DYNAMICS OF HELICOPTER FLIGHT

DYNAMICS OF HELICOPTER FLIGHT

GEORGE H. SAUNDERS

Lecturer
Institute of Safety and Systems Management
University of Southern California
Los Angeles, California

A Wiley-Interscience Publication

JOHN WILEY & SONS, INC.
New York • London • Sydney • Toronto

Published by John Wiley & Sons, Inc.

Library of Congress Cataloging in Publication Data:

Saunders, George H 1940–
Dynamics of helicopter flight.

"A Wiley-Interscience publication."
Bibliography: p.
Includes index.
1. Helicopters—Aerodynamics. 2. Helicopters—
Handling characteristics. I. Title.

TL716.S37 629.132′3 74-30261

ISBN 0-471-75509-5

Printed in the United States of America

10 9 8 7 6 5 4 3 2

To three inspirational men I have been fortunate to know:

Professor Holt Ashley

Dr. Robert Laidlaw

and with a special sadness at the recent passing of my first aerodynamics teacher,

Professor John Ruptash

PREFACE

This book is intended to fill the large gap in the existing helicopter literature between elementary manuals on "How-to-Fly-a-Helicopter" and the few advanced engineering texts on helicopter design. The former are replete with oversimplifications and homey analogies that do not provide the fundamentals for analyzing current problems. The latter are equally unhelpful in that they resort to, and often hide behind, complex mathematical descriptions.

The book is written for the intelligent pilot and for the engineering student who has had little previous exposure to the topic. It blends a theoretical treatment with the wisdom of experimental evidence and operational experience. Mathematics is used to the level of high school algebra, and then only to illustrate important quantitative relationships. A rudimentary acquaintance with the basic concepts of physics, especially mechanics, will be helpful to the reader; however, the most important of these are reviewed in Chapter 1.

Some basic concepts of the generation of aerodynamic forces are considered in Chapter 2 before applying these concepts to the particular case of an entire rotor system. Chapters 3 and 4 analyze in some detail the generation of lift, drag, torque, and power in hover and forward flight and relate these parameters to how and why the helicopter performs the way it does.

Perhaps the least understood subject is the stability (or lack of it) and the control of modern helicopters. What effects are present, and what role do they play in the sometimes peculiar motions helicopters exhibit about their pitch, roll, and yaw axes? This is the subject of Chapter 5 and includes the rapidly advancing application of stability augmentation concepts to helicopters.

Chapter 6 should be of particular interest to helicopter pilots in that it specifically examines certain flying problems. The most important and the most extensively treated of these is the autorotation maneuver. Operation at high gross weight and density altitude, external sling load problems, instrument flying, winds and turbulence, retreating blade stall, and wake turbulence are also discussed from the pilot's viewpoint.

Chapter 7 discusses, in a concise and integrated form, a subject not covered in most books—the elements of helicopter structures from strength requirements to crashworthiness.

At the end of each chapter are problems that indicate the depth of understanding the student should possess at that point. Any quantitative responses that are needed are provided at the back of the book. There is also a bibliography for the reader interested in pursuing the subject. Furthermore, a list of symbols and units appears at the end of the text.

Much of the material was developed while I was teaching engineering—notably helicopter performance, stability, and control—to U.S. Army aviators in the Army Safety Officers program at the Institute of Safety and Systems Management, University of Southern California. I am grateful for the many suggestions that the engineering staff and particularly my students made about the subject matter and its treatment. The manuscript reviews by Ms. Dennie Stansell, John Sinacori, Richard Lewis II, Dr. Harold Roland, Dr. Julian Wolkovitch, Harry Hurt, and John Hoffman were especially helpful.

I am also indebted to my wife, Dixie, for her continued support and encouragement during such particularly demanding phases of my career as the writing of this book.

George H. Saunders

Palos Verdes, California
December 1974

CONTENTS

DYNAMICS OF HELICOPTER FLIGHT

INTRODUCTION

1

In this book a number of the recognized disciplines brought to bear on the conception, detailed design, manufacture, flight testing, and operation of modern helicopters are discussed. The word "dynamic" in the book title is meant in its broadest sense to encompass all such disciplines. Figure 1.1 shows the relationship between some of these fields. It is clear that one individual cannot, and should not attempt to, be expert in all of them. This book aims to acquaint the reader with each to a sufficient depth that he can perform his duties in one or two of them with a greater perception of the role of the others, and the important interfaces that exist between them.

At all times we apply the discipline to the helicopter, rather than to other vehicles. Many books on helicopters rely heavily on fixed wing analogies to illustrate a point, on the assumption that anyone interested in helicopters will have some knowledge of fixed wing flight principles. This text, however, can be read and understood, for example, by a helicopter pilot who has never seen the inside of a fixed wing aircraft. Naturally, prior knowledge of flight of any kind will aid in digesting the more difficult concepts of helicopter flight. It has been said by helicopter pilots that a fixed wing aviator is one who is interested in aviation but does not have the nerve to try it. Nonetheless, we welcome aviation enthusiasts of all types.

Though the presentation here is kept simple, the reader should be familiar with some basic ideas of mathematics and physics. Mathematics is the language of the helicopter engineer, and physics provides the funda-

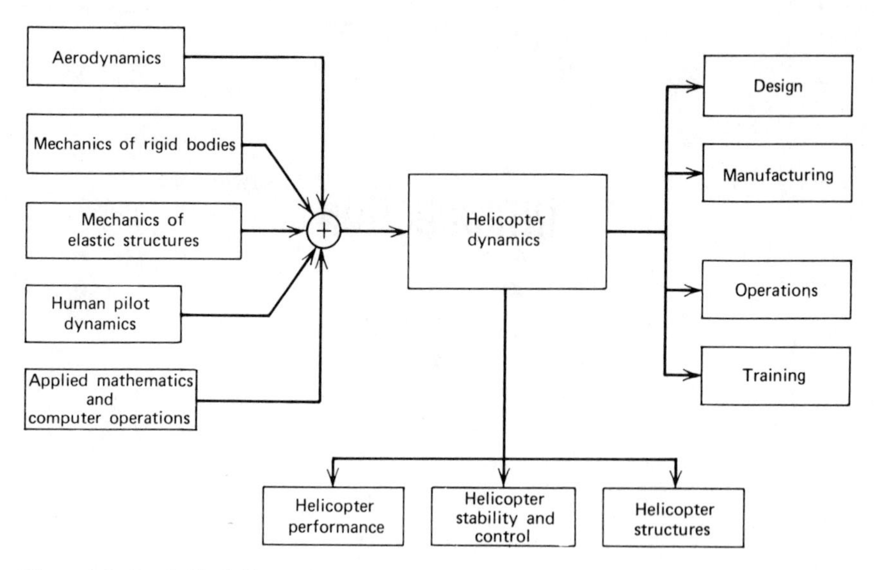

Figure 1.1 Basic disciplines of helicopter dynamics.

mental laws that all helicopter motions must obey. We now briefly review some necessary ideas. Engineering students may skip on to Chapter 2; others may wish to treat the next few paragraphs as a review of the branch of physics called mechanics; still others may wish to examine some of the texts listed in the bibliography.

Basic Quantities and Units

Although the National Aeronautics and Space Administration (NASA) has made some effort to convert to the metric system of units, other organizations, including the helicopter industry, have not indicated any special interest in doing so. In our numerical examples we therefore use the English system. In this system the fundamental units are the following:

Force: pounds = lb
Distance: feet = ft
Time: seconds = sec

All other quantities are derived from this basic set:

Velocity: distance per unit time = ft/sec (fps)
Area: distance · distance = ft · ft = ft^2

Volume: ft^3
Pressure: force per unit area = lb/ft^2 (psf)
Acceleration: change in velocity per unit time = ft/(sec)/(sec)
= ft/sec^2

Other units will be used where it is convenient or traditional to do so. Velocity, for example, is often given in knots (nautical miles per hour) or mph (statute miles per hour), and rate of descent is usually talked about in feet per minute. Some useful conversion factors are given below:

knots · 1.69 = ft/sec (fps)
knots · 1.15 = mph
mph · 1.47 = ft/sec (fps)
ft/sec · 60 = ft/min (fpm)

Weight and Mass

Weight is a force and is measured in pounds. It is the force that results from the fundamental attraction of any two objects for each other. Since here we are not concerned with the gravitational attraction of the moon, sun, or other planetary bodies, we always consider the force called weight that acts on a body to be directed toward the center of the earth. Thus even when the helicopter is at some unusual attitude, its weight at that time is a force directed straight down.

Mass, on the other hand, is a measure of the amount of material contained in the body. A given body has the same mass no matter where it is located in the universe. Its weight, however, depends on the mass *and* location of other bodies in the universe, as well as its own mass. Considering bodies close to the surface of the earth (including altitudes up to the helicopter's maximum ceiling) the weight of the body is directly proportional to the mass of the body:

$$W = mg$$

where W is the body's weight, m the body's mass, and g the constant of proportionality. For our purposes g is a constant. For earth, and in the English system, g has a magnitude of 32.2 and the units of acceleration:

$$g = 32.2 \text{ ft/sec}^2$$

The units for mass fall out from the equation for weight and mass:

$$m = \frac{W}{g} = \frac{\text{lb}}{\text{ft/sec}^2}$$

This set of units is called a slug:

$$1 \text{ slug} = 1 \frac{\text{lb}}{\text{ft/sec}^2}$$

$$\text{lb} = \text{slug} \cdot \frac{\text{ft}}{\text{sec}^2}$$

The reason why g has the same units as acceleration will come apparent when we discuss Newton's second law. One also hears the term "G-forces" of just G. This is a shorthand notation for force or acceleration. A 3 G force simply means a force equal to three times the body's weight. Thus an 8000 lb helicopter in a 2 G pull-up is experiencing a 16,000 lb force along its "normal" axis (up-down axis, in the aircraft axis system).

Scalar and Vector Quantities

The study of helicopter flight introduces two types of quantities—scalars and vectors. Scalar quantities are those that can be described by size alone. Vector quantities are described when their size (magnitude) is known *and* their direction is indicated. Area, volume, time, and mass all are scalar quantities. When we say that the volume is 26 ft^3 we have completely described the property called volume. It is not sufficient, however, to say that a helicopter has a velocity of 50 knots. We have no idea of the *direction* of that velocity. In the mechanics of flight the directions of vector quantities are just as important as their magnitude.

All forces, from whatever sources, are vectors. Weight is a vector, and so are lift and drag. A vector is not completely described until both magnitude and direction are specified. The force due to the main rotor produces different results when its line of action passes through the center of gravity of the helicopter and when it does not. Besides force, other important vector quantities include velocity and acceleration.

When two or more scalar quantities come into play simultaneously, the result is the same as if a single scalar quantity, equal in magnitude to the simple arithmetic sum, were present. Adding 40 gal of fuel to tanks already containing 80 gal of fuel produces tanks containing 120 gal of fuel—obviously. Not so with vector quantities. The addition of a vertical 40 lb force on a body to an already existing 80 lb horizontal force *does not* produce a net 120 lb force in any direction. The addition of vector quantities must include consideration of their respective directions, and this is fundamentally different from scalar addition.

Vectors are most conveniently added if the vector quantity is indicated by an arrow, whose length represents the magnitude of the quantity and whose orientation represents its directional property. For example, the airspeed vector of a helicopter in horizontal flight may be 80 knots, northbound, and may be represented by an arrow:

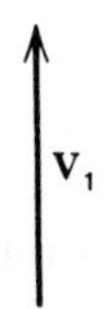

Here it is assumed that north is at the top of the page, and the length of the line represents the 80 knot size. If there were no wind the airspeed and groundspeed vectors would be identical. Suppose, however, that a 40 knot westerly wind is blowing. The groundspeed vector now becomes the *vector sum* of the airspeed and the wind vectors. Graphically, this addition is carried out by placing the tail of the second vector to the head of the first. The result of the vector addition is a new vector, represented by joining the tail of the first to the head of the second:

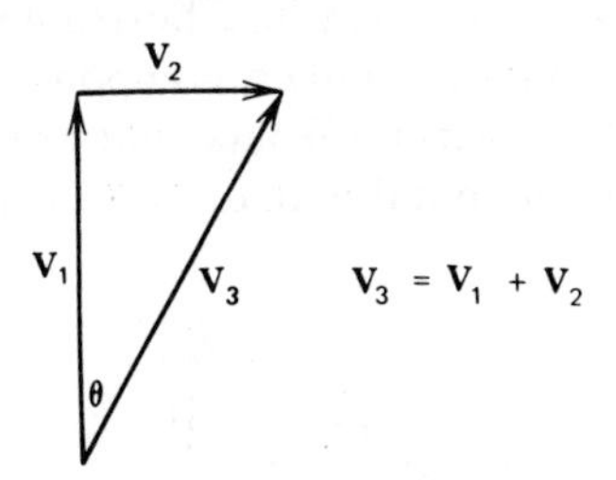

The magnitude and direction of the groundspeed vector ($\mathbf{V}_3$) may be measured graphically, or computed trigonometrically. In the example shown, $\mathbf{V}_3$ is the hypotenuse of a right angled triangle. From the Pythagorean theorem:

$$V_3 = \sqrt{V_1^2 + V_2^2} = \sqrt{(80)^2 + (40)^2} = \sqrt{6400 + 1600}$$

$$= \sqrt{8000} = 89.4 \text{ knots}$$

The direction of $\mathbf{V}_3$, relative to north, is given by the angle θ. Again this may be measured graphically, or computed trigonometrically:

$$\tan\theta = \frac{V_2}{V_1} = \frac{40}{80} = 0.5$$

$$\therefore \theta = 26.6°$$

Thus the aircraft has a groundspeed of 89.4 knots on a track of 027° (to the nearest degree).

In general a helicopter has many forces acting on it simultaneously. Reducing this force system to a single net force requires the vector addition of all the forces.

Vector Resolution

The opposite of adding many vectors into a vector sum is the breaking up of a single vector into "components." For example, what effect does a particular force have in a particular direction other than its own? Consider a body acted upon by a single inclined force of 80 lb as shown:

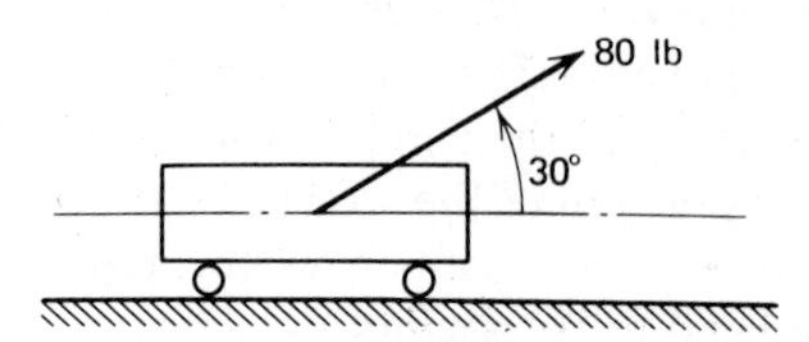

It is not the full force that is acting in a horizontal direction, tending to accelerate the body horizontally—only a component of the vector is. We must "resolve" the vector into its horizontal and vertical components before separately analyzing its horizontal and/or vertical motions. To do so, we form the vector triangle:

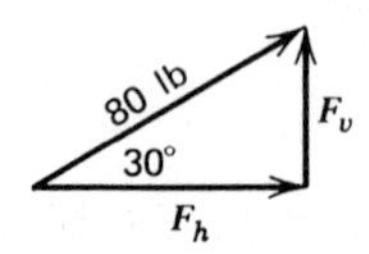

From trigonometry: $\cos 30° = F_h/80$. Or

$$F_h = 80 \cdot \cos 30° = 80 \cdot (0.866) = 69.3 \text{ lb}$$

Likewise

$$F_v = 80 \cdot \cos 60° = 80 \cdot \sin 30° = 80 \cdot (0.5) = 40 \text{ lb}$$

Thus a 80 lb force inclined 30° to the horizontal may be replaced by a horizontal force of 69.3 lb together with a 40 lb vertical force acting at the same point.

The general rule is the following: the magnitude of the component of any vector, in a particular direction, is equal to the magnitude of the vector times the cosine of the angle between the vector and the direction of interest.

Example. A helicopter is climbing on a 15° flight path at 100 knots. What is its rate of climb?

First draw the vector diagram:

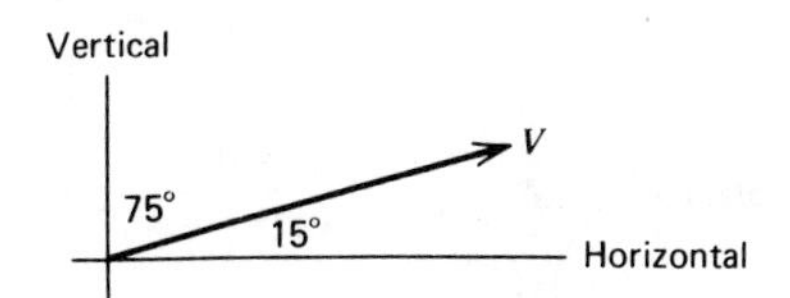

We are interested in the vertical component. Applying the rule, $V_v = 100 \cdot \cos(75°) = 100 \cdot (0.259) = 25.9$ knots [note that $\cos \theta = \sin(90 - \theta)$, hence $\cos(75°) = \sin(15°)$] and expressing the climb rate in feet per minute (fpm) we have

$$V_v = 25.9 \cdot 1.69 \cdot 60 = 2624 \text{ fpm}$$

Moments (Torque)

In our investigation of helicopter motions we consider rotation (e.g., pitch, roll, yaw) as well as translational, or straight line, motions. Rotational motion is caused by unbalanced moments, or torques. Consider the simple teeter-totter shown below:

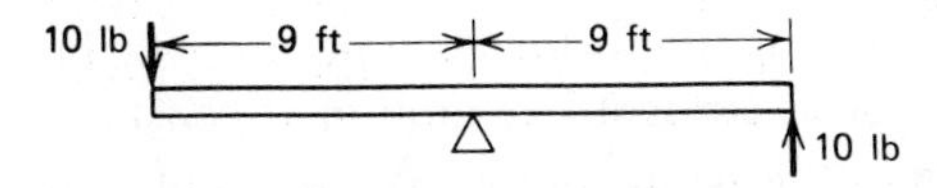

At this particular time the bar is experiencing zero *net* force (i.e. the 10 lb upforce cancels the 10 lb downforce). The bar will not translate if the net force is zero, but it will *rotate* since the net *moment* is not zero:

$$\text{moment} = \text{force} \cdot \text{distance} \qquad \text{(ft-lb)}$$

Here the distance is the shortest distance from the center of rotation to the line of action of the force (i.e., the perpendicular distance):

$$M = 10 \cdot (9) + 10 \cdot (9) = 10 \cdot (18) = 180 \text{ ft-lb counterclockwise}$$

It is important to specify the sense of the moment (clockwise or counterclockwise) about the center of rotation. In this example each force tends to rotate the bar counterclockwise about the fulcrum; hence their effects are additive.

Example. The main rotor torque of a helicopter in a certain flight condition is 7500 ft-lb. What tail rotor thrust force is necessary to balance the aircraft directionally?

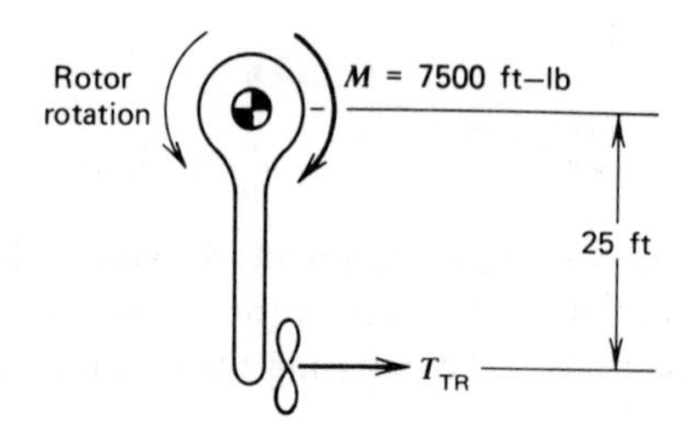

For directional equilibrium the moment produced on the fuselage by the main rotor, about the center of gravity, must be balanced by the moment produced by the tail rotor thrust acting through its moment arm (25 ft).

$$\therefore\ 7500 = T_{TR} \cdot 25$$

$$T_{TR} = \frac{7500}{25} = 300 \text{ lb}$$

Newton's First Law

Newton's first law states that "a body tends to remain at rest or in uniform motion in a straight line unless acted upon by external unbalanced forces." This also specifies the conditions for "equilibrium" flight. A hovering helicopter, or one executing straight line motion at constant speed, is in equilibrium. There are forces acting on the helicopter, of course, but the net or resultant of the forces is zero. All moments, too, add to zero. For equilibrium: $\Sigma \mathbf{F} = 0$ and $\Sigma \mathbf{M} = 0$. The second condition ensures that there is no rotational acceleration.

Example. A helicopter in forward horizontal flight may be represented in a simple way by three forces acting through the center of gravity:

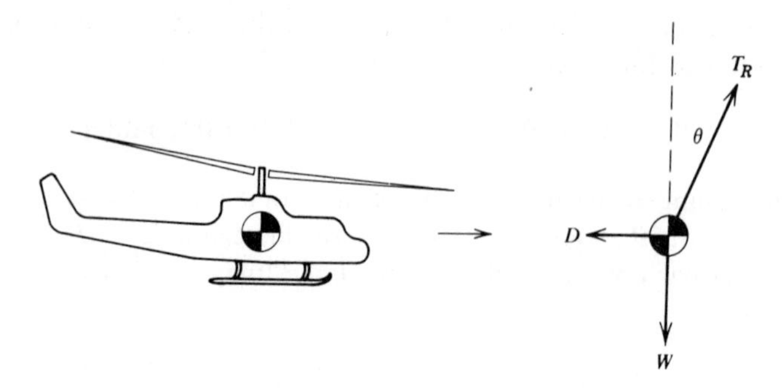

If $W = 8000$ lb and $D = 600$ lb, what value must T_R and the disc tilt angle θ have for equilibrium to exist? Since all forces act through the cg they produce no moment about the cg; hence the condition for rotational equilibrium is already satisfied. For translational equilibrium the vertical component of rotor thrust must balance weight, and the horizontal component must balance drag.

$$T_R \cos\theta = W \tag{1}$$

$$T_R \sin\theta = D \tag{2}$$

For the given values of W and D these two equations must be solved simultaneously for the two unknowns T_R and θ. Dividing equation 2 by equation 1, we obtain

$$\frac{T_R \sin\theta}{T_R \cos\theta} = \frac{D}{W}$$

Or

$$\tan\theta = \frac{D}{W} = \frac{600}{8000} = 0.075$$

$$\therefore \theta = 4.3°$$

Substituting into equation 1, we have

$$T_R = \frac{8000}{\cos(4.3)} = \frac{8000}{0.997} = 8030 \text{ lb}$$

Notice that the rotor thrust, though only slightly in excess of the weight, produces a substantial horizontal component if tilted a few degrees. This is a common situation, as we shall see.

Newton's Second Law

Newton's second law states that "the rate of change of motion of a body is directly proportional to the applied unbalanced force and inversely proportional to the body's mass." This is probably the most important law in describing helicopter motions. It is the only one that relates the size of a body and the direction of applied force to the resultant accelerations of that body. By "rate of change of motion" Newton meant acceleration:

$$\text{acceleration} = \frac{\text{change in velocity}}{\text{time}} \qquad (\text{ft/sec}^2)$$

If we denote acceleration by a, mass by m, and force by F, we have

$$a = \frac{F}{m} \qquad \text{or} \qquad \boxed{F = ma}$$

Recall that both force and acceleration are vector quantities, where mass is a scalar. The *direction* of the acceleration is the same as that of the unbalanced net force.

Example. What unbalanced force is required to accelerate a 10,000 lb helicopter forward at 0.5 g?

$$a = 0.5\,g = 0.5\,(32.2) = 16.1 \text{ ft/sec}^2$$

$$m = \frac{W}{g} = \frac{10{,}000}{32.2} = 311 \text{ slugs}$$

$$F = ma = (311) \cdot (16.1) = 5000 \text{ lb}$$

This force must, of course, be oriented in the direction of the desired acceleration, that is, "forward."

Example. An aircraft touches down at a forward velocity of 80 knots. If the net braking force is a constant 1000 lb and the aircraft weighs 12,000 lb, how many seconds are needed for the aircraft to stop? From the definition of acceleration we have

$$a = \frac{\Delta V}{\Delta t}$$

We know that $\Delta V = 80$ knots and we wish to determine Δt. But what is a? From Newton's second law (with minus denoting deceleration) we obtain

$$a = \frac{F}{m} = \frac{F}{W/g} = \frac{-1000}{12{,}000/32.2} = -2.68 \text{ ft/sec}^2$$

Thus:

$$\Delta t = \frac{\Delta V}{a} = \frac{-80\,(1.69)}{-2.68} = 50.4 \text{ sec}$$

Newton's Third Law

Newton's third law states that "for every action there is an equal and opposite reaction." This law applies whether or not the body is in equilibrium. A block sitting on a table exerts a force, equal to its weight, on the table. The table in turn exerts an equal and opposite force on the block. Now consider a helicopter rotor developing some thrust T_R. Where did this force come from? Clearly it is an aerodynamic force caused by the surrounding air acting on the rotor blades. According to Newton, then, the blades must be exerting an equal and opposite force on the air. Because the air is unrestrained, it must accelerate under the action of this unbalanced force. That is,

$$T_R = \text{mass of air} \cdot \text{acceleration of air}$$
$$= \frac{\text{mass} \cdot \text{change in velocity}}{\text{time}}$$
$$= \text{mass flow rate} \cdot \text{change in velocity}$$
$$= \frac{\text{slugs}}{\text{sec}} \cdot \frac{\text{ft}}{\text{sec}} = \text{lb}$$

Thus the rotor thrust is a function of the flow rate through the rotor disc and the velocity of the air through the disc. Changing rotor diameter and/or velocity through the disc will change rotor thrust proportionally. Helicopters tend to have large mass flows at low velocity, while rockets and pure jet engines have low mass flow and high velocity.

Constant Acceleration Relations

Many flight problems involve, or may be approximated by, periods of time in which the acceleration is not changing (the unbalanced force is constant in the direction of interest). Landing forces and decelerations are often analyzed as follows:

$$a = \frac{\Delta V}{\Delta t} = \frac{V - V_0}{t - t_0}$$

where V_0 = velocity at time t_0
V = velocity at time t

It is usual to start the problem at time zero:

$$t_0 = 0$$

Then

$$a = \frac{V - V_0}{t} \quad \text{or} \quad \boxed{V = V_0 + a \cdot t}$$

A graph of velocity plotted versus time is a straight line of slope a, starting at V_0 when $t = 0$.

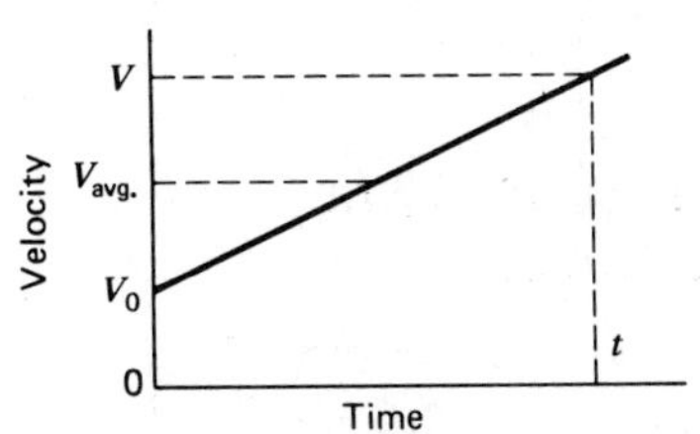

If the final velocity at time t is V, then the average velocity during the period of constant acceleration is

$$V_{avg} = \left(\frac{V + V_0}{2}\right)$$

The *distance* traveled during the period is simply the product of the average velocity and the time:

$$s = V_{avg} \cdot t$$
$$= \left(\frac{V + V_0}{2}\right) \cdot t$$

But $V = V_0 + at$; hence

$$s = \left(\frac{V_0 + at + V_0}{2}\right) \cdot t \quad \text{or} \quad \boxed{s = V_0 t + \tfrac{1}{2}at^2}$$

The graph of distance versus time is not a straight line but a curve of ever-increasing slope:

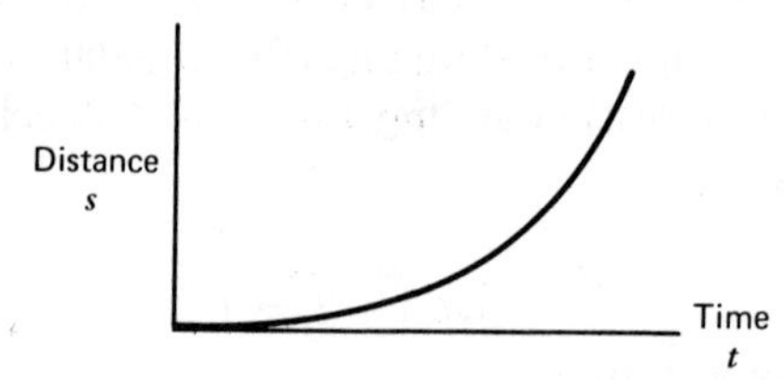

For constant acceleration, the distance traveled in a given period is greater than any previous period. A third and useful relationship comes from combining the two previous equations, eliminating t:

$$\boxed{V^2 - V_0^2 = 2as}$$

Example. What deceleration does a helicopter experience when it hits the ground in vertical flight at 2000 fpm and the gear compresses a maximum of 8 in.? Treating the deceleration from 2000 fpm to zero as a constant deceleration; we have

$$V = 0$$
$$V_0 = 2000 \text{ fpm} = 33.3 \text{ fps}$$
$$s = 8 \text{ in.} = 0.667 \text{ ft}$$
$$a = \frac{V^2 - V_0^2}{2s} = \frac{0 - (33.3)^2}{2(0.667)} = -831 \text{ ft/sec}^2$$

This deceleration corresponds to $831/32.2 = 25.8\ G$. From the pilot's viewpoint, he would be experiencing "1 G flight" before impact and $25.8 + 1 = 26.8\ G$ flight during impact. This analysis excludes gear dynamics, which is discussed in Section 7.6 on crashworthiness.

Work, Energy, and Power

The terms work, energy, and power have definite meanings in physics and should not be used loosely in discussing helicopter flight. *Work* is the product of a force times a distance. The distance involved is the distance over which the body moved as a result of the force, and is therefore measured in the same direction as the force. Pushing on an immovable object does no work (although the one pushing may disagree). Pushing a moving shopping cart does require positive work:

$$\text{work (ft-lb)} = \text{force (lb)} \cdot \text{distance (ft)}$$

Power is the *rate* at which work is accomplished:

$$\text{power}\left(\frac{\text{ft-lb}}{\text{sec}}\right) = \frac{\text{force (lb)} \cdot \text{distance (ft)}}{\text{time (sec)}}$$

Two events can involve the same amount of work, but the event that takes the least time acquires the higher level of power. Power is often quoted in units of horsepower (HP):

$$1 \text{ horsepower} = 550 \text{ ft-lb/sec}$$

Example. What is the minimum horsepower motor required to winch a helicopter sling load of 1500 lb vertically at the rate of 1 fps? Here the distance itself is not specified, but the rate at which the distance is traveled is:

$$\begin{aligned}\text{power} &= \text{force} \cdot \frac{\text{distance}}{\text{time}} \\ &= \text{force} \cdot \text{velocity} \\ &= 1500 \cdot 1 = 1500 \text{ ft-lb/sec} \\ \text{HP} &= \frac{1500}{550} = 2.72 \text{ HP}\end{aligned}$$

Note that this is the minimal horsepower needed to do the job without considering friction losses, heat losses, and so on. Note also that the amount of work actually done cannot be specified unless the distance or the time is specified independently.

Energy is a measure of a body's capacity to do work. It can come in many forms, such as chemical, nuclear, heat, and mechanical. We are interested primarily in the two types of mechanical energy—potential and kinetic. Potential energy is the capacity to do work by virtue of the body's position in a graviational field. That is, if a body of weight W is positioned at a height h above the surface of the earth, it has the capacity, when released, to do work equal to the force it exerts, W, times the distance it travels, h.

$$\text{potential energy} = \text{weight} \cdot \text{height}$$

$$\boxed{\text{PE} = W \cdot h} \qquad \text{ft-lb}$$

Note that energy has the same units as work.

Kinetic energy is that capacity to do work which a body has by virtue of its velocity. In other words, if a moving body is brought to rest, it will do so by experiencing a deceleration force over some distance. It can be shown that this capacity is proportional to the mass of the body and the square of its velocity:

$$\text{kinetic energy} = \tfrac{1}{2} \cdot \text{mass} \cdot \text{velocity}^2$$

$$\boxed{\text{KE} = \tfrac{1}{2} m V^2 = \tfrac{1}{2} \frac{W}{g} V^2} \qquad \text{ft-lb}$$

The principle of conservation of energy is often helpful in flight analysis. Simply stated, energy can neither be created nor destroyed. The total energy in a system is always constant. There is no restriction on the *type* of energy, however. Thus the kinetic energy of the air in the downwash of a hovering helicopter is ultimately being supplied from the chemical energy in the fuel. A *transformation* of energy types has occurred, but the total amount of energy is constant.

Example. Speed (kinetic energy) can be traded for altitude (potential energy) without an increase in the rate of conversion of fuel energy—by a "zoom" climb. How much speed will be sacrificed by a helicopter at 160 knots in "zooming" 1000 ft above its previous altitude? According to the law of conservation of energy, the *change* in potential energy (gained) must equal the change in kinetic energy (lost).

$$W \cdot \Delta h = \tfrac{1}{2} \frac{W}{g} V_1^2 - \tfrac{1}{2} \frac{W}{g} V_2^2$$

$$\Delta h = \frac{1}{2g} (V_1^2 - V_2^2)$$

or

$$\begin{aligned} V_2^2 &= V_1^2 - 2g\,\Delta h \\ &= (160 \cdot 1.69)^2 - 2(32.2)(1000) \\ &= 73{,}116 - 64{,}400 = 8716 \\ \therefore\ V_2 &= \sqrt{8716} = 93.6 \text{ fps} = 55.2 \text{ knots} \end{aligned}$$

Example. A 160 lb man runs up six stories of a building, each of which is 15 ft high, in 1 min. How much potential energy did he gain? How much horsepower did he exert?

$$\Delta \text{PE} = W \cdot h = 160(15 \cdot 6) = 14{,}400 \text{ ft-lb}$$

$$\text{HP} = \frac{14{,}400}{60 \cdot 550} = 0.436 \text{ HP}$$

Rotational Motion

Rotational motion plays a very important part in helicoptor flight, since even when the aircraft itself is not rotating, its main rotor, tail rotor, tail rotor shaft, engine components, and so on, are in circular motion. An element of a rotor blade maintaining constant rate (rpm) has its velocity vector continuously changed, not in magnitude but in direction. Since acceleration involves the rate of change of velocity, if *either* the magnitude *or* the direction of the velocity vector changes, acceleration has occurred, by definition. To change the direction of the velocity vector it is necessary to exert a force on the body *perpendicular* to the velocity vector direction. In the case of a blade element this force is provided by the blade structure itself in a direction toward the center of rotation. This force is called the centripetal force. The element exerts an equal and opposite centrifugal force, so that the entire blade is in tension. Without derivation, some important relationships between force and motion variables are given below:

1. The translational velocity of any body rotating about an axis is

$$\boxed{V_r = \frac{r \cdot \text{RPM}}{9.55}} \quad \text{fps}$$

where r is the distance of the body from the axis of rotation. Thus doubling the rate of rotation doubles speed, as does doubling the distance r.

2. The centrifugal force experienced by a weight W is given by

$$\boxed{\text{CF} = \frac{W \cdot V_r^2}{g \cdot r}} \quad \text{lb}$$

or

$$\boxed{CF = \frac{W \cdot r \cdot (\text{RPM})^2}{2937}} \qquad \text{lb}$$

Thus doubling the rate causes a fourfold increase in centrifugal force, while doubling r doubles centrifugal force.

Example. How many Gs would one experience if he were at the tip of a 44 ft diameter rotor turning at 400 RPM?

$$CF = \frac{W(22)(400)^2}{2937} = 1199W$$

$$\therefore \frac{CF}{W} = 1199 \qquad \text{or} \qquad 1199\ G$$

Example. How much sideward force must friction supply to prevent a 10,000 lb aircraft, taxiing around a 250 ft radius circle at 50 knots, from sliding off?

$$CF = \frac{W \cdot V_r^2}{g \cdot r} = \frac{10{,}000(50 \cdot 1.69)^2}{32.2(250)} = 8869 \text{ lb}$$

Example. A helicopter executes a steady level turn at a 60° bank angle and 100 knots. What is its radius of turn? For level flight:

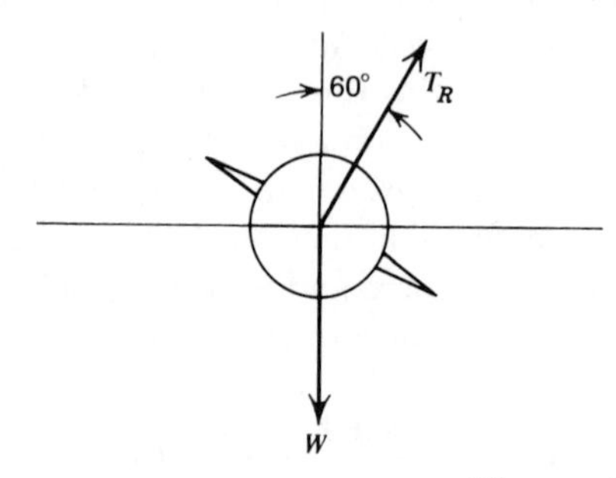

$$T_R \cdot \cos 60° = W \qquad \therefore T_R = \frac{W}{\cos 60°} = \frac{W}{0.5} = 2W$$

$$CF = T_R \cdot \sin 60° = 2W(0.866) = 1.73W$$

$$\therefore 1.73W = \frac{W(100 \cdot 1.69)^2}{32.2r}$$

$$\therefore r = \frac{(100 \cdot 1.69)^2}{1.73(32.2)} = 513 \text{ ft}$$

Concluding Remarks

In this chapter we have taken a very quick look at some of the principles that we apply later so as to gain a fuller appreciation of helicopter dynamics discussed in the chapters to come. The serious student should become familiar with these ideas, those interested in a more qualitative understanding may proceed without mastering them thoroughly. The text is still readable, albeit at the expense of greater depth, by those interested in the latter approach. It should be emphasized, however, that many aspects of helicopter behavior are necessarily complicated, involving the simultaneous application of many forces and moments. To adequately sort out all the important influences, as well as to arrive at a conclusion about the nature of the resultant motion, it is absolutely essential that the student be able to deal quantitatively with the subject, at least to the depth illustrated by the examples in this chapter.

Where possible we use diagrams, sketches, and charts as aids to understanding, as well as mathematical descriptions. Some topics cannot be adequately treated at the level of mathematical skill that this book assumes. In such cases the problem is at least formulated and the important conclusions of such analyses are given. Wherever practical, real aircraft and real tasks are used as examples, although the helicopters are not identified by make or model.

PROBLEMS

1.1 A helicopter hovering out of ground effect (OGE) and weighing 8500 lb accelerates forward to 50 knots in 8 sec at a constant rate. (*a*) How much rotor thrust and (*b*) what disc tilt angle are required to accomplish this at constant altitude? (Ignore buildup in drag).

1.2 To test helicopter windshields for birdstrikes, a 4 lb chicken is fired through a cannon at a test windshield in a laboratory. (*a*) At what speed should it strike the windshield to produce the same energy transfer as would occur in a head-on collision between a 20 lb goose at 10 knots and a helicopter at 120 knots? (*b*) Estimate the total force transmitted to the windshield by decelerating the chicken completely in its 1 ft length.

1.3 During a nap-of-the-earth mission a blade strike caused the loss of 3 lb of blade tip of a 24 ft radius rotor rotating at 324 RPM. Calculate the unbalanced force of this weight loss on the helicopter, ignoring changes in aerodynamic forces.

Figure 1.2 Courtesy Bell Helicopter Company.

BASIC LAWS OF AERODYNAMICS

2

2.1 INTRODUCTION

All flying machines designed for operation in the earth's atmosphere rely on the laws of fluid mechanics for the generation of their lift and propulsive forces. These forces arise from the physics of fluids, and are fundamentally the same for a submarine "flying" in the water (hydrodynamics) and a helicopter flying in the atmosphere (aerodynamics). This chapter examines those elements of aerodynamics that directly affect the helicopter's design, performance, and operational utility. What is the source of these aerodynamic forces? On what factors do they depend? How can we maximize needed aerodynamic forces and minimize unwanted ones? How can we obtain the necessary forces with minimal power output? We attempt to answer some of the questions in an effort to understand and make use of the principles of aerodynamics on which successful helicopter flight is based. Such understanding is a prerequisite to the discussion of helicopter performance, stability, control, and special piloting problems.

2.2 PROPERTIES OF THE ATMOSPHERE

The aerodynamic forces and moments acting on a helicopter component are due in great part to the properties of the air mass on which the aircraft is operating. The chemical composition of the atmosphere, which varies somewhat with altitude, is approximately 78% nitrogen, 21% oxygen, and 1% water vapor, argon, carbon dioxide, and other gases. The particular chemistry of the air is not important to helicopter flight. At hypersonic speeds (those five times the speed of sound or greater) local surface temperatures may cause such great changes in the gas properties (due to ionization, etc.) as to significantly influence the aerodynamic forces. At the low speeds of helicopter flight, air can be considered to be a homogeneous mixture of its constituent gases. The most important properties of this gaseous mixture that are observed to influence its aerodynamic behavior are static pressure, temperature, density, and viscosity.

Static Pressure

The static pressure of the air at any altitude results from the mass of air above that level. If we weighed a column of air 1 ft^2 in area, extending from the altitude of interest up to the physical boundary of the sensible atmosphere, that weight, in pounds per square foot (psf), would be the static pressure. Clearly, the higher we go, the less air remains above, thus reducing the static pressure. At any one time the static pressure at the surface of the earth varies from place to place around the world. Likewise, a given location experiences changes in static pressure from day to day. For convenience, a standard sea level reference static pressure, p_0, has been defined:

$$\begin{aligned} p_0 &= 2116 \text{ pounds per square foot (psf)} \\ &= 14.7 \text{ pounds per square inch (psi)} \\ &= 29.92 \text{ inches of mercury (in. Hg)} \\ &= 1013 \text{ millibars (mb)} \end{aligned}$$

For most of our work pounds per square foot or pounds per square inch are the most convenient units. Aviation weather reports and forecasts often specify the pressure in millibars and give the altimeter setting in inches of mercury (since altimeters are calibrated this way). It is often convenient to speak of the static pressure as a ratio of the standard reference value. This is called the pressure ratio and is denoted by δ (delta):

$$\boxed{\delta = \frac{p}{p_0}}$$

Thus a pressure ratio of 0.5 means that the existing static pressure is one half the standard sea level value. In a standard atmosphere δ has a value of 1.0 at sea level and values less than 1.0 at higher altitudes. For example, the pressure has dropped to one half of its sea level value at about 18,000 ft and to one fifth of p_0 at about 37,500 ft.

Temperature

Temperature measures the kinetic energy of the gas on a molecular level. We are used to measuring temperature on the Fahrenheit or Centigrade (now called Celcius) scales. These scales were based somewhat arbitrarily on the boiling and freezing points of water. Thus 0°C corresponds to 32°F for the freezing point, and 100°C corresponds to 212°F for the boiling point:

$$\boxed{\begin{aligned} °C &= \tfrac{5}{9}\,(°F - 32) \\ °F &= \tfrac{9}{5}°C + 32 \end{aligned}}$$

At −40° both scales happen to have the same value. A much more fundamental temperature scale is one that has a value of zero at absolute zero. Absolute zero is the condition under which no molecular kinetic energy is observable. This is found to occur at −273°C or −460°F. By simply shifting the zero point down to absolute zero we can derive two absolute temperature scales—the Kelvin scale and the Rankine scale:

$$\begin{aligned} °K &= °C + 273 \\ °R &= °F + 460 \end{aligned}$$

Figure 2.1 defines all four scales. The absolute scales have fundamental physical significance and are used in computations. Scientifically, it is not correct to say that the temperature doubles by going from 50°F to 100°F. The kinetic energy has not doubled. The true increase is reflected by the ratio of the two temperatures on the appropriate *absolute* scale:

$$\frac{T_2}{T_1} = \frac{100 + 460}{50 + 460} = \frac{560}{510} = 1.1$$

Again, a standard sea level temperature T_0 has been defined as 59°F or 15°C, corresponding to 519°R or 288°K. Likewise, a temperature ratio is defined as the ratio of the existing temperature to the standard value, on an absolute scale. This quantity is denoted by Θ (theta):

$$\boxed{\Theta = \frac{T}{T_0}}$$

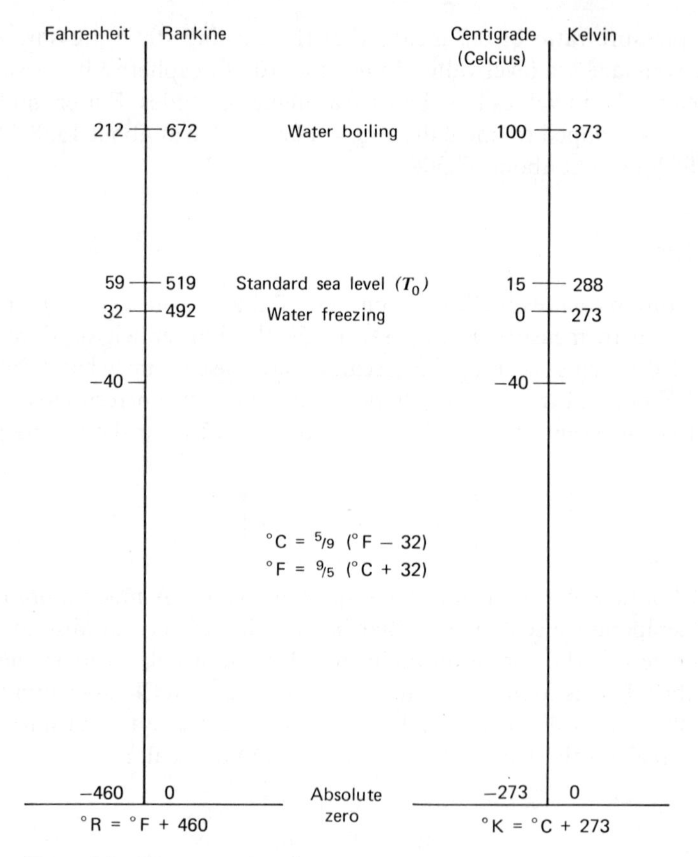

Figure 2.1 Temperature scales.

Like static pressure, temperature normally decreases with altitude, at least up to the limits of the troposphere. Therefore Θ starts out at 1.0 at sea level and decreases as altitude increases.

Density

The density of the air is a property of utmost importance to the study of aerodynamics. It is defined as the mass of the air per unit volume and is denoted by ρ (rho):

$$\rho = \frac{\text{mass}}{\text{unit volume}} \qquad (\text{slug/ft}^3)$$

In our system of units density is therefore expressed in slugs per cubic foot. The standard sea level value, ρ_0, is 0.00238 slug/ft^3. Density decreases with altitude in a normal atmosphere, reaching a value of $\frac{1}{2}\rho_0$ at about 22,000 ft and a value of $\frac{1}{4}\rho_0$ at about 40,000 ft. Clearly, once we run out of density we have depleted the very thing that provided aerodynamic force. Thus, as we shall see, helicopter performance is seriously degraded at low density conditions.

The symbol σ (sigma) has been assigned to the density ratio:

$$\boxed{\sigma = \frac{\rho}{\rho_0}}$$

We learned in high school chemistry and physics experiments that pressure, temperature, and density are related. If we change one we must change one or both of the others. The relationship is summarized by the universal gas law:

$$\boxed{p = K\rho T}$$

Here K is a constant of proportionality whose numerical value varies with the gas being considered and the units for the other variables. When pressure and density are expressed in their usual units, and temperature is in degrees Rankine, for air K has a value of 1718.

The universal gas law specifies the relationship that must exist in any gas. If density is held constant, for example, pressure and temperature are directly proportional.

An increase in one variable causes a corresponding increase in the other. Or, if temperature is constant, increases in pressure cause increases in density, and vice versa. If we know the values of any two of the variables, we can determine the values of the third by applying the law. Thus if pressure and temperature are known, density can be calculated.

An interesting relationship between δ, Θ, and σ can be derived in the following way:

$$p = K\rho T$$
$$p_0 = K\rho_0 T_0$$

Dividing the first equation by the second yields:

$$\delta = \sigma\Theta$$

or

$$\boxed{\sigma = \frac{\delta}{\Theta}}$$

Viscosity

Viscosity is a measure of the resistance of air to flow. It becomes important in discussing the aerodynamics of the area very close to the surface of the aircraft (the "boundary layer") and in determining skin friction drag. It is not a very important variable in helicopter performance, except to wind tunnel designers and operators interested in the details of the flow field. The "absolute" viscosity is denoted by μ (mu). In a gas, unlike a liquid, absolute viscosity increases with temperature.

In many computational problems of viscous flow the ratio of absolute viscosity to density appears, called "kinematic viscosity" and denoted by ν (nu):

$$\boxed{\nu = \frac{\mu}{\rho}} \qquad \text{ft}^2/\text{sec}$$

ICAO Standard Atmosphere

To provide a common denominator for comparison of various aircraft and a calibration standard for manufacturers of aircraft systems, the International Civil Aviation Organization has defined a standard atmosphere. It is partly shown in Table 2.1. This represents a set of conditions averaged over the entire globe and over a year's cyclic variation. We use this chart often in performance calculations. Note that pressure and density decrease continuously, although not at the same rate, as altitude increases in the standard atmosphere. Temperature decreases to a point called the tropopause, at the lower boundary of the stratosphere, occurring at 36,089 ft. Thereafter it is constant.

The speed of sound has also been included in this table, since it becomes an important variable in flights close to or beyond its value. Although helicopters themselves seldom approach flight speeds at which these effects become important, the outboard portions of their main rotor blades may encounter the effects even in hover, as we shall see. The speed of sound will be shown to be a function only of temperature. Thus when the temperature stops decreasing in the standard atmosphere, so does the speed of sound (Table 2.1).

Perhaps the greatest benefit of a standard atmosphere lies in the concepts of pressure altitude and density altitude. Pressure altitude is that altitude in the standard atmosphere which corresponds to a particular pressure. For example, instead of a pressure of 1455 psf (or a pressure ratio of 0.6877)

Table 2.1 ICAO Standard Atmosphere

Altitude (ft)	Density (slugs/ft³)	Density Ratio	Pressure (psf)	Pressure Ratio	Temperature		Temperature Ratio	Kinematic Viscosity (ft²/sec)	Speed of Sound (knots)
					°F	°C			
h	ρ	σ	p	δ			Θ	ν	a
0	0.002377	1.0000	2116	1.0000	59.00	15.00	1.0000	0.000158	661.7
1,000	0.002308	0.9711	2041	0.9644	55.43	13.02	0.9931	0.000161	659.5
2,000	0.002241	0.9428	1968	0.9298	51.87	11.04	0.9862	0.000165	657.2
3,000	0.002175	0.9151	1897	0.8962	48.30	9.06	0.9794	0.000169	654.9
4,000	0.002111	0.8881	1828	0.8637	44.74	7.08	0.9725	0.000174	652.6
5,000	0.002048	0.8617	1761	0.8320	41.17	5.09	0.9656	0.000178	650.3
6,000	0.001987	0.8359	1696	0.8014	37.60	3.11	0.9587	0.000182	647.9
7,000	0.001927	0.8106	1633	0.7716	34.04	1.13	0.9519	0.000187	645.6
8,000	0.001868	0.7860	1572	0.7428	30.47	−0.85	0.9450	0.000192	643.3
9,000	0.001811	0.7620	1513	0.7148	26.90	−2.83	0.9381	0.000197	640.9
10,000	0.001755	0.7385	1455	0.6877	23.34	−4.81	0.9312	0.000202	638.6
11,000	0.001701	0.7156	1400	0.6616	19.77	−6.79	0.9244	0.000207	636.2
12,000	0.001648	0.6933	1346	0.6361	16.21	−8.77	0.9175	0.000212	633.8
13,000	0.001596	0.6714	1294	0.6115	12.64	−10.76	0.9106	0.000217	631.4
14,000	0.001545	0.6500	1243	0.5874	9.07	−12.74	0.9037	0.000223	629.0
15,000	.0001496	0.6292	1194	0.5643	5.51	−14.72	0.8969	0.000229	626.7
20,000	0.001266	0.5328	972.5	0.4595	−12.32	−24.62	0.8625	0.000262	614.6
25,000	0.001065	0.4481	785.3	0.3711	−30.15	−34.53	0.8281	0.000302	602.2
30,000	0.000889	0.3741	628.4	0.2970	−47.98	−44.43	0.7937	0.000349	589.5
35,000	0.000737	0.3099	498.0	0.2353	−65.82	−54.34	0.7594	0.000405	576.6
36,089	0.000706	0.2971	472.7	0.2234	−69.70	−56.50	0.7519	0.000419	573.8
40,000	0.000585	0.2462	391.7	0.1851	−69.70	−56.50	0.7519	0.000506	573.8
50,000	0.000362	0.1522	242.2	0.1145	−69.70	−56.50	0.7519	0.000818	573.8
60,000	0.000224	0.0941	149.8	0.0708	−69.70	−56.60	0.7519	0.001323	573.8

we can talk about a pressure altitude of 10,000 ft. The pressure altitude has nothing to do with the physical altitude of the aircraft, either above ground or above sea level. It is only an alternate and very useful way of expressing pressure. Meteorologists will quote the pressure either directly (usually in millibars or inches of mercury) or by pressure altitude. All altimeters are calibrated on the basis of a sea level pressure of 29.92 in. Hg. If the altimeter indicator is set to this value, the instrument reads pressure altitude directly.

Density altitude is that altitude in the standard atmosphere which corresponds to a particular density. A density of 0.001545 slug/ft^3 can also be expressed as a density altitude of 14,000 ft. Density altitude greatly affects helicopter performance, as will be reflected in performance charts. If the pressure and temperature were known, we could calculate density using the universal gas law. Another method is to find the pressure *altitude* and temperature, and then determine the density *altitude*. Figure 2.2 illustrates the relationship between pressure altitude, density altitude, and temperature. For example, a pressure altitude of 4000 ft and a temperature of +24°C result in a density altitude of 6000 ft. It is the density altitude that the helicopter will "feel" and will respond to. Aviation computers can produce the same result, though perhaps less accurately.

Note that as temperature drops with increasing altitude, so does the absolute viscosity μ. However, the density is decreasing at an even faster rate; hence kinematic viscosity ($\nu = \mu/\rho$) increases with altitude.

2.3 BERNOULLI'S PRINCIPLE AND AIRSPEED MEASUREMENT

All aerodynamic forces bearing on a surface are the result of air pressure (perpendicular to the surface) or air friction (parallel to the surface). Friction effects, associated with the property of viscosity, are generally confined to a thin boundary layer and usually are not dominant. As a first approximation we can therefore neglect the effects of viscosity and concentrate on pressure distribution.

Consider the uniform flow of a fluid through the converging-diverging channel of Figure 2.3. Represent the conditions upstream by p_1, T_1, ρ_1, and the velocity and cross-sectional area by V_1 and A_1 respectively. Assign the subscript 2 to the parameters at the throat. We do not inject any fluid into the flow between sections 1 and 2, nor do we allow any to escape.

An important initial concept is that of conservation of mass: what goes in must come out. To put it more exactly, the rate of mass flow by section 1 must be equal to that of section 2 if no fluid is being injected or extracted in between. The volume of air per unit time is simply the product of the cross-

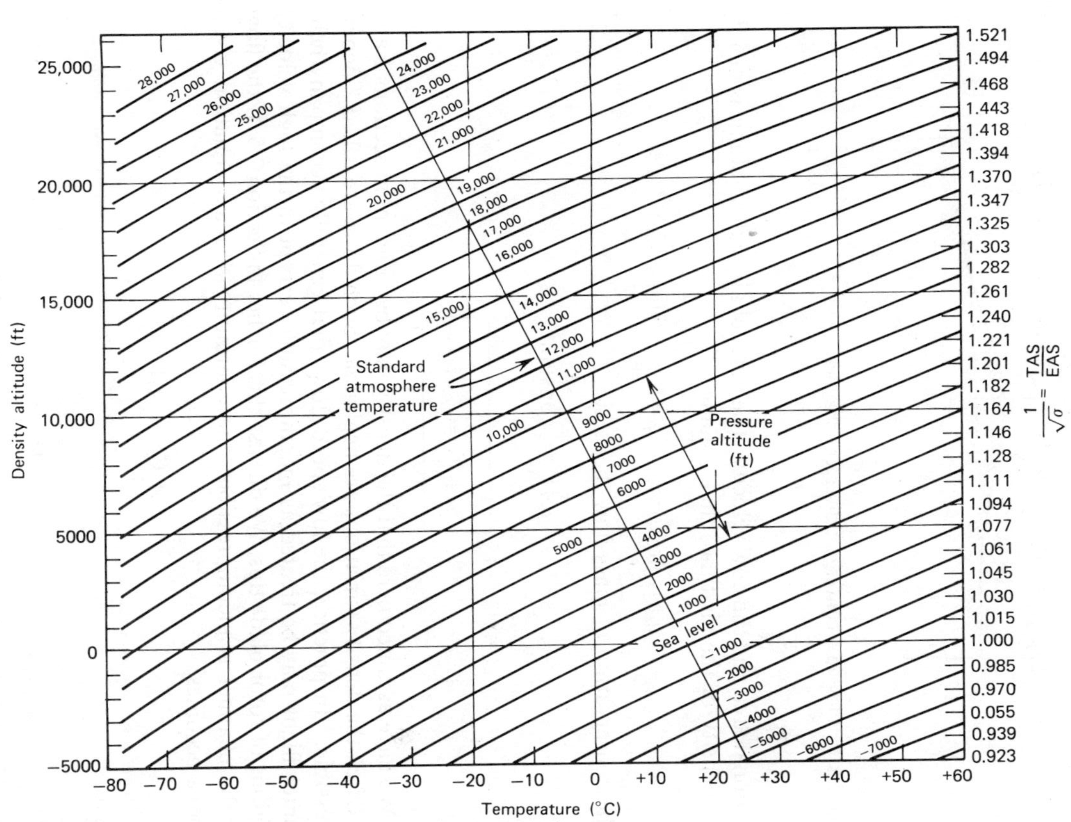

Figure 2.2 Density altitude, pressure altitude, and temperature.

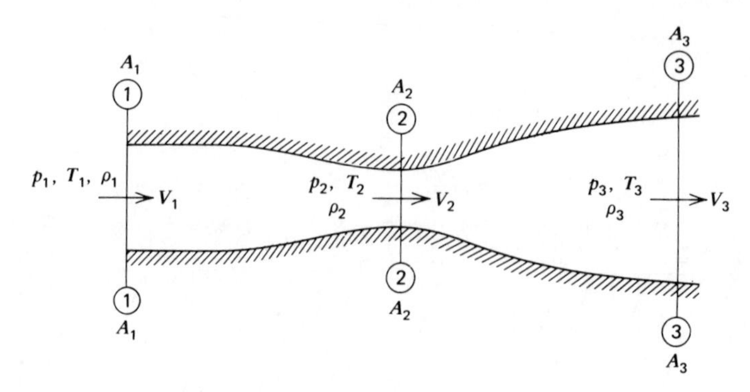

Figure 2.3 Flow in a convergent-divergent channel.

sectional area and the flow velocity. The mass of air in this volume is merely the density of the air times that volume:

$$\text{mass flow rate} = \rho A V \qquad \text{(slugs/sec)}$$

The conservation of mass flow then says:

$$\rho A V = \text{constant}$$

or

$$\boxed{\rho_1 A_1 V_1 = \rho_2 A_2 V_2}$$

We have assumed here that the density may be different at sections 1 and 2. Often the density variations are negligible. Such flows are called "incompressible." In practice, the low speed flows that generally accompany helicopter flight may be treated as incompressible, except in the high velocity regions of rotor blade tips. We discuss this further in Section 2.5. If the flow in the channel is incompressible, the continuity of mass equation given above becomes:

$$A_1 V_1 = A_2 V_2$$

or

$$\frac{V_2}{V_1} = \frac{A_1}{A_2}$$

Thus if A_1 is greater than A_2 (as it is in our example) V_2 must be greater than V_1 in compressible flow. This is also known as the Venturi effect and simply says that the flow of an incompressible fluid speeds up through a restriction in direct proportion to the reduction in area.

Bernoulli's Principle

If the flow velocity increases, its kinetic energy level has increased. We know from the concept of conservation of energy that a corresponding decrease in some other kind of energy must have taken place (since we did not add any energy between the two sections). In aerodynamics, the equivalent of potential energy is static pressure. If the kinetic energy increases, the static pressure decreases. Viewed another way, the flow was accelerated from section 1 to section 2. According to Newton's second law this could have come only from an unbalanced force. This force is provided by the pressure change.

Bernoulli's equation is essentially an energy conservation statement, which says:

$$p + \tfrac{1}{2}\rho V^2 = \text{constant}$$

or

$$\boxed{p_1 + \tfrac{1}{2}\rho_1 V_1^2 = p_2 + \tfrac{1}{2}\rho_2 V_2^2}$$

For incompressible flow $\rho_1 = \rho_2$. Bernoulli's equation relates, quantitatively, velocity changes to pressure changes. Since pressure, acting on an area of the aircraft, produces a force, Bernoulli's equation is extremely useful in aerodynamics.

It should be appreciated that the term $\frac{1}{2}\rho V^2$ has the units of pressure. If density is in slugs per cubic feet and velocity in feet per second, then $\frac{1}{2}\rho V^2$ has the units of pounds per square foot. This term is also called the "dynamic" pressure and is denoted by q:

$$\text{dynamic pressure } q = \tfrac{1}{2}\rho V^2$$

Thus Bernoulli's equation states that the sum of the static and dynamic pressures in a flow is constant. Table 2.2 gives typical values of dynamic

Table 2.2 Effect of Speed and Altitude on Dynamic Pressure

Velocity (TAS)		Dynamic Pressure, q (psf)					
knots	fps	SL	5000	10,000	15,000	20,000	30,000
50	84.5	8.48	7.30	6.25	5.34	4.51	3.17
100	169	33.9	29.2	25.0	21.3	18.1	12.7
150	254	76.2	65.7	56.1	47.9	41.0	28.5
200	338	135.6	116.8	100	85.2	72.4	50.8
400	676	542.0	467	400	341	289	203
600	1013	1221	1051	902	769	651	457

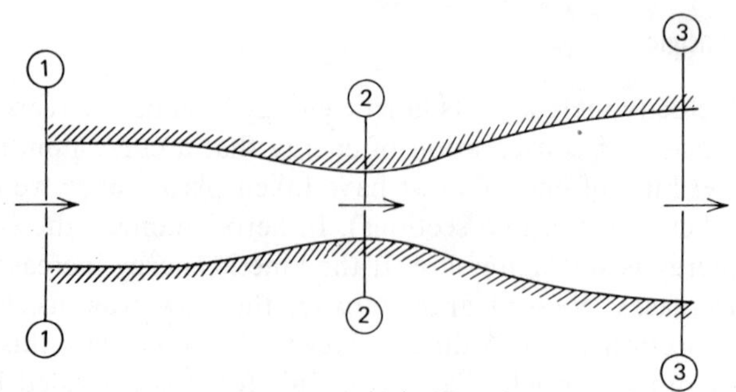

Figure 2.4 Variation of flow parameters for incompressible fluid.

$A_1 = 10\ \text{ft}^2$	$A_2 = 5\ \text{ft}^2$	$A_3 = 15\ \text{ft}^2$
$V_1 = 100$ knots	$V_2 = 200$ knots	$V_3 = 66.6$ knots
$\rho_1 = 0.00238\ \text{slug/ft}^3$	$\rho_2 = 0.00238\ \text{slug/ft}^3$	$\rho_3 = 0.00238\ \text{slug/ft}^3$
$p_1 = 2116$ psf	$p_2 = 2014$ psf	$p_3 = 2135$ psf
$q_1 = 34$ psf	$q_2 = 136$ psf	$q_3 = 15$ psf

pressure for various true airspeeds and altitudes in the standard atmosphere. Notice that the dynamic pressure at some fixed velocity varies directly with the density ratio at any altitude. Also, appreciate the fact that at an altitude of 40,000 ft (where $\sigma = 0.25$) twice the airspeed is needed to produce the same dynamic pressure.

Figure 2.4 is a numerical illustration of flow in a channel.

Airspeed Measurement

If a symmetrically shaped object is placed in a moving airstream, a flow pattern such as shown in Figure 2.5 results. There is a point at the very nose of the object at which the flow is brought to rest. This point is called the stagnation point, and the streamline ending in this point is the stagnation streamline. Streamlines above this line go over the top of the object; all

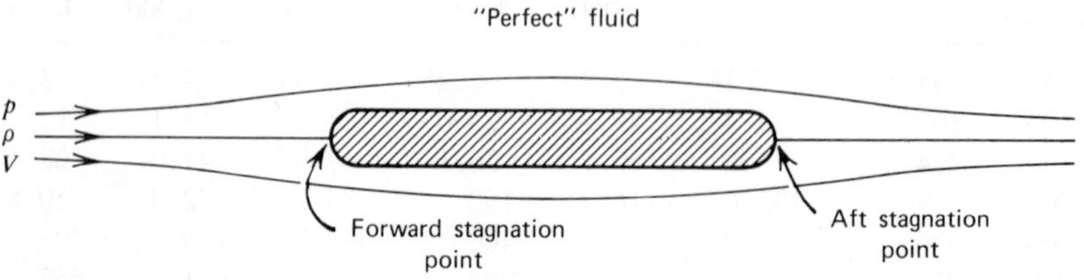

Figure 2.5 Flow pattern around a symmetrical object. Stagnation pressure $p_s = p + \frac{1}{2}\rho V^2$.

others pass below. Since the velocity at this point is zero, the stagnation pressure must be

$$p_s = p + \tfrac{1}{2}\rho V^2$$

where p and V are the upstream conditions. A pitot tube, such as shown in Figure 2.6, has a stagnation point at its entrance (at zero angle of attack); there is no flow through the tube. A pitot tube alone, hooked up to pressure sensitive bellows and an indicator, would therefore measure the sum of the upstream static and dynamic pressure. If a source of static pressure can be found on the aircraft, equal in magnitude to the upstream static pressure (which implies that the local velocity past the static port is equal to the upstream velocity), it can be fed to the other side of the bellows. The indicator then measures only dynamic pressure, since static pressures are balanced on either side of the diaphragm.

If we assume, as most airspeed indicators do, that the density is constant at 0.00238 slugs, the indicator displays true airspeed (note that doubling true airspeed quadruples dynamic pressure so that the scale on the face of the indicator is nonlinear). There are a number of reasons why the airspeed so indicated may not be an accurate measure of the true airspeed of the helicopter:

1. Position and/or installation error, ΔV_i: the instrument is calibrated for greatest accuracy at a particular flight condition, usually for straight and level flight at some usual cruise speed. At other conditions the stagnation point may migrate, lowering the pressure in the pitot tube and, often

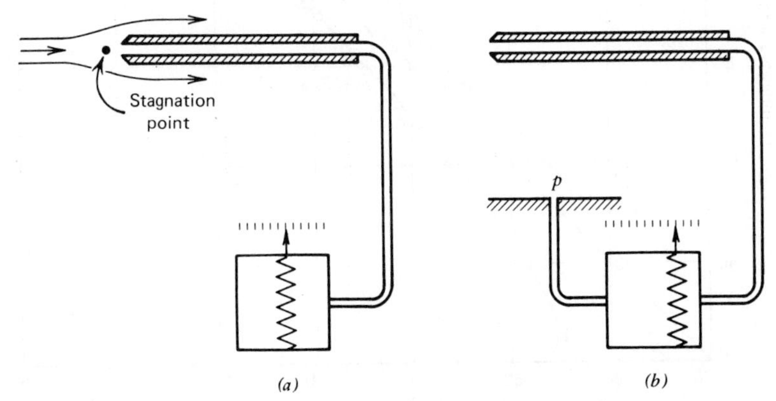

Figure 2.6 Airspeed measurement. (*a*) Pitot tube measures stagnation pressure $p_s = p + \frac{1}{2}\rho V^2$. (*b*) Pitot/static system measures $p_s - p = \frac{1}{2}\rho V^2$ (i.e., dynamic pressure).

more important, changing the pressure at the static ports because of local flow condition changes. Good engineering can minimize these errors. Note that the error in the installation shown in Figure 2.7*a* is essentially zero at 100 knots straight and level, but increases to as much as 20 knots in autorotation at 50 knots. In this installation the indicator reads too high in climbs and too low in descents. Other installations, such as that shown in Figure 2.7*b*, have opposite effects. Calibrated airspeed (CAS) is the indicated airspeed (IAS) corrected for position error.

2. Compressibility effects, ΔV_c: a further source of error comes about at high speed (greater than about six tenths the speed of sound) where density changes occur that affect dynamic pressure independent of velocity. Within the speed and altitude range of conventional helicopters this effect is small, and will be ignored for computational purposes. Equivalent airspeed (EAS) is the result of corrections in CAS for compressibility errors.

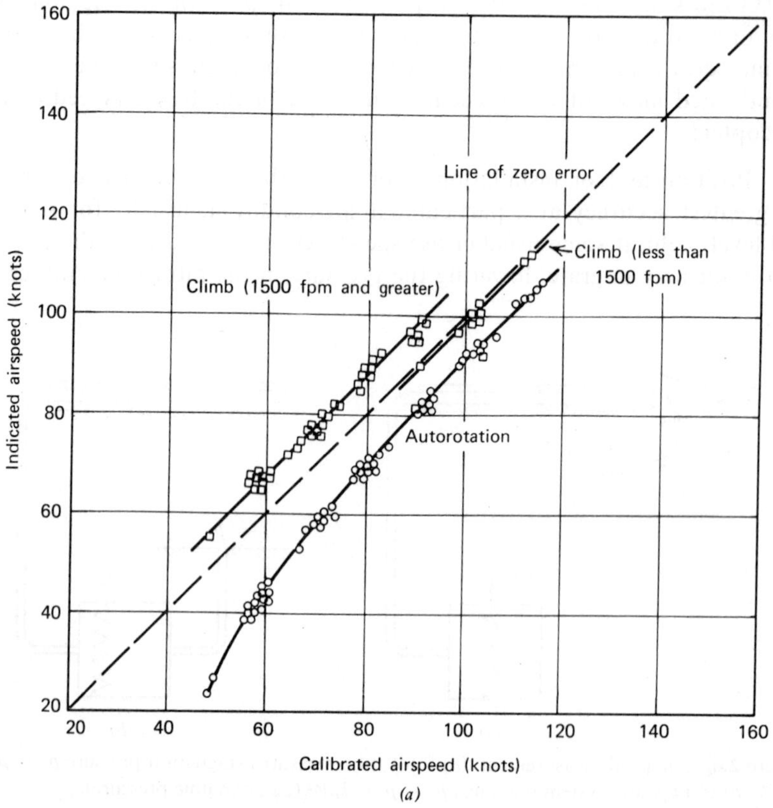

(*a*)

Figure 2.7 (*a*) Airpseed calibration in tandem rotor cargo helicopter. (U.S. Army data.)

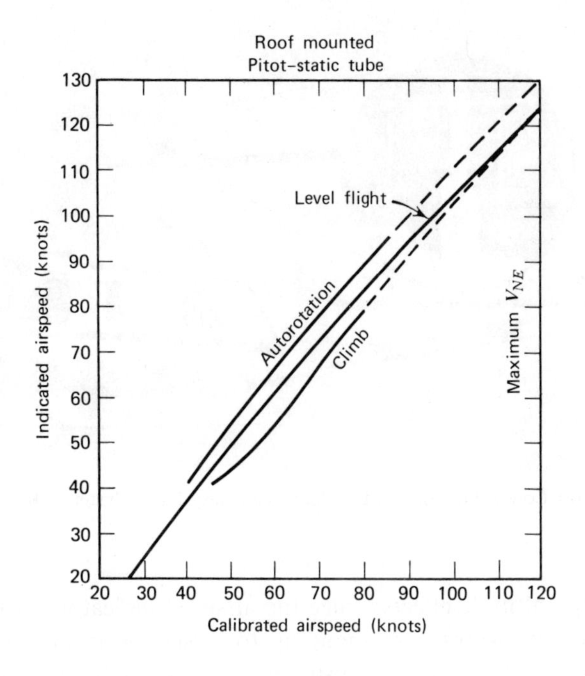

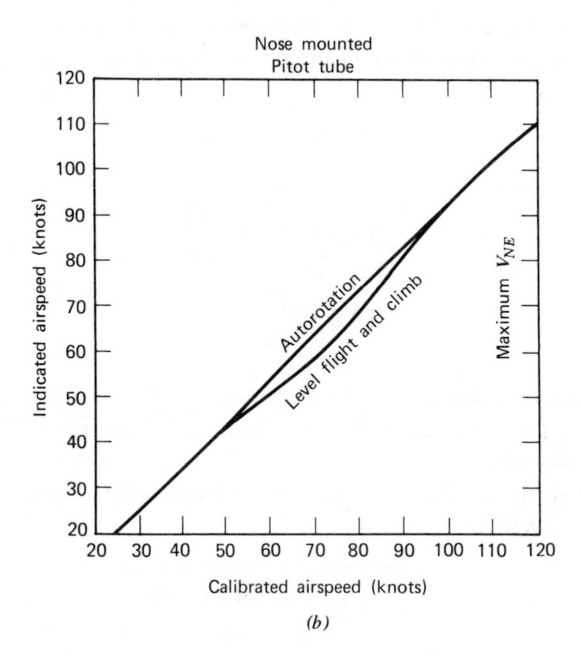

(b)

Figure 2.7 (*b*) Airspeed calibration in utility helicopter. (U.S. Army data.)

Figure 2.7 (*c*) Low range airspeed system. (Courtesy Pacer Systems, Inc.)

3. Density altitude effects: since the airspeed indicator is calibrated for the dynamic pressures corresponding to airspeeds at standard sea level conditions, variations in air density must be accounted for. The true airspeed (TAS) coupled with the existing density, produces the same dynamic pressure as the equivalent airspeed (EAS) coupled with standard sea level density. That is,

$$(\text{TAS})^2\rho = (\text{EAS})^2\rho_0$$

or

$$\text{TAS} = \text{EAS}\sqrt{\frac{\rho_0}{\rho}}$$

$$\text{TAS} = \frac{\text{EAS}}{\sqrt{\sigma}}$$

This latter effect is very important and must be taken correctly into account in helicopter performance problems. Figure 2.2 gives the value of $1/\sqrt{\sigma}$ for any density altitude.

Combining all these effects results in the following formula for conversion from IAS to TAS:

$$\boxed{\text{TAS} = \frac{\text{IAS} + \Delta V_i + \Delta V_c}{\sqrt{\sigma}}}$$

Example. The helicopter shown in Figure 2.7*a* is in autorotation at 60 knots IAS. The pressure altitude is 4000 ft and the temperature is +24°C. Ignoring compressibility, what is the aircraft's TAS (knots)? From Figure 2.7*a*, $\Delta V_i = +11$ knots, and from Figure 2.2 $1/\sqrt{\sigma} = 1.094$

$$\therefore \text{TAS} = (60 + 11)1.094 = 71(1.094) = 77.9 \text{ knots TAS}$$

The accuracy and sensitivity of conventional airspeed systems deteriorates rapidly at speeds below 30 knots, and new methods must be devised for this situation if IFR flight and/or speed stability augmentation is contemplated. Various new ultrasonic, electronic, and laser systems demonstrate improved accuracy, but often at high cost and complexity. It must be remembered that any measuring device measures conditions at the location of the sensor, which may or may not be the quantity sought. For helicopters, the main rotor wake greatly influences local flow conditions around the aircraft, and the airspeed of the helicopter itself, relative to the undisturbed airmass, may be very difficult to measure. We cannot here discuss the relative merits of all the different engineering approaches to the problem. We examine only one system, which has shown promise in helicopter application. The device is shown installed above a rotor in Figure 2.7*c*. It consists of a small constant speed rotor with shielded pitot tubes on each end. The difference in pressure between the two is sensed by a transducer in the hub. When the helicopter velocity is zero, the pressures are identical and no signal is produced. If the vehicle is moving (or the wind is blowing past the helicopter) the relative velocity is increased on the "advancing" side and decreased on the "retreating" side; hence a difference in dynamic pressure is measured, proportional to the square of the airspeed. Notice also that by knowing the rotor azimuth when it experiences the maximum pressure difference, the *direction* as well as the magnitude of the airspeed are obtained. Thus an accurate measurement of sideslip is possible. Measurement of airspeed, both forward and sideward components, have been measured with an average error less than 1 knot down to zero airspeed. Backward velocities are measured with equal precision. A system of this type, with its plane of rotation mounted vertically, measures forward and downward velocity components, hence aircraft angle of attack.

2.4 DEVELOPMENT OF LIFT AND DRAG ON AIRFOILS

The cross-sectional size and shape of a helicopter blade is carefully chosen to give the best overall lift, drag, and pitching moment that are possible within given structural, aeroelastic, and manufacturing constraints. Symmetrical airfoils are the most common but cambered airfoils are increasingly being used in newly designed aircraft. In symmetrical airfoils the upper and lower surfaces have exactly the same shape and are equidistant from a straight line joining the leading and trailing edge (chordline).

Consider such an airfoil aligned in the direction of the upstream flow (i.e., angle of attack is zero), as illustrated in Figure 2.8. At the leading edge is a stagnation point where the flow is brought to rest. This point divides the flow over the top and bottom of the airfoil. The local pressure here is equal, from our previous derivation, to the sum of the upstream static and dynamic pressure. The difference between the pressure at the stagnation point and the static pressure upstream is equal to the upstream dynamic pressure. Since the airfoil itself is symmetrical and is placed at zero incidence to the flow direction, the streamline patterns above and below it are identical. From the stagnation point (zero velocity) the flow

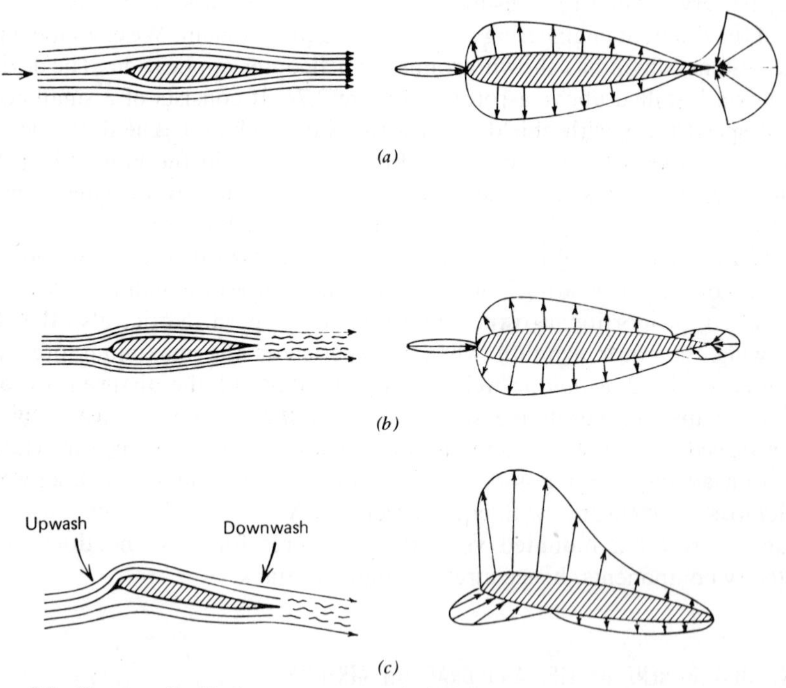

Figure 2.8 Pressure distribution over symmetrical airfoils. (*a*) Perfect fluid—zero angle of attack. Completely symmetrical pressure distribution: net aerodynamic force = 0. (*b*) Real fluid—zero angle of attack. Nonsymmetrical force/aft: net force aft (drag). (*c*) Real fluid—positive angle of attack. Completely nonsymmetrical: net force up and aft (lift and drag).

velocity increases as we move along the surface. In a smoke tunnel, where the streamlines can be seen, this is indicated by the streamlines' converging and producing the Venturi effect, which increases velocities. When the velocity increases up to the upstream value, the pressure has dropped back to the upstream static value. As the velocity continues to increase, the pressure continues to decrease. At some point, near the point of maximum thickness, maximum velocity and minimum pressure are achieved. Thereafter the flow veolcity decreases back toward its free stream valve as it approaches the trailing edge.

The result is a pressure *distribution* over the airfoil, in this case symmetrical top and bottom. For the case of a so-called "perfect" fluid (one in which viscosity is zero) the streamlines close uniformly at the trailing edge, and eventually assume their parallel structure downstream, at the same velocity as upstream. In a "real" fluid this is not so. Viscosity effects have robbed the flow of some of its energy, and it is not quite able to fully recover from its experience. Consequently a "wake" of low dynamic pressure and some turbulence exists near the trailing edge. The resulting pressure distribution, while still symmetrical top and bottom, is not quite symmetrical fore and aft. In perfect fluid, the complete symmetry of the situation leads to zero net aerodynamic force. In a real fluid, we have a net aerodynamic force in the downstream direction (drag). (Figure 2.8)

Next consider the same symmetrical airfoil at a positive angle of attack (angle of attack is the angle between the chordline and the direction of the relative flow upstream). In this case the flow does not "see" a symmetrical situation. Its path over the top of the airfoil is different from the path beneath. In a smoke tunnel, the streamlines ahead of the airfoil are seen to turn upward (upwash), while a downward component of flow (downwash) is present behind the airfoil. In between, the flow has been turned as it negotiates the obstruction caused by the airfoil. The velocity distribution on the upper surface is different from that on the lower surface, as is the accompanying pressure distribution. Even the stagnation point has migrated below the leading edge.

Two adjacent particles of air approaching the airfoil above and below the stagnation streamline need not join again at the trailing edge. Bernoulli never said that, nor is it true in general. Figure 2.9 shows clearly that in an airfoil generating lift the flow over the top reaches the trailing edge sooner than does the flow over the bottom.

Each local pressure, multiplied by the area over which it acts, produces a force perpendicular to the local surface. The summation of all these forces generally creates an aerodynamic force inclined to the free stream direction. For convenience, and out of tradition, this total aerodynamic force is usually

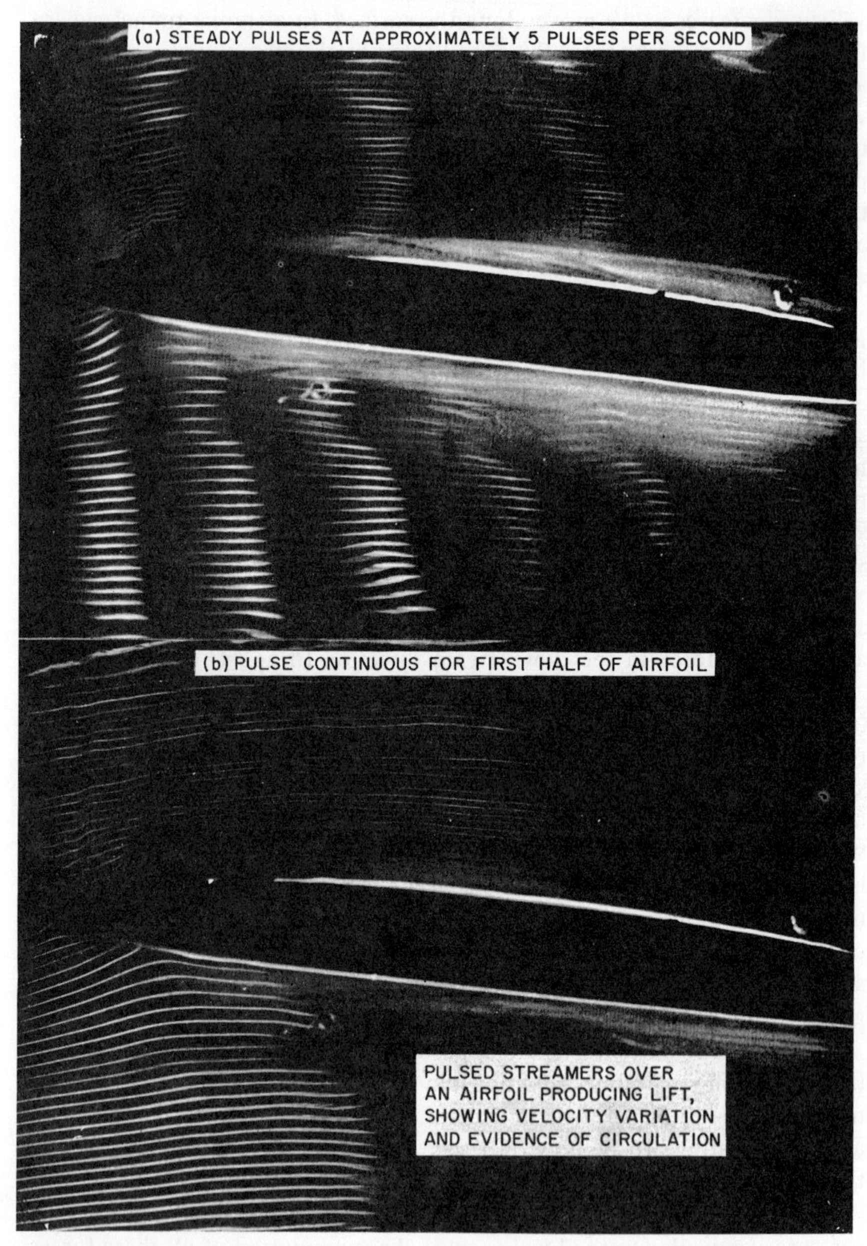

Figure 2.9 Velocity differences above and below an airfoil. (From Douglas Report ES 29075.)

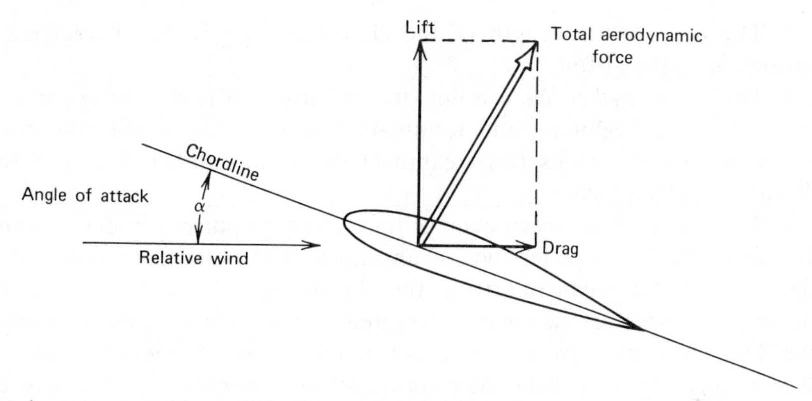

Figure 2.10 Definitions of lift, drag, and angle of attack.

broken into two components—one perpendicular and the other parallel to the free stream direction. These two force components, by definition, are the lift and drag of the airfoil (Figure 2.10).

Before discussing the factors affecting the magnitude of lift and drag, let us distinguish between size and shape. Shape is defined by the geometry of the airfoil. In Figure 2.11 the geometric properties usually used to describe airfoils are illustrated:

1. The *chordline* is a straight line connecting the leading and trailing edges of the airfoil.

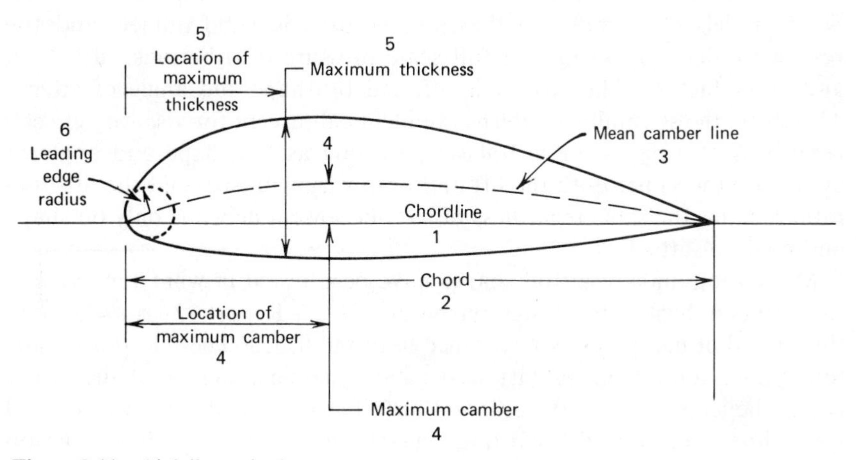

Figure 2.11 Airfoil terminology.

2. The *chord* is the length of the chordline, and is the characteristic dimension of the airfoil.

3. The *mean-camber line* is a line drawn halfway between the upper and lower surfaces, beginning and terminating at the ends of the chordline. For symmetrical airfoils (zero camber) the mean-camber line and the chordline are coincident.

4. The shape of the mean-camber line is very important in determining the aerodynamic characteristics of an airfoil. The *maximum camber* (displacement of the mean line from the chordline) and the *location* of the maximum camber are two parameters that help to define the mean-camber line. These quantities are expressed as fractions or percentages of the chord. Maximum camber on helicopter rotors seldom exceeds 4% and may be located as far aft as 40% from the leading edge. Some horizontal tail surfaces and helicopter sync-elevators have substantial negative camber.

5. The thickness and its distribution are also important to the aerodynamics of the airfoil. The *maximum thickness* and its *location* are also expressed as a percentage of chord. Most helicopter rotor blades are between 9 and 14% thick. Some tip sections on advanced blades are thinner.

6. The *leading edge radius* of an airfoil is a measure of the radius of curvature at this location. Relatively small changes in the geometry of the leading edge may significantly affect the total pressure distribution over the airfoil. Leading edge radii may vary from zero (knife edge shape of some supersonic configurations) to a more typical 2 to 3% on helicopter blades.

Notice an airfoil shape is described by dimensions that are percentages of the basic chord. Small and large *sizes* of the same shape are possible. Scale models of aircraft can therefore be used in wind tunnels and the results "scaled up" to predict full scale pressure distributions, lift, drag, and other factors. The airflow is affected by shape and angle of attack. Therefore, the streamline patterns are identical (except for viscosity effects) regardless of airspeed or airfoil size, as long as the shape and angle of attack are the same. Both the lift and drag vary with size, but the lift-drag ratio remains the same regardless of size, because it depends only on shape and angle of attack.

Many thousands of airfoil shapes have been tested in wind tunnels and the results published for design purposes. NACA Report 824 is a classic in this area, but many others have since been published. The selection of airfoil shape is a fundamental task in the aerodynamic design of all aircraft. A typical helicopter may have different airfoil shapes for the main rotor, tail rotor, horizontal tail, vertical tail, sync-elevator, and wing, depending on the requirements for lift, drag, and pitching moment, and the aerodynamic environment in which the airfoil finds itself.

Factors Affecting Lift and Drag

The magnitude of lift and drag experienced on a body is a function of the following important variables:

1. Airstream velocity.
2. Air density.
3. Surface area.
4. Angle of attack.
5. Shape.
6. Compressibility (Mach number).
7. Viscosity (Reynolds number, p. 49).

The airstream velocity and air density combine in the form of dynamic pressure to influence the magnitude of the aerodynamic force. Doubling the dynamic pressure doubles the aerodynamic force, all other factors being the same. Notice that a change in dynamic pressure does not change the shape of the pressure distribution, but only its magnitude. Clearly, the size of the surface in the airstream will have a direct and proportional effect on the magnitude of the aerodynamic force. Thus:

$$F_a = C_f q S$$

where F_a = total aerodynamic force (lb)
C_f = aerodynamic force coefficient (dimensionless)
q = dynamic pressure $\frac{1}{2}\rho V^2$ (psf)
S = surface area (ft^2)

The force coefficient, C_f, must account for the remaining factors of angle of attack, shape, compressibility, and viscosity. For most of our purposes we can consider compressibility (speed of sound) and viscosity effects to be negligible. We identify particular areas in which they play a role in later discussions. For now, consider C_f to be a function of shape and angle of attack only. Lift and drag are simply components of the total aerodynamic force and they depend on the same variables.

Lift

Lift has been defined as the net force developed perpendicular to the relative wind. It arises from the summation of all the pressure components in this direction, and may be expressed as

$$L = C_L q S$$

where L is the total lift force (lb) and C_L is the "lift coefficient." If the lift coefficient of a conventional airplane wing were plotted versus angle of attack, a typical result would be the graph of Figure 2.12. Such a graph was determined from wind tunnel tests in which lift was measured directly and divided by the product of the dynamic pressure and reference area.

It should be realized here that for a total body or wing at a given angle of attack the pressure distribution is influenced not only by the shape characteristics of the airfoil section, but also by the plan shape of the entire body. Some wings are rectangular, others triangular; some have straight leading edges, others sweep back; some have constant chords, others are tapered. While the planforms of fixed wings vary widely, helicopter blades do not. Most are rectangular and have a large span-to-chord ratio. A familiar shape parameter is aspect ratio, defined in the following way:

$$\boxed{AR = \frac{b^2}{S}}$$

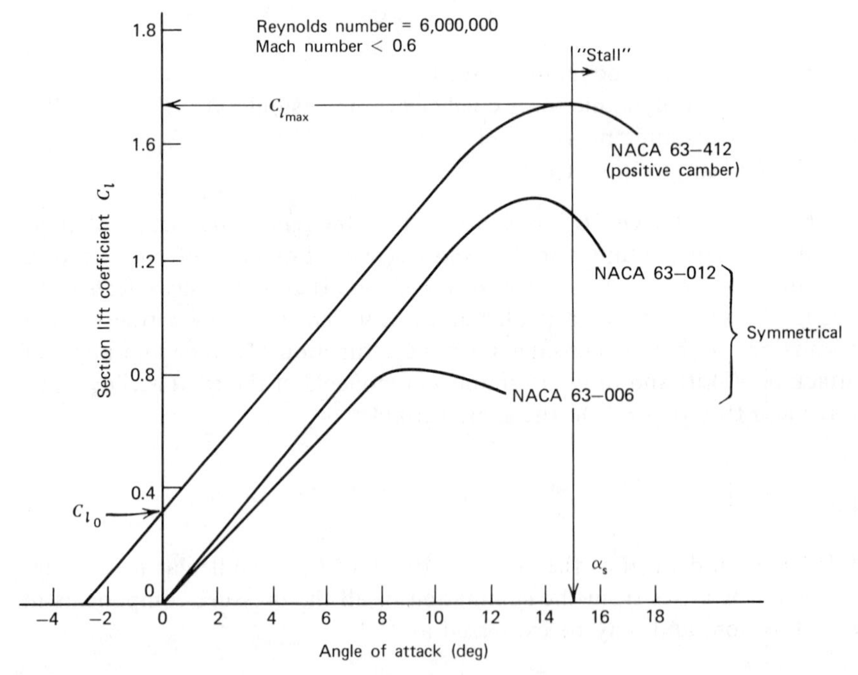

Figure 2.12 Typical lift curves. (From reference 6.)

where b is the total tip-to-tip span or, in the case of a rotor blade, its diameter (ft). For a rectangular planform S, the surface area is equal to the span times the chord (c)

$$\text{rectangular planforms: } AR = \frac{b^2}{b \cdot c} = \frac{b}{c}$$

Returning to Figure 2.12, several lift curve characteristics should be noted:

1. Even at zero angle of attack some positive lift may be generated in positively cambered airfoils (C_{l_0}). Symmetrical airfoils, as we have seen, generate no lift at zero angle of attack, and it follows that negatively cambered airfoils would have a negative lift in this condition.
2. The lift coefficient has a relatively linear relationship to angle of attack for a certain range. The slope of this line is an indication of the sensitivity of lift to changes in the angle of attack. The steeper the slope, the higher the sensitivity. This "lift curve slope" is important to the gust response of the aircraft and to its longitudinal static stability.
3. The curve has a maximum value, $C_{l_{max}}$, corresponding to the angle of attack for static stall. Beyond the stall angle of attack, lift decreases. The shape of the curve past this point contributes to, but is not the only influence on, the poststall behavior of the aircraft. It must be appreciated that such curves are determined by placing the airfoil at fixed angles of attack and measuring lift. The curves then depict the *static* lift characteristics of the airfoil. In helicopter flight, as we see in the next two chapters, a blade airfoil section may experience *dynamic* conditions, that is it may experience an ever-changing angle of attack. The "instantaneous" lift produced while passing through a given angle of attack is in general different from the value achieved at that angle of attack in steady flight. Similarly, $C_{l_{max}}$ and α_s are different under unsteady conditions, as we discuss in Section 4.3. The picture at the end of this chapter depicts an airfoil oscillating in pitch and showing the unsteady vorticies shed from the leading edge once in every cycle.

All wing sections in a fixed wing aircraft experience the same velocity, and a total aircraft C_L-α curve may be generated. For straight and level flight where $L = W$ we obtain:

$$W = C_L q S \quad \text{lb}$$
$$W = C_L \tfrac{1}{2} \rho V^2 S \quad \text{lb}$$

Thus, for a fixed weight, density, and wing reference area, C_L must increase as speed decreases. There will be a higher trim angle of attack at lower speed. The lowest possible speed corresponds to maximum C_L, that is, at the $C_{L_{\max}}$ and α_s. Thus the 1 g stall speed of a fixed wing aircraft is determined by $C_{L_{\max}}$. Also, as weight increases at fixed $C_{L_{\max}}$, speed must be increased. Thus the stalling speed of a fixed wing aircraft increases with increasing weight.

Higher lift, when needed (e.g., in slow speed flight, heavy weight flight, and/or maneuvering) has been achieved in most fixed wing aircraft by using "high lift devices." Applied to the trailing edge of a section, a high lift device consists of a flap that is usually 15 to 25% of the chord. The deflection of a flap produces the effect of a large amount of camber added well aft on the chord. The usual types of flaps and their effects are shown in Figure 2.13. The main effect of this kind of trailing edge device is to shift the lift curve upward without appreciable change in lift curve slope. Even though the stalling angle is decreased somewhat, the upward shift increases $C_{l_{\max}}$. Also shown is a "drag polar" in which the drag characteristics are plotted together with the lift coefficient. Note that a drag penalty always accompanies lift increases. Note also that at low values of lift coefficient all such devices tend to have higher drag than does the basic section. In any case, the lift-to-drag ratio is highest for the basic, "clean" section. Flaps are of course primarily used in landing where the highest C_l provides the lowest approach speed for a given weight. The accompanying drag increase must be compensated for with additional thrust.

High lift devices applied to the leading edge of a section consist of slots, slats, and small amounts of local camber. The fixed slot in a wing conducts flow of high energy air into the boundary layer on the upper surface and delays airflow separation to some higher angle of attack and lift coefficient. Since the slot alone effects no change in camber, the higher maximum lift coefficient is obtained at a higher angle of attack, that is, the slot simply delays stall to a higher angle of attack, as shown in Figure 2.14.

The devices that control boundary layers also serve to increase the maximum lift coefficient of a section. They are used in some operational fixed wing aircraft where the thin layer of airflow adjacent to the surface of an airfoil shows reduced local velocities from the effect of skin friction. At high angles of attack this boundary layer on the upper surface tends to stagnate and come to a stop. The airflow then separates from the surface, and a stall occurs. By blowing or sucking through ports in the wing surface the boundary layer can be energized, delaying separation to higher angles of attack, with accompanying increases in maximum lift coefficient. In complicated flap arrangements, which attempt to turn the air through a large angle without separation, stalling of the flap section itself can be troublesome. Gaining increasing attention and application (especially in STOL aircraft) is the "blown flap" or "jet flap" device, one arrangement of

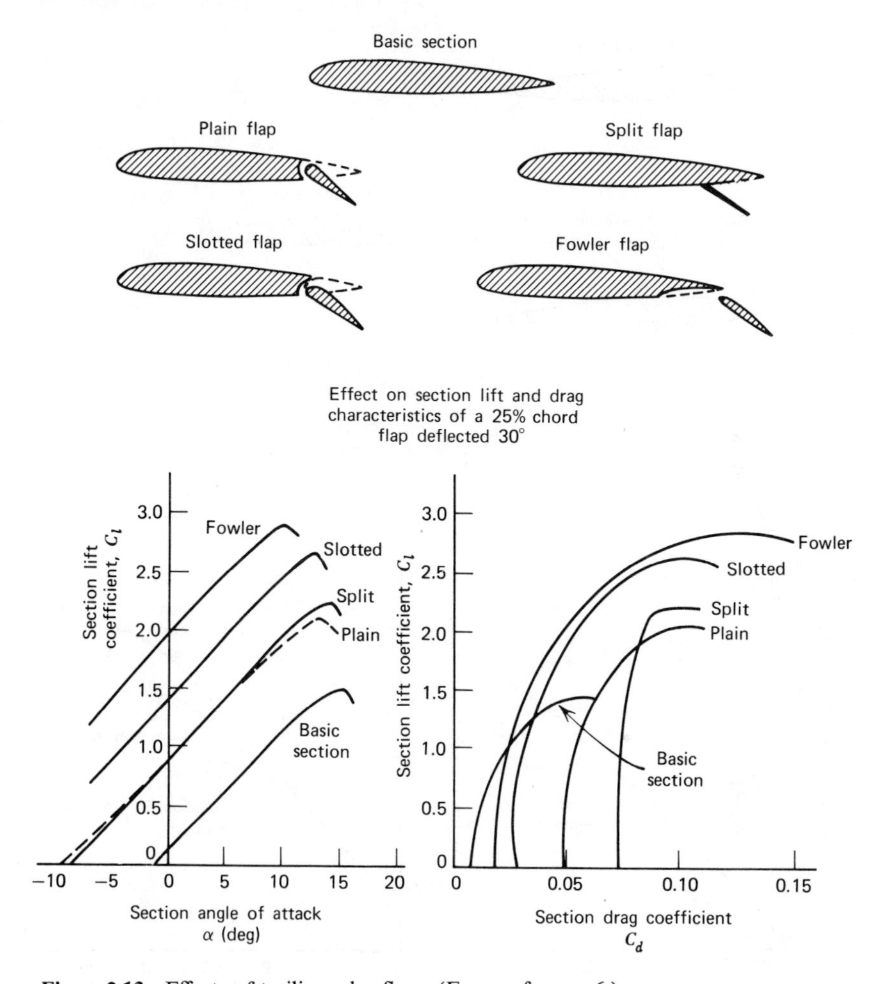

Figure 2.13 Effects of trailing edge flaps. (From reference 6.)

which is shown in Figure 2.15. This combination of a trailing edge device with boundary layer control has produced exceptionally high lift coefficients. Naturally, boundary layer control involves mechanical complexity and weight; it demands a source of air, hence some engine power for operation.

High lift devices are not widely used in helicopter rotors, being limited to experimental and research activity. One drawback is the mechanical complexity of the required control systems to the rotating blades. Moreover, there is less need for such devices in the helicopter rotor, because it operates over a very limited airspeed range by virtue of its rotational velocity com-

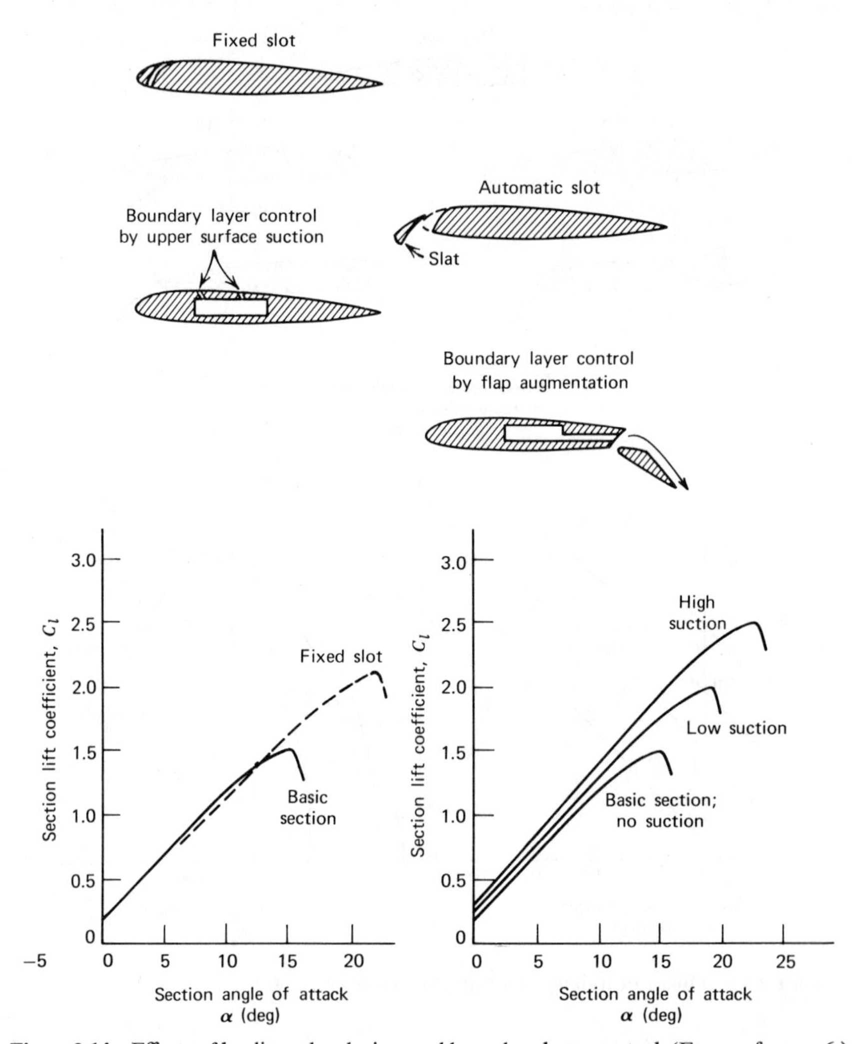

Figure 2.14 Effects of leading edge devices and boundary layer control. (From reference 6.)

ponent. For example, if the tip speed of a typical helicopter is 700 fps and the maximum helicopter speed is 200 fps, the maximum TAS seen by the blade is 900 fps. In hover, the tip speed is 700 fps, so that the tip sees only a 28.6% variation in TAS. A commercial airliner might have an approach speed at sea level of 120 knots and a maximum cruise speed of 600 knots for a variation of 500%. Thus the fixed wing aircraft has a much wider envelope, often requiring solutions that involve complex devices. There is

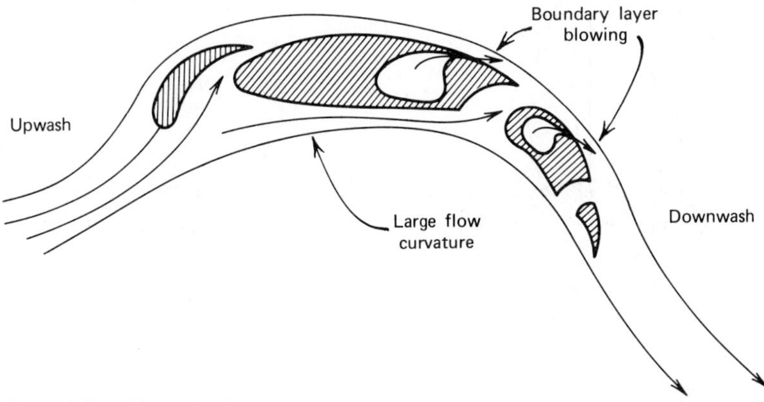

Figure 2.15 Blown jet flap.

also the problem of pitching moments associated with cambered airfoils and flapped airfoils. Besides a net aerodynamic force, the pressure distribution on cambered airfoils also produces a net pitching moment, as shown in Figure 2.16. As angle of attack changes, there is one point in the airfoil, called the aerodynamic center, where pitching moment does not change. For most helicopter blade sections this point is located between 23 and 27% of the chord aft of the leading edge. The entire pressure distribution may then be replaced by a constant pitching moment about the aerodynamic center and a variable lift and drag acting through the aerodynamic center. For positively cambered airfoils a nosedown pitching moment is obtained, a zero moment for symmetrical sections, and a noseup one for negatively cambered airfoils. For helicopter blades, which by nature have low torsional stiffness, pitching moments may cause intolerable amounts of structural twist, as well as excessive loads on the pitch control linkages. This is another reason why cambered airfoils have not been used in the past. The greater structural stiffness, without severe weight penalties, that is now being introduced allows designers to achieve the desirable characteristics of cambered airfoils, which are thus becoming increasingly popular.

Stall

The maximum lift capability of any airfoil is associated with its stalling behavior. To understand the stall mechanism, consider the flow immediately adjacent to the surface. This so-called "boundary layer" is the region of the flow in which local velocities are reduced by the surface itself through the

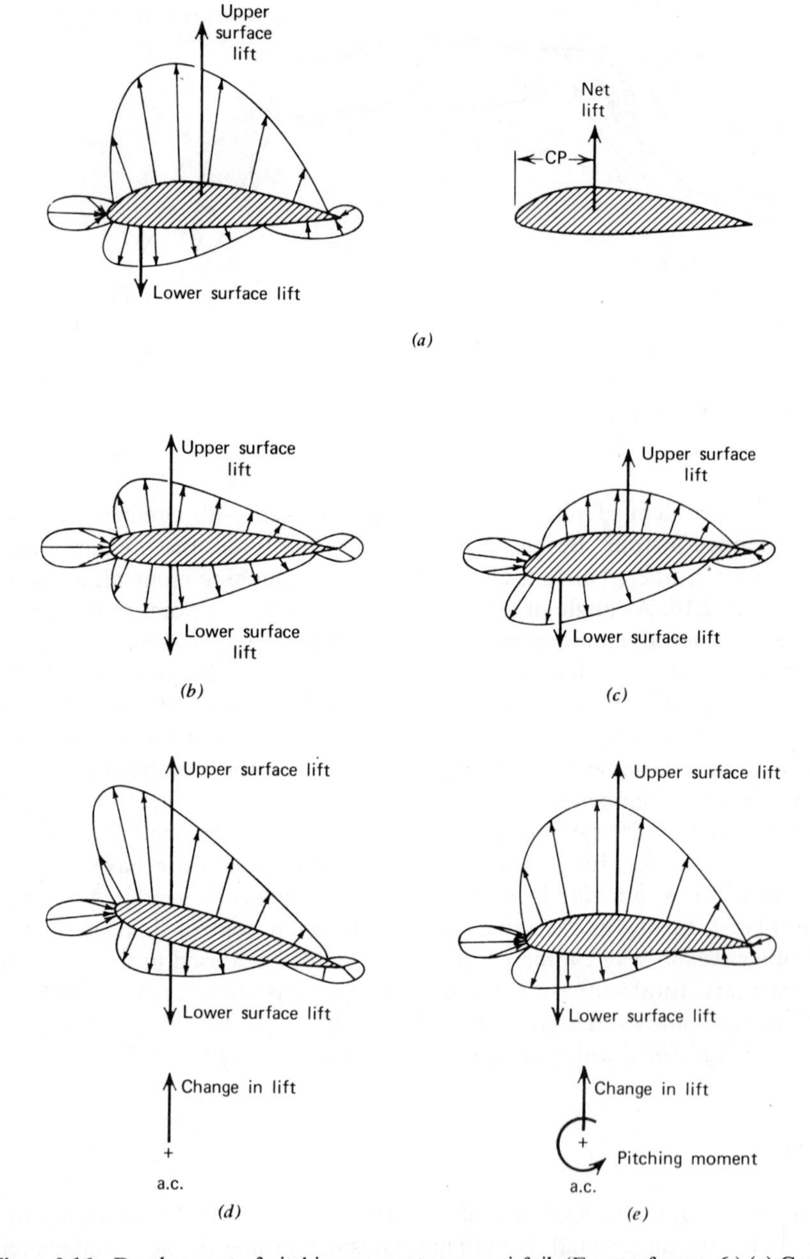

Figure 2.16 Development of pitching moments on an airfoil. (From reference 6.) (*a*) Cambered airfoil developing positive lift. (*b*) Symmetrical airfoil at zero lift. (*c*) Cambered airfoil at zero lift. (*d*) Symmetrical airfoil at positive lift. (*e*) Cambered airfoil at positive lift.

resistance to flow characteristics of the fluid's viscosity. Although the boundary layer is usually very thin, it greatly affects the character of the entire flow field. It grows in thickness downstream from the stagnation point as the friction effect on the fluid (and conversely the skin friction drag on the surface) is progressively increased.

Two "types" of boundary layers have been classified. The "laminar" boundary layer has low energy, is smooth, and has little transfer of momentum between parallel layers. The "turbulent" boundary layer, as its name implies, has a lot of mixing, is of high energy and produces more skin friction drag. The "transition" from laminar to turbulent occurs naturally on an airfoil at a location dependent on airfoil shape, angle of attack, free stream velocity, and fluid viscosity. Viscosity effects are often discussed in terms of Reynold's number, which is defined by

$$\mathrm{RN} = \frac{Vc}{\nu}$$

where V = free stream velocity (fps)
c = chord (ft)
ν = kinematic viscosity ($\mathrm{ft}^2/\mathrm{sec}$)

This nondimensional number is an indicator of the viscosity effects. It has been clearly demonstrated that aerodynamic forces and moments depend strongly on RN, independently of the other variables. Typically RN can range from 1 to 6,000,000 for helicopter rotor sections.

Consider the flow over the top of an airfoil at high angle of attack. From a place near the point of maximum thickness and thence aft, the pressure gradient is "adverse," that is, the velocities are decreasing, hence the pressures are increasing. The flow thus sees an uphill climb from a low to a high pressure area. The success in negotiating this gradient depends on the momentum of the flow. In the boundary layer the flow has less momentum than elsewhere; hence it has a more difficult time. As angle of attack is increased further, the pressure gradient becomes even more adverse than before. Eventually, insufficient energy in the turbulent boundary layer causes it to become detached from the surface at some "separation point." Further increases in angle of attack cause the separation point to migrate upstream, thus adversely affecting the aerodynamics over an increasing portion of the airfoil. The result is rapid loss of lift and increase in drag—a stall.

The stall described above is the so-called trailing edge stall. It is characterized by a gentle stall in both lift and pitching moment. The "thin airfoil stall" shown in Figure 2.17 is caused by separation of the laminar boundary layer at the nose, which produces a "bubble" whose upper surface flow is

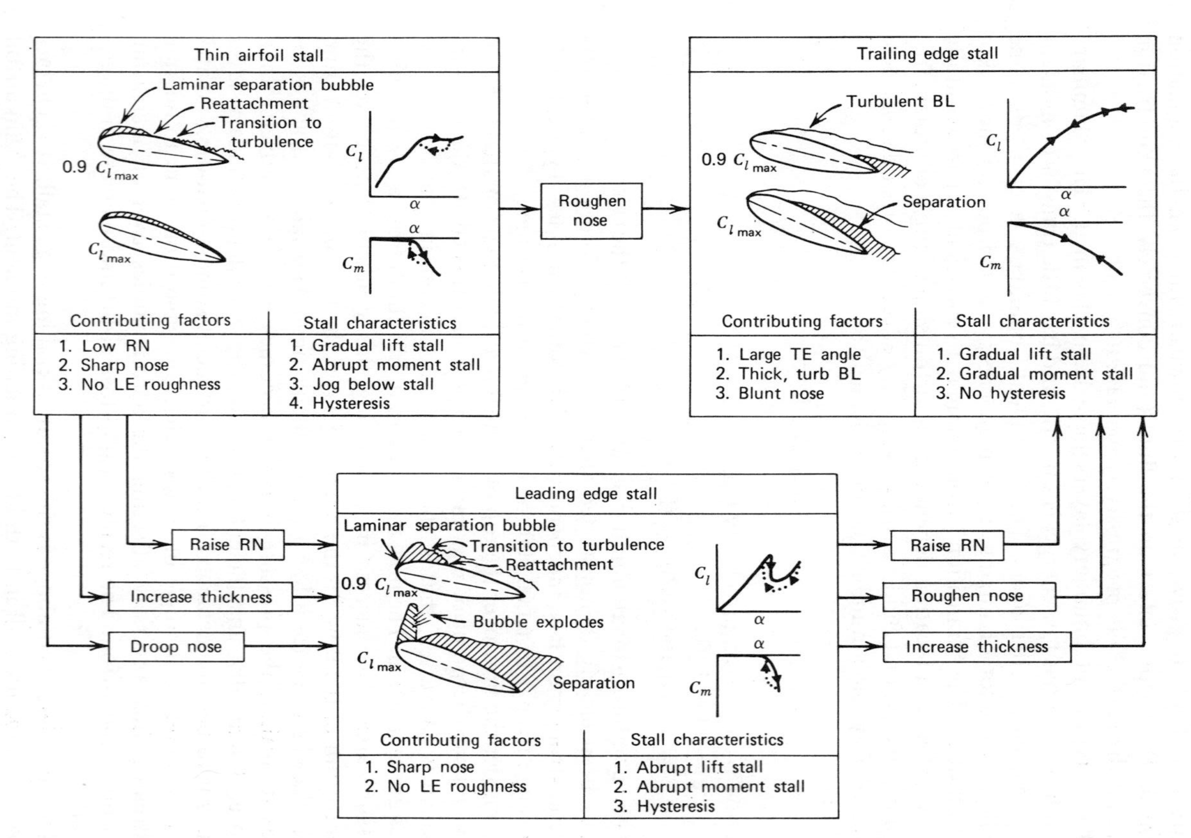

Figure 2.17 Airfoil stall characteristics.

laminar over the full chord length. Thin airfoil stall occurs at low RN and has a gentle lift stall but a severe pitching moment. Leading edge roughness produces either the same or larger maximum lift coefficient.

The "leading edge stall" is caused by separation of the laminar boundary layer at the nose, which produces a bubble whose upper surface may have a transition to turbulent flow before it goes the full chord length. An abrupt stall both in lift and in pitching moment results. Adding leading edge roughness decreases $C_{l_{\max}}$. Figure 2.17 summarizes these effects.

Figure 2.18 illustrates a number of typical helicopter blade sections, showing $C_{l_{\max}}$ values and the type of stall encountered. Figure 2.19 depicts the effect of both Mach number (to be discussed in Section 2.5) and Reynold's number.

Drag

Drag is the net aerodynamic force parallel to the relative wind. The components of pressure in this direction and skin friction are its source. Large, thick, bluff bodies show a predominance of drag due to unbalanced pressure distribution fore and aft (called "form" drag). This effect is mini-

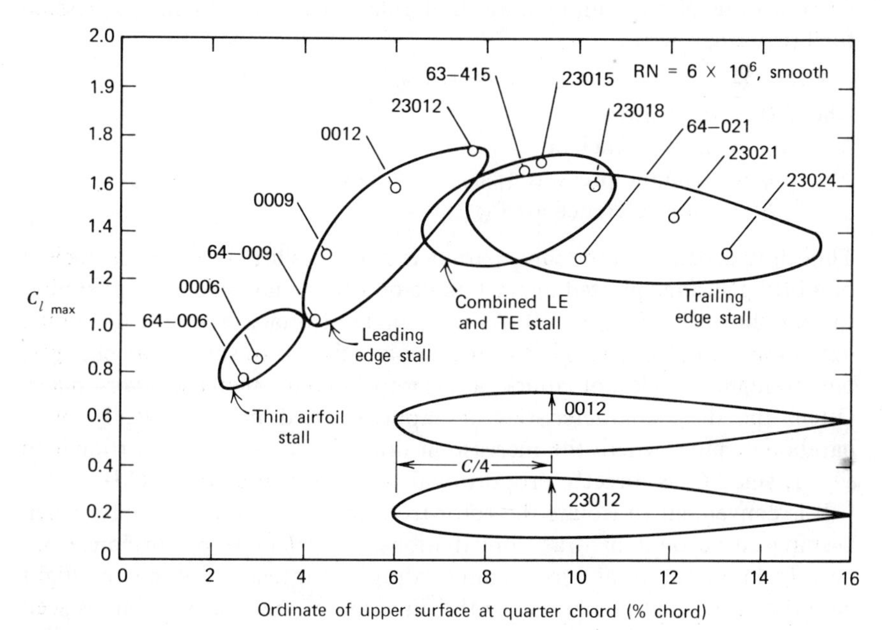

Figure 2.18 Maximum lift coefficient of several airfoils at low Mach numbers.

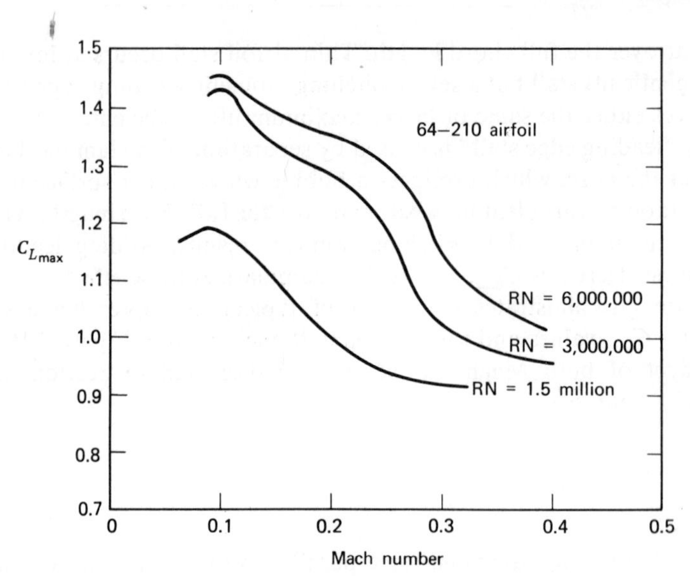

Figure 2.19 Effect of Mach and Reynolds numbers on maximum lift coefficient.

mized in slender streamlined bodies with smooth contours, where the skin friction drag plays a more important role. Analogous to the expression for lift, we can write

$$D = C_d q S$$

where D = drag (lb)
C_d = drag coefficient
q = dynamic pressure (psf)
S = wing reference area (ft^2)

Thus drag depends on the same parameters as does lift. The drag coefficient of a lifting surface plotted against angle of attack may give a result similar to that shown in Figure 2.20. At zero angle of attack a small, but finite, drag exists. Small changes in the angle of attack lead to small drag changes, but at higher angles of attack a disproportionate increase takes place. Often, the drag characteristics are approximated mathematically by a parabolic shape, where the increase in drag above C_{d_0} is proportional to α^2 (or, since C_l is directly proportional to α prior to stall, to C_l^2).

It is convenient to isolate the rotor from the rest of the helicopter when keeping an account of drag contributions. To calculate performance, we need to know the total aerodynamic "drag" as measured along the flight path direction, that is, parallel to the direction of the relative wind as seen by the fuselage. Each blade element, however, "sees" a different relative

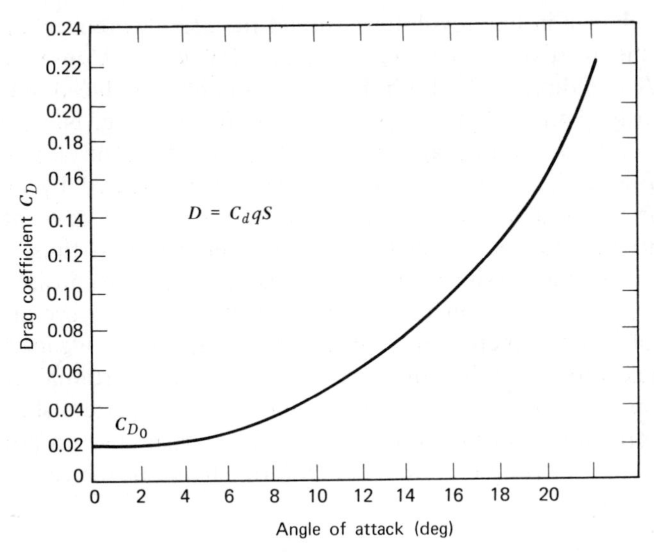

Figure 2.20 Drag characteristics.

wind, because of its velocity of rotation, for example. The rotor blade is examined in considerable detail later. For now let us identify the following "kinds" of drag:

1. *Parasite drag.* Parasite drag is associated with the nonlifting portions of the fuselage, including cockpit, engine cowlings, rotor hub, landing gear, and tail boom. It is measured in the direction of flight, and includes all form drag and skin friction associated with these components.
2. *Profile drag.* Profile drag is the equivalent of parasite drag for the rotor blades themselves. Its direction on a blade section changes continuously relative to the aircraft axis system, though not relative to a rotating axis system in the blade. Profile drag includes all form drag and skin friction that occur at a local zero lift condition ($C_l = 0$) and does not change appreciably with angle of attack of the section.
3. *Induced drag.* Induced drag is associated with the production of lift, sometimes called "drag due to lift." Fuselage sections such as fixed wings, sync-elevators, and horizontal tail surfaces produce additional drag when they are lifting. A requirement for increased lift necessarily incurs an increased induced drag penalty. Induced drag of fixed surfaces is a function of fuselage angle of attack and surface incidence. Rotor blade sections also produce increased drag as a function of *local* angle of attack. As we shall see, the local angle of attack of a rotor blade element may undergo con-

siderable change in one revolution around the disc. Moreover, the magnitude of the relative velocity may change drastically. Consequently the magnitude and direction of both the profile and blade induced drag may be continuously changing and may require careful tracking. Nonethless, the basic reason for induced drag is the same for any lifting surface, as may be seen in Figure 2.21. The upwash-downwash field created by any lifting surface produces an average relative wind that is inclined downwards. The section lift therefore is inclined aft by the same amount, thus creating a component parallel to the remote free stream. Hence if we insist on measuring drag in the direction of the upstream flow, we measure an increase as angle of attack is increased. Since the magnitude of the lift itself (as well as the angle with which it is inclined backward) is proportional to angle of attack, the "drag due to lift" is proportional to the square of the angle of attack (or the square of the lift coefficient). The constant of proportionality is found to be a strong function of planform shape. In the case of a fixed wing or surface:

$$C_{D_i} = \frac{C_L^2}{\pi e AR}$$

where C_{D_i} = wing induced drag coefficient
C_L = wing lift coefficient
AR = aspect ratio
e = span efficiency factor

The span efficiency factor is a number that reflects the efficiency of the entire surface in sharing the lift load. It has been demonstrated that when the lift is distributed spanwise in an elliptical manner, minimum induced drag occurs, in which case e has a value of 1.0. In less efficient circumstances e is less than 1.0 (the elliptical lift distribution idea is not strictly valid for rotor blades where velocity varies spanwise). The importance of aspect ratio is evident in the expression above. Aircraft such as gliders have large span-to-chord ratios, large aspect ratios, and low induced drag. Low span delta planforms, found on some jet fighters, suffer from high induced drag when high lift is required.

Lift-Drag Ratio

A factor of considerable importance to some aspects of both fixed wing and helicopter flight, is the ratio of lift to drag:

$$\frac{L}{D} = \frac{C_L q S}{C_D q S} = \frac{C_L}{C_D}$$

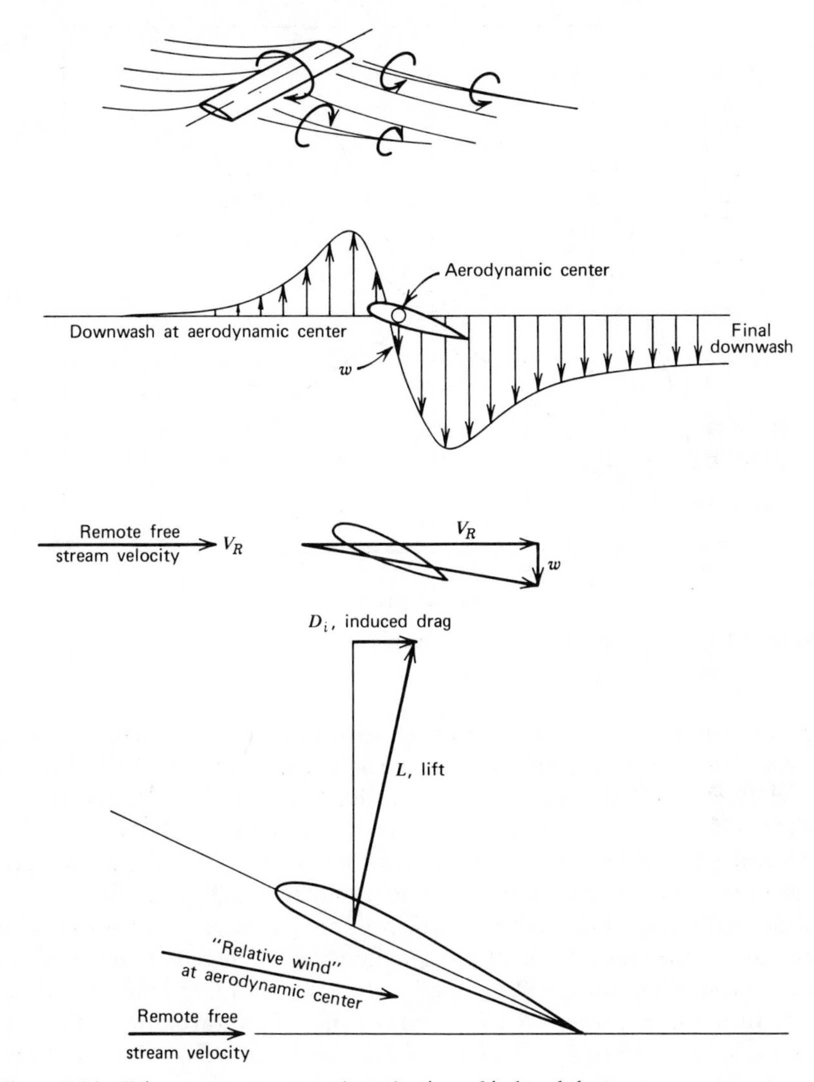

Figure 2.21 Wing vortex system and production of induced drag.

Figure 2-12 showed how C_l typically varies with angle of attack and Figure 2.20 showed a typical drag variation. For a symmetrical airfoil at zero angle of attack C_l is zero, while C_D is finite, yielding a zero value for L/D. Conversely, at high angles of attack near the stall lift is maximum, but drag is disproportionately greater. Thus there is some angle of attack in between, where L/D is maximum, as shown in Figure 2.22. Note that dynamic pres-

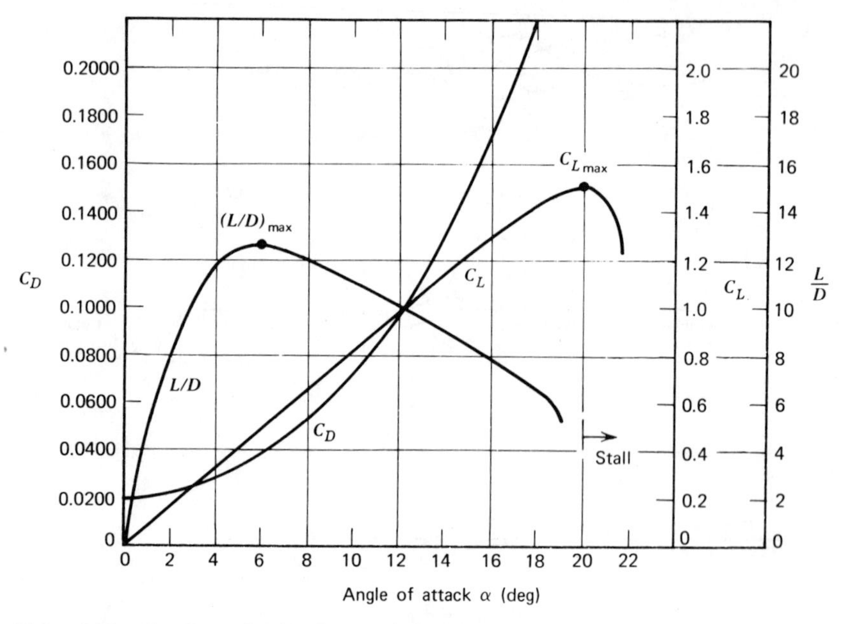

Figure 2.22 C_L, C_D, and L/D characteristics.

sure and surface area do not affect the lift-to-drag ratio. It depends only on shape (not size) and angle of attack. The old story about a lead airplane and a balsa wood airplane of the same shape having the same power-off gliding distance is true, since that performance is directly linked to L/D. Both aircraft would have to fly at the same angle of attack to achieve maximum L/D, but of course the heavier one would have to fly *faster* in order to produce the required lift. While certain sections of the rotor blades may be experiencing the angle of attack for maximum L/D, in general most of the blades, most of the time, will be in off-optimum conditions from this viewpoint. In terms of power-off glide performances in autorotation, the helicopter displays overall L/D's of 4 to 6 (although individual blade sections may display much higher values)—a ratio comparable to that for some supersonic fighters but, far short of the 10 to 15 achieved by many general aviation aircraft or the 25 to 40 achieved by high performance sailplanes.

2.5 COMPRESSIBLE FLOW

The relatively high velocity of helicopter rotor tips, especially on the advancing side in high speed flight, may produce "compressibility" effects, that is, local density changes, causing fundamentally different aerodynamics than are experienced at lower speed. The formation of shock waves on the blade, with an accompanying increase in drag, large pitching moments, and noise, has significance in helicopter dynamics.

Nature of Compressibility

At low flight speeds air experiences relatively small changes in pressure and only negligible changes in density. This airflow is termed *incompressible*, since the air may undergo changes in pressure without apparent changes in density. Such a condition of airflow is analogous to the flow of water, hydraulic fluid, or any other incompressible fluid. However, at high flight speeds large changes in air pressure and significant changes in air density occur. The study of airflow at high speeds must account for these changes in air density, must consider the air to be compressible, hence vulnerable to "compressibility effects."

A very important factor in the study of high speed airflow is the speed of sound. The speed of sound is the rate at which small pressure disturbances are propagated through the air; this speed of propagation is solely a function of air temperature. Table 2.3 illustrates the variation of the speed of sound in the standard atmosphere.

As an object moves through the airmass, velocity and pressure changes occur that create pressure disturbances in the airflow surrounding the object.

Table 2.3 Variation of Temperature and Speed of Sound with Altitude in the Standard Atmosphere

Altitude (ft)	Temperature		Speed of Sound (knots)
	°F	°C	
Sea level	59.0	15.0	661.7
5,000	41.2	5.1	650.3
10,000	23.3	−4.8	638.6
15,000	5.5	−14.7	626.7
20,000	−12.3	−24.6	614.6
25,000	−30.2	−34.5	602.2
30,000	−48.2	−44.4	589.6
35,000	−65.8	−54.3	576.6
40,000	−69.7	−56.5	573.8
50,000	−69.7	−56.5	573.8
60,000	−69.7	−56.5	573.8

These pressure disturbances are, of course, propagated through the air at the speed of sound. If the object is traveling at low speed, the pressure disturbances are propagated ahead of the object, and the airflow immediately ahead of the object is influenced by the pressure field on the object. Actually, these pressure disturbances are transmitted in all directions and extend indefinitely in all directions. Evidence of this "pressure warning" is seen in the typical subsonic flow pattern of Figure 2.23, where there is upwash and flow direction changes well ahead of the leading edge. If the object is

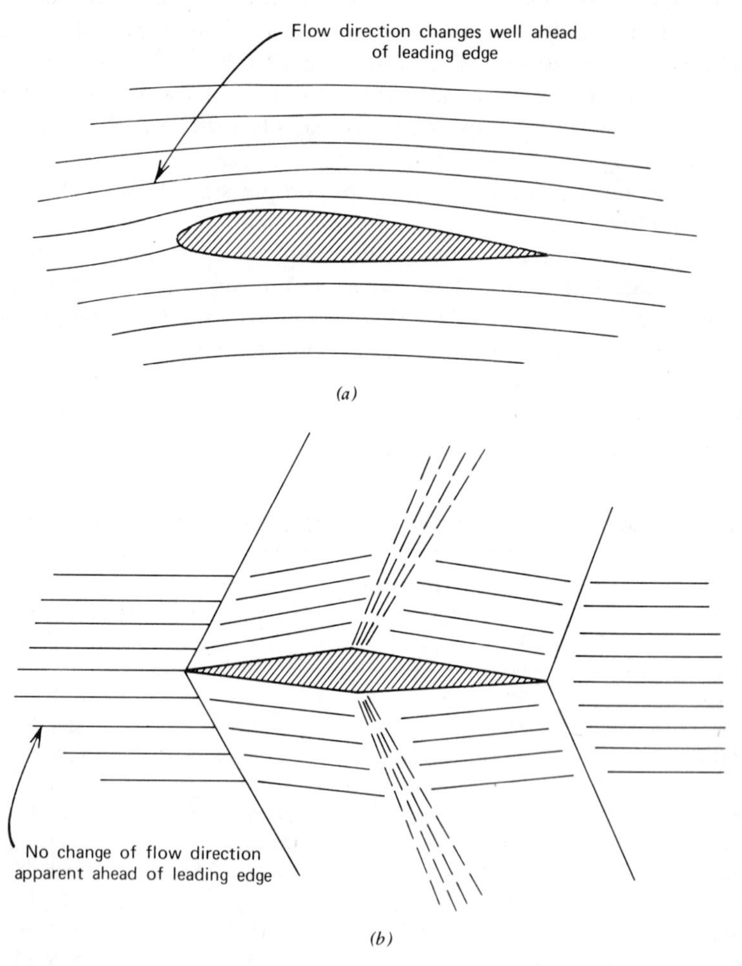

Figure 2.23 Compasiron of subsonic and supersonic flow patterns. (*a*) Typical subsonic flow pattern. (*b*) Typical supersonic flow pattern. (From reference 6.)

traveling at some speed above the speed of sound, the airflow ahead of the object is not influenced by the pressure field on the object, since pressure disturbances cannot be propagated ahead of the object. Thus, as the flight speed nears the speed of sound, a compression wave forms at the leading edge, and all changes in velocity and pressure take place quite sharply and suddenly. The airflow ahead of the object is not influenced until the air particles are suddenly forced out of the way by the concentrated pressure wave set up by the object. Evidence of this phenomenon is seen in the typical supersonic flow pattern of Figure 2.23.

The analogy of surface waves on the water may help to clarify these phenomena. Since a surface wave is simply the propagation of a pressure disturbance, a ship moving at a speed much below the wave speed does *not* form a "bow wave." As the ship's speed nears the wave propagation speed, the bow wave forms and becomes stronger as speed is increased beyond the wave speed.

At this point it should become apparent that all compressibility effects depend on the relationship of airspeed to the speed of sound. The term used to describe this relationship is the Mach number, M, which is the ratio of the true airspeed to the speed of sound:

$$M = \frac{V}{a}$$

where M = Mach number
V = true airspeed (knots)
a = speed of sound (knots)

It is important to note that compressibility effects are not limited to speeds at and above the speed of sound. Since a blade section has an aerodynamic shape, hence develops lift, there are local flow velocities on the surfaces that are greater than the section's flight speed. Thus a section may experience compressibility effects at speeds well below the speed of sound. The helicopter itself may have zero speed.

At a low rate of rotation in hover, pure subsonic airflow is most likely to exist on all parts of the blades. At higher speeds flow on the outboard sections may be partly subsonic and partly supersonic.

The principal differences between subsonic and supersonic flow are due to the *compressibility* of the supersonic flow. Thus a change in the velocity or pressure of a supersonic flow produces a related change in density that must be considered and accounted for. Figure 2.24 compares incompressible and compressible flow through a closed tube. Of course, the condition of continuity must exist in the flow through the closed tube; the mass flow at

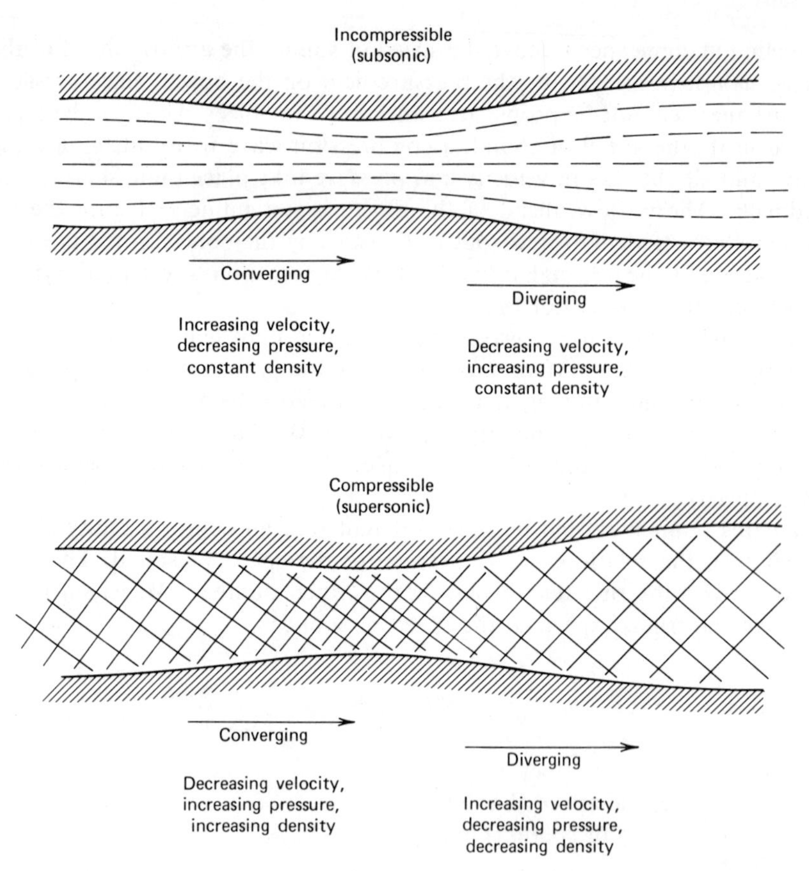

Figure 2.24 Comparison of compressible and incompressible flows through a channel. (From reference 6.)

any station along the tube is constant. This qualification must be present in both compressible and incompressible cases.

The example of subsonic incompressible flow is simplified by the fact that the density of flow is constant throughout the tube. Thus as the flow approaches a constriction and the streamlines converge, velocity increases and static pressure decreases. In other words, a convergence of the tube requires an increasing velocity to accommodate the continuity of flow. Also, as the subsonic incompressible flow enters a diverging section of the tube, velocity decreases and static pressure increases, but density remains unchanged. Thus convergence causes expansion (decreasing pressure), while a divergence causes compression (increasing pressure).

The example of supersonic compressible flow is complicated by the fact that the variations of flow density are related to the changes in velocity and static pressure. Thus a convergence causes compression, while a divergence causes expansion. As the supersonic compressible flow approaches a constriction and the streamlines converge, velocity decreases and static pressure increases. Continuity of mass flow is maintained by the increase in flow density that accompanies the decrease in velocity. As the supersonic compressible flow enters a diverging section of the tube, velocity increases, static pressure decreases, and density decreases to accommodate the condition of continuity.

Three significant differences between supersonic compressible and subsonic incompressible flows are thus evident:

1. Compressible flow includes the additional variable of flow density.
2. Convergence of flow causes acceleration of incompressible flow but deceleration of compressible flow.
3. Divergence of flow causes deceleration of incompressible flow but acceleration of compressible flow.

Formation of Shock Waves on Airfoils

Any object in subsonic flight that has some finite thickness or is producing lift encounters local velocities on the surface that are greater than the free stream velocity. Hence compressibility effects can be expected to occur at flight speeds below the speed of sound.

Consider a conventional airfoil shape (Figure 2.25). If this airfoil is at a local Mach number of 0.50 and a slight positive angle of attack, the maximum local velocity on the surface is greater than the flight speed, but most likely smaller than sonic speed. Assume that an increase in local Mach number to 0.72 would produce *first evidence of local sonic flow*. This condition of flight would be the highest flight speed possible without *supersonic* flow and would be termed the "critical Mach number." Thus critical Mach number is the boundary between subsonic and transonic flight and is an important point of reference for all compressibility effects encountered in transonic flight. By definition, critical Mach number is the "free stream Mach number that produces first evidence of local sonic flow." Therefore, shock waves, buffet, airflow separation, and so on, take place above critical Mach number.

As critical Mach number is exceeded, an area of *supersonic* airflow is created, and a normal shock wave forms as the boundary between the supersonic and subsonic flows on the aft portion of the airfoil surface. The accel-

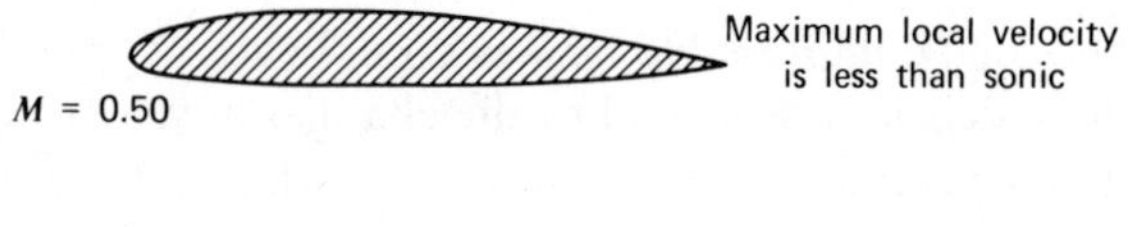

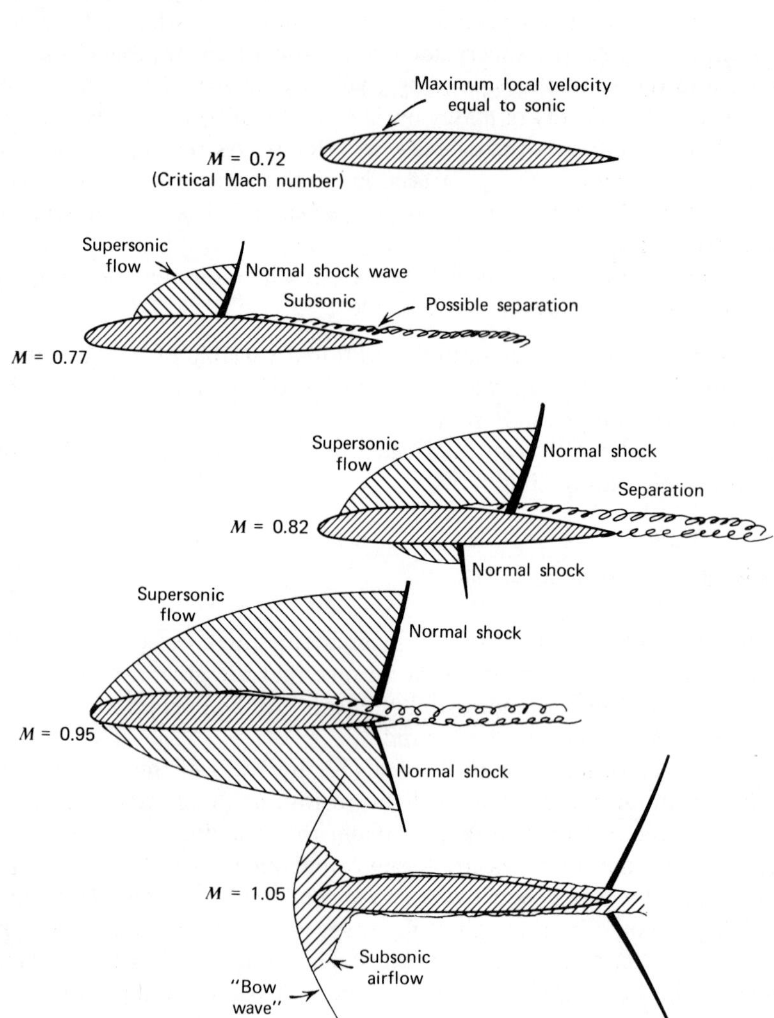

Figure 2.25 Formation of shock waves on an airfoil. (From reference 6.)

eration of the airflow from subsonic to supersonic is smooth and unaccompanied by shock waves if the surface is smooth and the transition gradual. However, the transition of airflow from supersonic to subsonic is always accompanied by a shock wave and, when there is no change in direction of the airflow, the wave is a normal shock wave.

Recall that one of the principal effects of the normal shock wave is a large increase in the static pressure of the airstream behind the wave. If the shock wave is strong, the boundary layer may not have sufficient kinetic energy to withstand the large, adverse pressure gradient, and separation occurs. At speeds only slightly beyond critical Mach number the shock wave formed is not strong enough to cause separation or any noticeable change in the aerodynamic force coefficients. However, an increase in speed above critical Mach number sufficient to form a strong shock wave can cause separation of the boundary layer and produce sudden changes in the aerodynamic force coefficients. Such a flow condition is shown in Figure 2.25 by the flow pattern for $M = 0.77$. Notice that a further increase in Mach number to 0.82 can enlarge the supersonic area on the upper surface and form an additional area of supersonic flow and normal shock wave on the lower surface.

As the flight speed approaches the speed of sound, the areas of supersonic flow enlarge and the shock waves move nearer the trailing edge. The boundary layer may remain separated or may reattach depending on the airfoil shape and angle of attack. When the flight speed exceeds the speed of sound the "bow" wave forms at the leading edge; this typical flow pattern is illustrated in Figure 2.25 by the drawing for $M = 1.05$. If the speed is increased to some higher supersonic value, all oblique portions of the waves incline more, and the detached normal shock portion of the bow wave moves closer to the leading edge.

Of course, all components of the aircraft are affected by compressibility in a manner somewhat similar to that of a basic airfoil. The tail, fuselage, nacelles, canopy, and other components and the effect of the interference between the various surfaces of the aircraft must be considered.

Effects on Lift and Drag

The airflow separation induced by shock wave formation can create significant variations in the aerodynamic force coefficients. When the free stream speed is greater than critical Mach number, such effects on an airfoil section as the following occur:

1. An increase in the section drag coefficient for a given section lift coefficient.

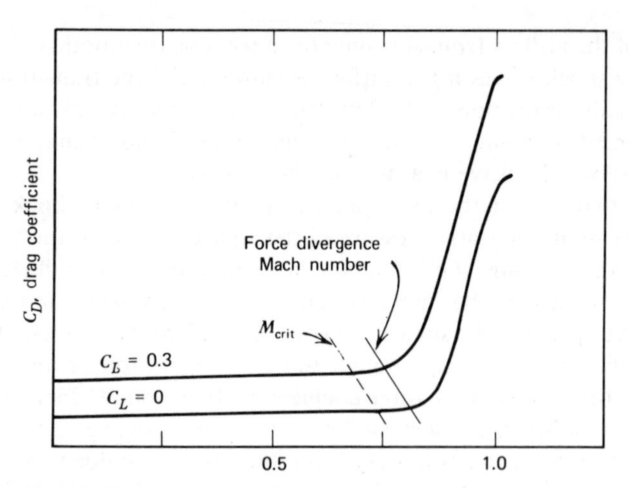

Figure 2.26 Compressibility drag rise.

2. A decrease in section lift coefficient for a given section angle of attack.
3. A change in section pitching moment coefficient.

A reference point is usually taken by a plot of drag coefficient versus Mach number for a constant lift coefficient. Such a graph is shown in Figure 2.26. The Mach number that produces a sharp change in the drag coefficient is termed the "force divergence" Mach number and, for most airfoils, usually exceeds the critical Mach number at least 5 to 10%. This condition is also referred to as the "drag divergence" or "drag rise."

Associated with the drag rise are buffet and generally unsteady flow phenomena. This is especially true for helicopter rotor blades, since the torsional flexibility, particularly at the tips, causes rapid migration of the shock waves fore and aft. Of course, a very severe and prolonged buffet may do structural damage, if such operation is in violation of operating limitations.

Shape Effects

To counter the adverse effects of local transonic flow on helicopter rotor blades, new design ideas, adopted from fixed wing technology, have begun to appear. The critical Mach number may be increased as follows, thus allowing a larger flight envelope without compressibility effects:

1. By selecting thinner airfoils for the tip sections.
2. By a sweepback of the leading edge.

A thinner airfoil, common on high speed fixed wing aircraft, has a smaller velocity increase over its surface than does a thicker airfoil at the same angle of attack. Thus an outboard section of a blade composed of such thin airfoils has a higher M_{crit}. Conversely, increased camber, such as caused by excessive nose droop, increases compressibility effects. These points are illustrated in Figures 2.27 and 2.28.

The effects of sweepback can be seen in Figure 2.29. The swept wing shown has the streamwise velocity broken down into a component of velocity perpendicular to the leading edge and a component parallel to the leading edge. The component of speed perpendicular to the leading edge is less than the free stream speed (by the cosine of the sweep angle), and it is this velocity component that determines the magnitude of the pressure distribution.

The component of speed parallel to the leading edge could be visualized as moving across constant sections and, in doing so, does not contribute to the pressure distribution on the swept wing. Hence sweep of a surface produces a beneficial effect in high speed flight, since higher flight speeds may be obtained before components of speed perpendicular to the leading edge produce critical conditions on the wing. This is one of the most important advantages of sweep, since there is an increase in critical Mach number,

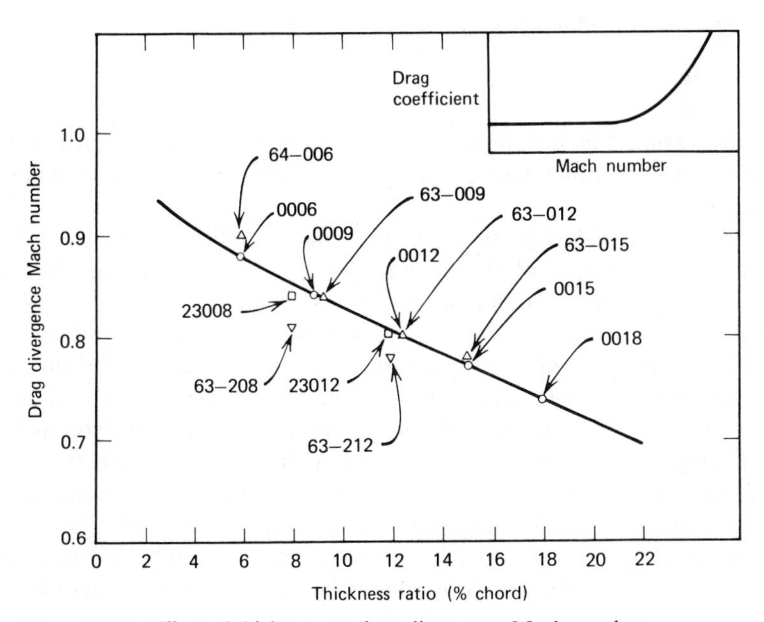

Figure 2.27 Effect of thickness on drag divergence Mach number.

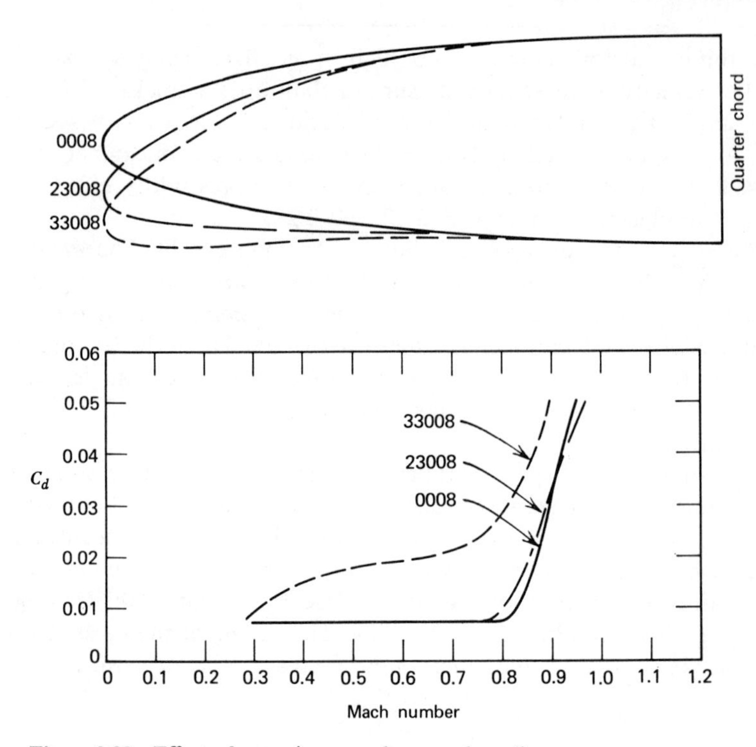

Figure 2.28 Effect of excessive nose drop on drag divergency.

force divergence Mach number, and the Mach number at which the drag rise will peak. In other words, sweep *delays* the onset of compressibility effects.

In addition to *delaying* the onset of compressibility effects, sweepback reduces the magnitude of the changes in force coefficients due to compressibility. Since the component of velocity perpendicular to the leading edge is less than the free stream velocity, the magnitude of all pressure forces on the wing is reduced (approximately by the square of the cosine of the sweep angle). Since compressibility force divergence occurs because of changes in pressure distribution, the use of sweepback will "soften" the force divergence. This effect is illustrated in Figure 2.29, which shows the typical variation of drag coefficient with Mach number for various sweepback angles. The straight wing shown begins drag rise at $M = 0.70$ and reaches a peak near $M = 1.0$. Note that the use of sweepback then *delays* the drag rise to some higher Mach number and *reduces* the magnitude of the drag rise.

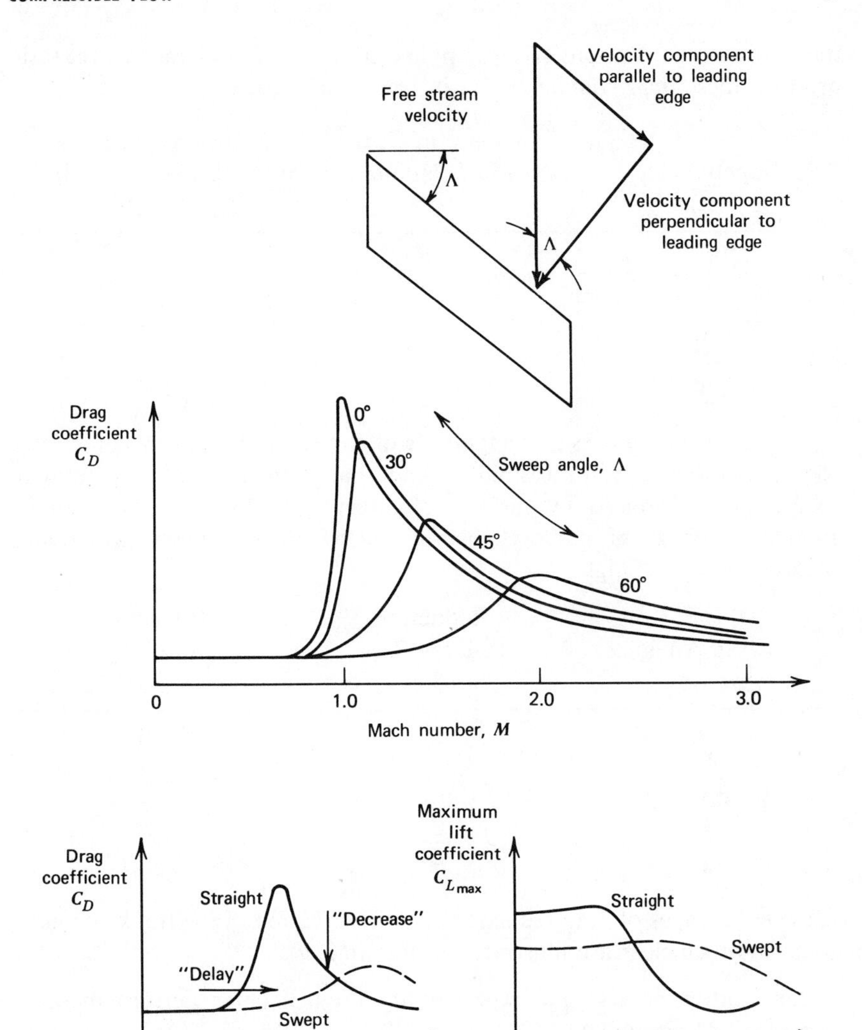

Figure 2.29 Effects of sweepback. (From reference 6.)

To summarize, sweepback has the following principal advantages:

1. Sweepback *delays* the onset of all compressibility effects. Critical Mach number and force divergence Mach number increase, since the velocity component affecting the pressure distribution is less than the free stream velocity. Also, the peak of drag rise is delayed to some higher supersonic speed—approximately the speed that produces sonic flow perpendicular to

the leading edge. Various sweeps applied to wings of moderate aspect ratio produce these *approximate* effects in transonic flight:

Sweep Angle (Λ)	Increase in Critical Mach Number (%)	Increase in Drag Peak Mach Number (%)
0°	0	0
15°	2	4
30°	8	15
45°	20	41
60°	41	100

2. Sweepback reduces the magnitude of change in the aerodynamic force coefficients due to compressibility. Any change in drag, lift, or moment coefficients is reduced by the use of sweepback. Various sweep angles applied to wings of moderate aspect ratio produce these *approximate* effects in transonic flight:

Sweep Angle (Λ)	Reduction in Drag Rise (%)	Reduction in $C_{L_{max}}$ (%)
0°	0	0
15°	5	3
30°	15	13
45°	35	30
60°	60	50

These advantages of drag reduction and preservation of the transonic maximum lift coefficient are illustrated in Figure 2.29.

Quantitative effects of compressibility on helicopter performance are discussed in Section 4.5.

2.6 POWERPLANTS

The engine must supply the main rotor, by way of the main rotor torque at a specified rate of rotation, with the power required to continuously provide the desired rotor thrust. At the same time the tail rotor needs power to do its job, the accessory drives are taking their share to drive electrical generators, hydraulic pumps, and the like, and there are always power losses caused by friction in the transmission drive system. A typical breakdown of

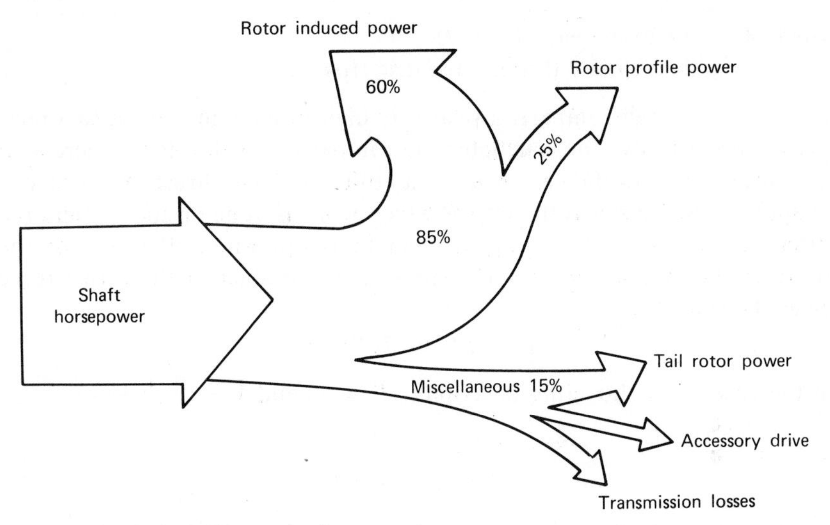

Figure 2.30 Typical power usage in hover.

power dissipation is shown in Figure 2.30. The rotor power source and requirements for a helicopter in hover are treated in the next chapter. Though many helicopters still use reciprocating engines, the many advantages of the shaft turbine engine have led to its widespread use in all types of helicopters. Let us now examine the basic operational principles of both engines, their operational limitations, and their characteristics as seen by the pilot.

Fundamental Principles of Propulsion

Though engines differ greatly in their engineering details and complexities, certain basic principles govern their performance. Any air-breathing propulsion system, be it a pure jet, an engine-propeller combination, or an engine-rotor combination, derives its net thrust by adding momentum to a volume of air. We developed in Chapter 1, using Newton's laws of motion, the relationship

$$\text{thrust} = \text{mass flow rate} \cdot \text{change in velocity}$$

Thus, in hover, where the air is accelerated from rest, the change in velocity equals the velocity through the disc v_i. The mass flow rate, Q slugs/sec, is the product of disc area, density, and v_i. Hence in hover:

$$T_r = \rho A v_i^2 \qquad \text{lb}$$

where A = the disc area (πR^2) (ft^2)
v_i = the velocity through the disc (fps)

Whereas a jet engine imparts a relatively high velocity increment to a relatively low mass flow, the helicopter rotor imparts a small velocity increment to a large mass flow. Power is a quantity different from thrust. As we saw in Chapter 1, the former is the rate at which work is done on the air, and the latter is a force imparted to the air (equal and opposite to the force on the aircraft). The work done per unit time is the product of the thrust force times the velocity:

$$P = TV \qquad \text{ft-lb/sec}$$

In the case of the hovering helicopter, $T = T_r$ and $V = v_i$; hence:

$$P_{\text{hover}} = T_r v_i$$

$$P_{\text{hover}} = \rho A v_i^3$$

It is fundamental to all air-breathing powerplants that both thrust and power depend on density—no air means no thrust or power. Thus the thrust and power available decrease with increasing density altitude. This plays a basic role in deteriorating aircraft performance under those conditions. We see in the standard atmosphere tables (Table 2.1) that the density ratio drops to 73.9% at 10,000 ft and to roughly 50% at 22,000 ft. We must then also expect a decrease in power available of roughly similar magnitudes. Actually, the variation of thrust with altitude is not quite so severe as the density variation in turbine engines because favorable decreases in temperature occur. The decrease in inlet air temperature provides relatively more combustion gas energy and allows a greater exit velocity from the combustion chamber, thus somewhat offsetting the decrease in mass flow. Typically, the available net power may decrease to 78.5% at 10,000 ft and 58% at 22,000 ft in such an engine. In reciprocating engines supercharging must be added to prevent this loss of power with density altitude. Since the basic engine is able to process air only by the basic volume displacement, the function of the supercharger is to compress the inlet air and provide a greater weight of air for the engine to process. Of course, shaft power is necessary to operate the engine-driven supercharger, and a temperature rise occurs through the supercharger compression.

The working cycle of a gas turbine engine is similar to that of a four-stroke piston engine. However, combustion here occurs at a constant pressure, rather than at a constant volume as in the piston engine. Both engine cycles (Figure 2.31) show that in each instance there is induction, compression, combustion, and exhaust. In the piston engine the cycle is intermittent, the piston being involved in all four strokes. The turbine engine, in contrast, has a continuous cycle with a separate compressor,

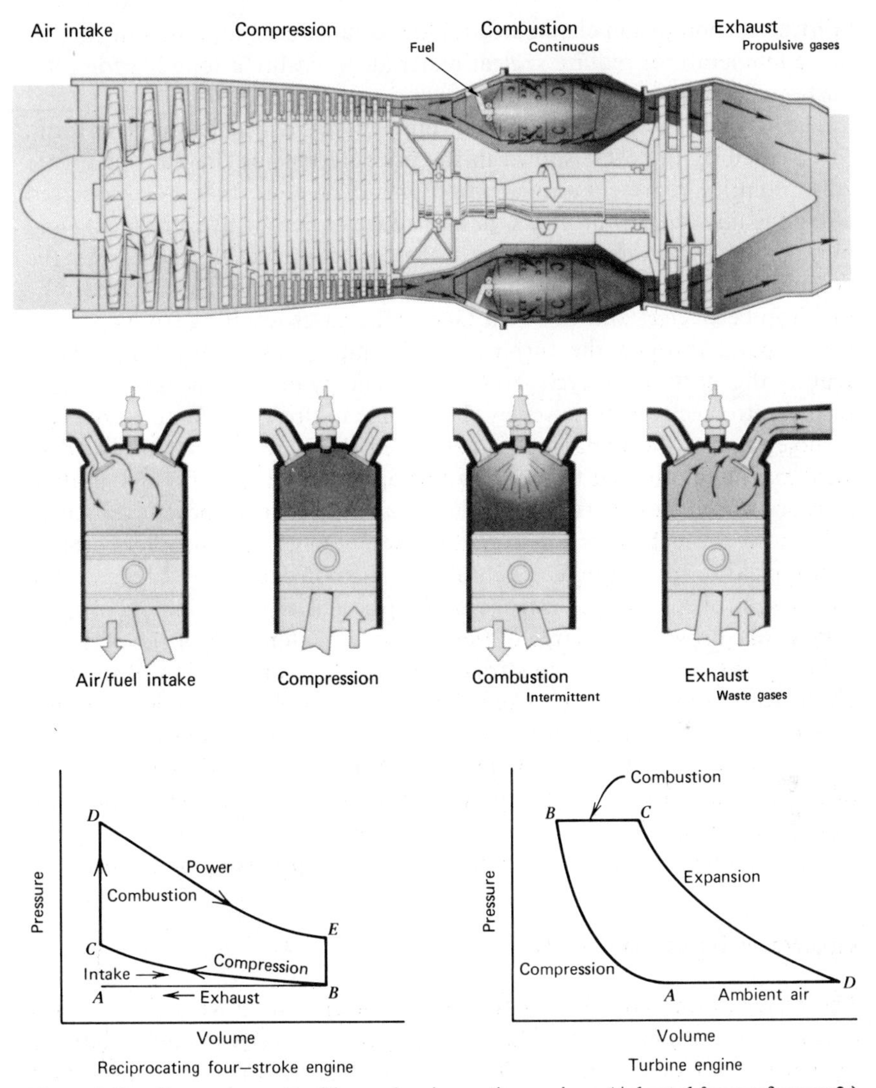

Figure 2.31 Comparison of turbine and reciprocating engines. (Adapted from reference 2.)

combustion system, turbine, and exhaust system. The continuous cycle and absence of reciprocating parts give a smoother running engine and allow more energy to be released for a given engine size.

As already stated, combustion occurs in the gas turbine engine at a constant pressure with an increase in volume. Therefore the peak pressures that occur in a piston engine are avoided. This allows the use of lightweight, fabricated combustion chambers and low octane fuels, although the higher flame temperatures require special materials to ensure a long life for combustion chamber and turbine components (see Chapter 7).

The working cycle of the gas turbine engine is, in its simplest form, represented by the cycle shown in the pressure-volume diagram of Figure 2.31. Point *A* represents air at atmospheric pressure that is compressed along the line *AB*. From *B* to *C* heat is added to the air by introducing and burning fuel at constant pressure, thereby considerably increasing the volume of air. Pressure losses in the combustion chambers are indicated by the drop between *B* and *C*. From *C* to *D* the gases resulting from combustion expand through the turbine and jet pipe back to the atmosphere. During this part of the cycle, some of the energy in the expanding gases is turned into mechanical power by the turbine to drive the compressor. In a turbojet engine the remainder is exhausted through a nozzle designed to yield maximum pure jet thrust. In a turboprop or turboshaft configuration a second turbine extracts most of the remaining energy and converts it to shaft power, which is then delivered to the propeller or helicopter rotor.

A typical reciprocating engine utilizes a four-stroke cycle (Figure 2.31). The first stroke is the downstroke of the piston with the intake valve open. This stroke draws in a charge of fuel-air mixture along *AB* of the pressure-volume diagram. The second stroke accomplishes compression of the fuel-air mixture along line *BC*. Combustion is initiated by a spark ignition apparatus, and combustion takes place in essentially a constant volume. The combustion of the fuel-air mixture liberates heat and causes the rise of pressure along line *CD*. The power stroke utilizes the increased pressure through the expansion along line *DE*. Then the exhaust begins by the initial rejection along line *EB* and is completed by the upstroke along line *BA*.

Reciprocating Engine Characteristics

The reciprocating engine is both a very efficient and a very complicated engine. However, part of the efficiency may be due to the engine's relatively long period of development. The thermal efficiency of the reciprocating engine is somewhat better than that of the turbine powerplant, which is currently used in aircraft. In addition, the propulsive efficiency of a rotor is higher than that of the turbine powerplant. It can therefore be stated that the combination of the reciprocating engine with the rotor is the most efficient powerplant available to date. Other considerations, such as reliability, maintainability, vibration, weight, and size, often overcome the advantages of reciprocating engine efficiency, and the shaft turbine engine is completely dominating new designs.

The horsepower produced by a reciprocating engine is a function of the pressure on the piston and the engine's rate of rotation. The horsepower may be measured by a brake or load device attached to the output shaft. The term brake horsepower (BHP) is derived from this power measuring instrument. The BMEP is not the actual peak pressure in the cylinders, but a mean pressure during the power stroke.

The more conventional pilot instruments are the manifold pressure gage and the tachometer, which read the intake manifold pressure and the speed of rotation of the output shaft, respectively. The controls are the throttle and the propeller pitch control.

The pilot, by manipulating the RPM and the manifold pressure of the engine, controls the power output of the engine. As the pilot opens the throttle, the manifold pressure increases, thus increasing the engine's power. As the RPM is increased, the pumping action of the engine and the power both increase. In addition, if the engine is supercharged, the impeller speeds up in proportion to the rotation and thus raises the manifold pressure. Of course, the pilot's manipulation of these two controls is not the only factor affecting the power output of the engine. The ambient density of the air that is mixed with fuel also affects it.

The air-to-fuel ratio of the mixture, too, controls the power output of the engine. The chemically correct proportion is 15 lb of air to 1 lb of fuel. This is called a stoichiometric mixture, which provides the maximum release of heat during the burning of the mixture. The mixture is normally spoken of as a fuel-air ratio or mixture. The stoichiometric mixture is 0.067. A lean mixture is one that provides less fuel in the mixture than 0.067. A rich mixture provides more fuel per pound of air, or a number larger than 0.067.

A mixture either richer or leaner than 0.067 does not release the amount of heat that is released at the stoichiometric ratio. It is therefore preferable to always operate the reciprocating engine at one mixture setting, but for a number of reasons this is not possible or practical.

Variations in flame speed, total mixing of the fuel-air mixture, and variations in the mixture temperature cause the maximum power of a reciprocating engine to occur at a fuel-air ratio slightly richer than 0.067. This ratio is about 0.07. Combustion is supported by fuel-air ratios as lean as 0.04 and as rich as 0.20. However, because of pumping losses and engine mechanical friction, the energy release is not sufficient to develop power. Therefore, useful power output of the reciprocating engine is available only between 0.05 and 0.15. Figure 2.32 shows this effect.

Economically the best mixtures occur near the stoichiometric ratio. The best power occurs at a mixture ratio slightly richer than stoichiometric. The takeoff mixture setting must be somewhat richer to suppress detonation.

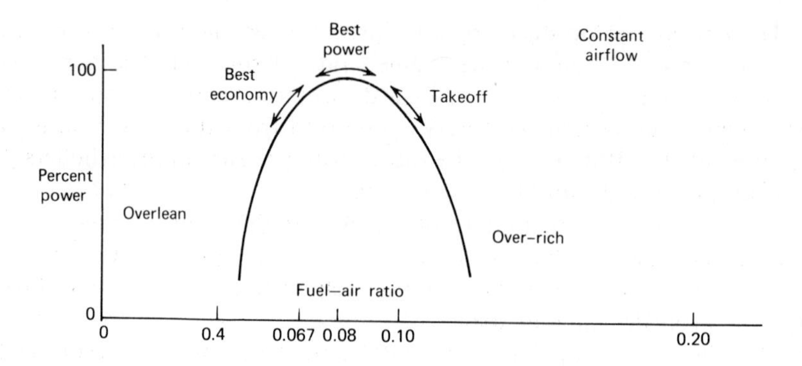

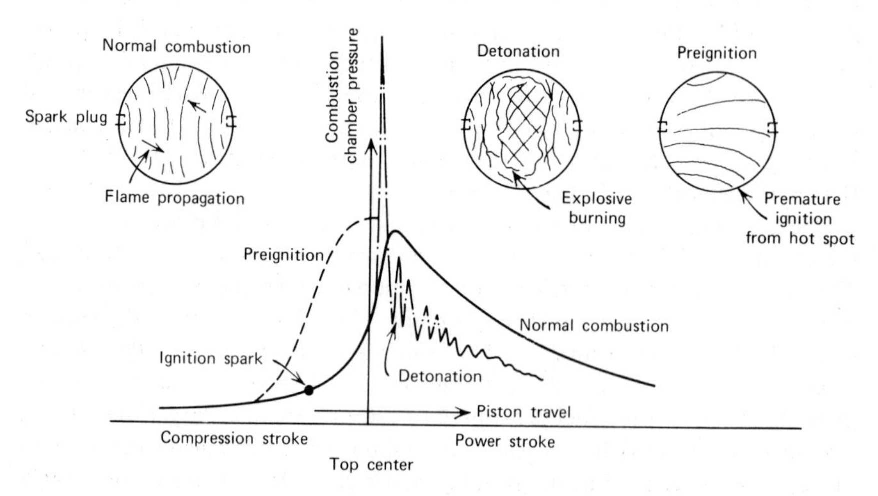

Figure 2.32 Reciprocating engine characteristics. (From reference 6.)

The mixture that is compressed in the cylinder during the compression stroke of the piston is ignited by the sparkplug. The spark starts ignition normally at two points in the aircraft cylinder, where burning begins at the time that the engine designers have specified as providing optimum pressure rise in the cylinder to obtain the best power. The ignition of the cylinder mixture normally occurs before top dead center of the piston, so that burning takes place during the compression stroke. The twin flame fronts proceed smoothly at a predictable rate through the cylinder, causing a gradual pressure rise during the latter part of the compression stroke and during the early part of the power stroke. Pressure variation during the piston travel must be carefully controlled to achieve the greatest network from the cycle of operation. The timing of the ignition is very important, as is the correct burning rate for the proper power output of the engine.

Figure 2.32 depicts the rise in pressure with the correct ignition timing and burning rate.

If the flame front can be accelerated, heat will be released more rapidly and pressure rise in the cylinders will be quicker. It is for this reason that high power aircraft engines have dual ignition. Dual ignition also adds to realiability and safety.

If ignition does not occur at the proper time or if the resulting burning is erratic, the optimum amount of power will not be released, possibly causing damage to the engine. Premature ignition may be caused by carbon deposits in the cylinder or a small piece of feathered metal that has become detached from the parent structure. The offending material will glow red under normal operating conditions and will then ignite prematurely. This is called *preignition*. Preignition leads to a premature rise in pressure in the cylinder, with a net reduction in engine torque and power. Moreover, higher cylinder temperatures are usually developed under these conditions.

Detonation is another nonnormal burning mode within the cylinder. It is more dangerous than preignition, and the loss of power is greater. In addition, there may be immediate damage to the engine. Damage will certainly occur if detonation is allowed to continue even for a short period of time. Detonation takes place at high temperature and pressure in the unburned portion of the mixture ahead of the flame front when the mixture burns excessively fast. Many small areas of ignition may occur simultaneously within the unburned portion of the mixture in the cylinder. As can be seen in Figure 2.32, this explosion sharply increases pressure in the cylinder, followed by a lowering of pressure and thus power. This loss of power, of course, is accompanied by a rise in cylinder temperature. Detonation always brings with it vibration, loss of power, and perhaps permanent engine damage.

Mixture controls in most aircraft are set so that the lean setting will give close to stoichiometric fuel-air ratio. The rich setting, on the other hand, is sufficiently above the lean setting to suppress detonation at the higher power outputs of the engine. The rich mixture then is adjusted to correspond to the octane rating of the fuel specified for the aircraft. If a lower octane or performance number of fuel is used, detonation may occur at the higher power outputs. If a higher octane or performance number is used, there is an additional safety margin in the mixture setting of the carburetor. It is, of course, not recommended that the pilot manually lean the mixture control to obtain better power for takeoff with fuels of higher than specified octane. The pilot has no way of determining the optimum amount of leaning that will prevent detonation and provide the maximum power output.

One of the factors that indicate the operating efficiency of the reciprocating engine is the *specific fuel consumption*, which is more formally called the brake specific fuel consumption. This is the ratio of the fuel flow to the brake horsepower. It may be written as

$$c = \frac{\text{lb/hr}}{\text{BHP}}$$

Typical minimum values of the specific fuel consumption range from 0.4 to 0.6. These values are obtained at the lean mixture setting or at stoichiometric ratio and at low power outputs of 30 to 60% of the maximum available power. The lowest values of specific fuel consumption are obtained at low speeds of rotation as well as at low power outputs. The slow rotation minimizes friction within the engine and improves operating efficiency. This effect is different for turbine engines, which are optimized for the 100% RPM condition.

The reciprocating engine, though reliable and efficient, is very sensitive to handling. Correct operating procedures must be observed and engine life limitations taken into account. When fuels are altered, the new operating limitations must be strictly observed.

If the engine is operated at excessively low temperatures because of low manifold pressures and RPM, carbon fouling of the sparkplugs takes place. If the engine is operated at high temperatures, lead deposits from the fuel additives may foul the plugs.

The manufacturer's handbook for the aircraft and engine places time limits on the engine's operation at high power settings. Minimizing the time spent at the high power outputs may lead to fewer overhauls. It has been found in commercial operations of reciprocating engines that utilizing the full amount of takeoff and climb power puts less wear on the engine, because less time is required for these maneuvers.

The most wear and damage to the reciprocating engine occurs under conditions of high RPM and low manifold pressure. This condition of operation is sometimes called the underboost condition of operation while the high power output at very high manifold pressure is called the overboost condition. It can be stated that while the time at high power outputs must be minimized by the correct operating techniques, the time at the underboost condition must be eliminated. Rules of thumb are available on most reciprocating powerplants which give the correct relation between RPM and manifold pressure to avoid the underboost condition of operation. This condition will most often occur during letdown from cruise altitude when

Figure 2.33 Typical helicopter turboshaft gas turbine engine. (Photo courtesy General Motors Corporation.)

the throttle is retarded for letdown without a corresponding decrease in RPM. This will result in the propeller motoring the engine with resultant forces in the engine acting in a direction and manner somewhat different from design. The wear can be excessive and, in extreme cases, severe bearing damage may result.

Turboshaft Engine Characteristics

A typical turboshaft gas turbine engine used in helicopters is shown in Figure 2.33. Its low weight, small size, and large power output make the gas turbine ideally suited to helicopter use.

The main part of a shaft turbine engine are the gas generator and the power turbine, as well as the inlet and exhaust. If the entire engine is examined with respect to the airflow through it, the components align as follows:

1. Air inlet or diffuser.
2. Gas generator compressor.
3. Combustion chamber.
4. Gas generator turbine.

5. Power turbine.
6. Exhaust nozzle.

It is the function of the inlet to take air of varying velocity and deliver it to the first stage of the compressor at the lowest possible velocity and the highest possible pressure. A poorly designed inlet, which does not deliver the air to the face of the compressor smoothly and with even distribution of pressure, results in poor engine performance.

The gas generator compressor and turbine are on a common shaft, and just enough energy is extracted from the airflow by the gas generator turbine to propel the compresor and any engine accessories that may be driven by a takeoff from the gas generator shaft. The function of the compressor is to increase the pressure of the airflow with the least increase in temperature and deliver this high pressure air to the combustion chamber. This process corresponds to the compression stroke in the reciprocating engine cycle. The compressor's efficiency is necessary to good turbine engine performance and is the reason why the prevention safety program must stress foreign object damage (FOD), since it is this damage that affects the efficiency of the compressor. It is further affected by grass blockage of the inlet, high ambient air temperatures, the operation of the emergency fuel control system, and use of bleed air.

The compressor may be an axial-flow type, a centrifugal-flow type, or a combination of both as shown in Figure 2.34. The choice should depend on the engine requirements. A number of small shaft turbine engines widey used in helicopters have axial-centrifugal combination-type compressors.

Each type of compressor has its advantages and disadvantages. The centrifugal wheel is simple in design and less susceptible to stalling or surging, but it is limited to pressure ratios of 4 to 5 for a single stage. A two-stage centrifugal compressor is the most advanced to date. It is used mostly in the small turbine engines.

The axial compressor employs alternate rows of rotor and stator blades to gain the required pressure rise; a large number of stages will lead to high pressure ratios. This compressor also allows the air to flow along a straight path from inlet to combustion chamber, thus foregoing a circumferential diffuser, which is needed for the centrifugal wheel. As a result, a smaller diameter engine produces the same output. The axial wheel is more susceptible to foreign object damage, however, and compressor stall and the blades accumulate fatigue and creep damage that may cause maintenance problems. The axial compressor can also provide very high efficiency in the compressor process, which means lower fuel consumption for the engine. The axial-centrifugal compressor combines the advantages of both types;

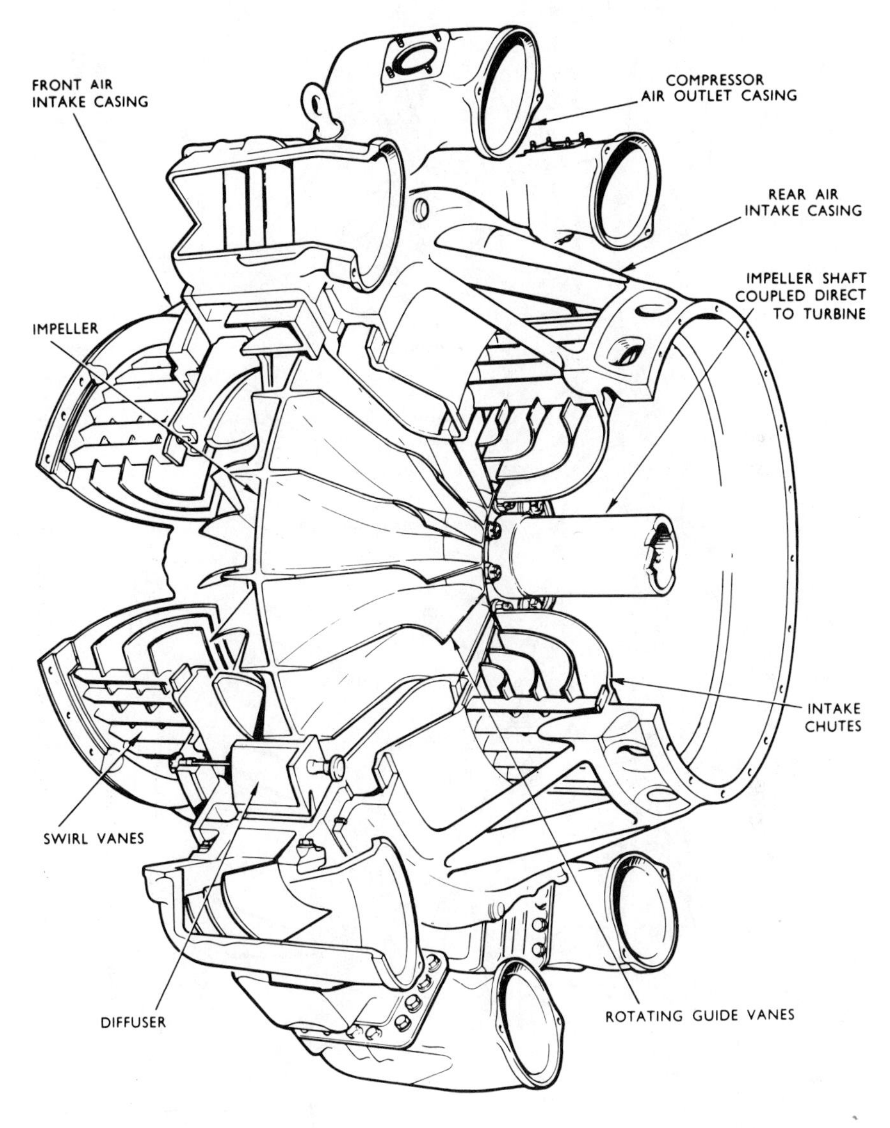

Figure 2.34 (*a*) Typical centrifugal compressor.

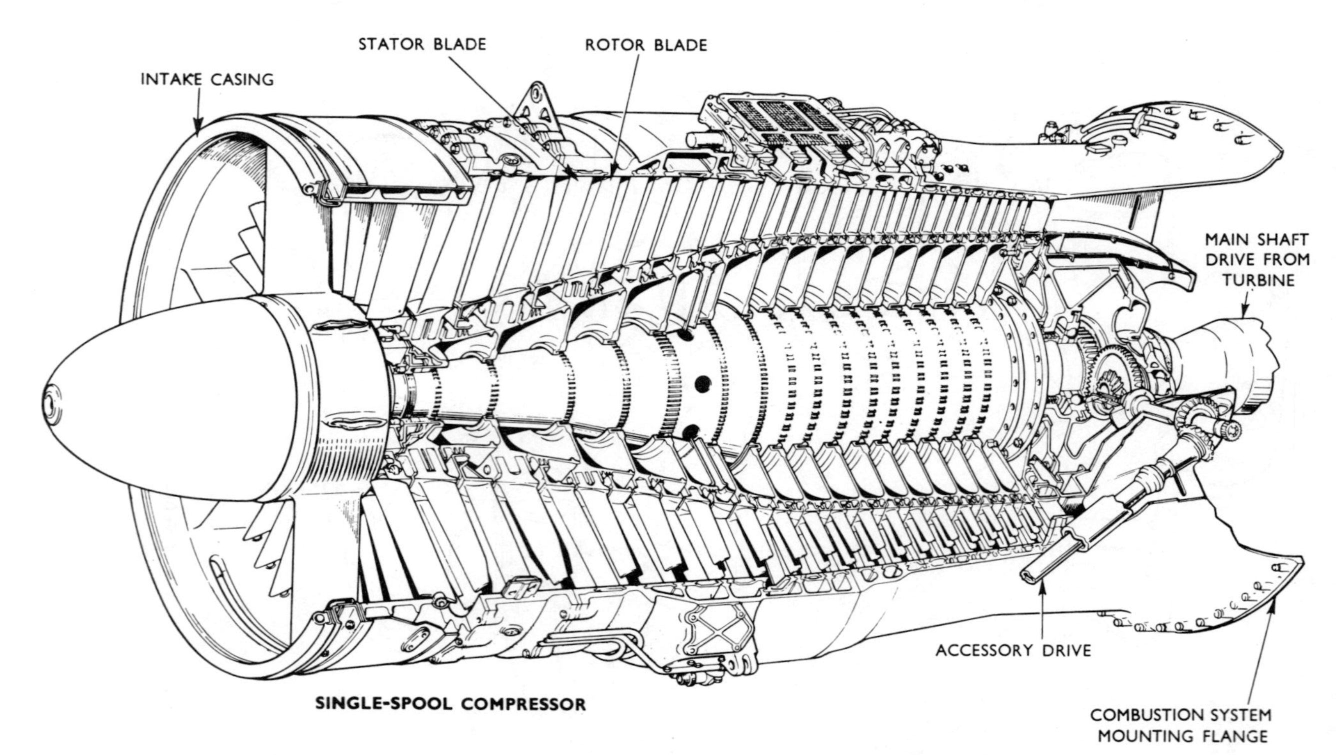

Figure 2.34 (*b*) Typical axial and centrifugal-axial compressors (Adapted from reference 2.)

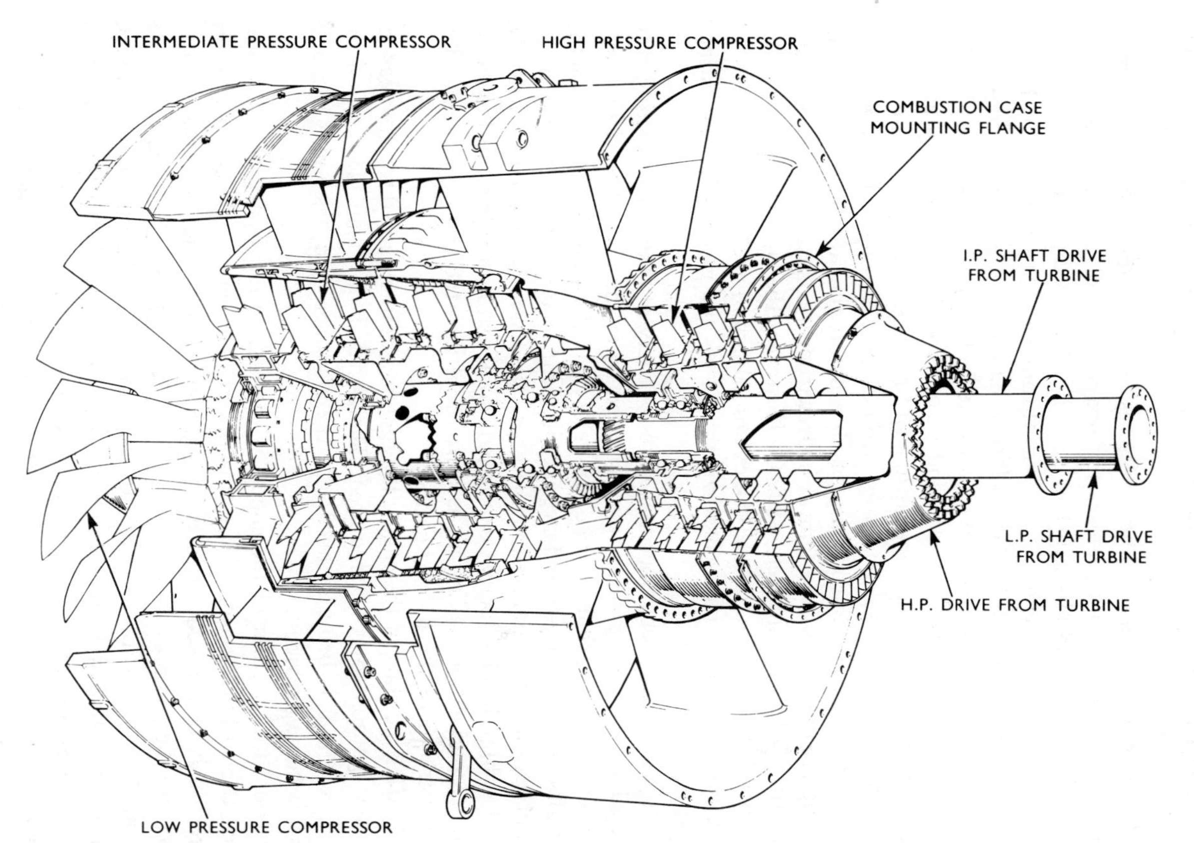

Figure 2.34b (*Continued*).

its pressure ratios are moderate, and it has the means to minimize the length of the engine.

In the combustion chamber energy is added to the airflow by burning fuel. This process rapidly raises the temperature of the gas flow while it remains at an essentially constant pressure. This means that the volume of gas must increase. Much air is flowing through a gas turbine engine. In fact, the mass flow is at least four times larger than the amount needed to provide the necessary oxygen to combine with the fuel. In the combustion chamber the air is divided into primary and secondary air. The primary air flows through the core of the combustion and has the fuel injected into it. The remaining, secondary, air flows around and through the combustion chamber and rejoins the primary gas flow before the flow enters the turbine.

The combustion of the typical hydrocarbon fuels can produce gas temperatures of approximately 1800°C. However, the maximum continuous temperatures that the turbine blades can withstand are from 800 to 1000°C. The temperature is reduced when the excess air mixes with the burned mixture.

The combustion chamber may take a variety of forms. Its function is to introduce the high pressure air, removed from the last stage of the compressor, at high turbulence and low velocity in the vicinity of the fuel spray nozzles. The velocity-turbulence requirement serves to keep the nucleus of combustion in the combustion chamber. The flame propagates very slowly, so that high local velocities can impair combustion or blow out the flame. The secondary or cooling air is introduced into the combustion chamber downstream of the flame nozzles.

If after the start of the engine the fuel flow is interrupted for any reason, a new ignition source is required. There may be a "lean blowout" if insufficient fuel is being sprayed into the chamber or a "richout" if excess fuel is being provided.

The "hot" section of the engine is the most critical part, which means that the turbine section is very important. The gas generator turbine, as previously mentioned, extracts enough energy from the combustion gases to drive the compressor and accessories. The high energy combustion gases from the combustion chamber are delivered to the turbine nozzle, which directs the airflow to the blades of the turbine wheels. In this expansion process, energy from the airflow is converted to mechanical energy as rotation of the turbine wheel, which of course is also the speed of rotation of the compressor, both being on the same shaft.

A large quantity of energy remains in combustion gas flow after it has passed through the gas generator turbine. In a turbojet engine this energy would be used to accelerate the gas flow to a high exhaust velocity to produce jet thrust. The shaft turbine, however, must produce shaft power; hence another turbine section, the power turbine, is placed in the engine. This combination of power turbine nozzle and power turbine blades extracts as much of the remaining energy in the airflow as possible, leaving only enough energy to exhaust the air at very low velocity out the exhaust nozzle. The power turbine can be an additional turbine stage on the gas generator turbine, as is the case on some turboprop engines that have only one rotating component.

More commonly, there are two separate components: the gas generator compressor and turbine on one shaft and the power turbine on a second shaft. The rotational speed for the gas generator is deonoted by N_{I} and that for the power turbine by N_{II}. A typical arrangement of the free power turbine on a concentric shaft with respect to the gas generator rotor is shown in Figure 2.35.

The two turbines in the free power turbine engine are linked aerodynamically only, since the same airflow drives both the gas generator turbine and the free power turbine. Thus differences in rotational speed can and

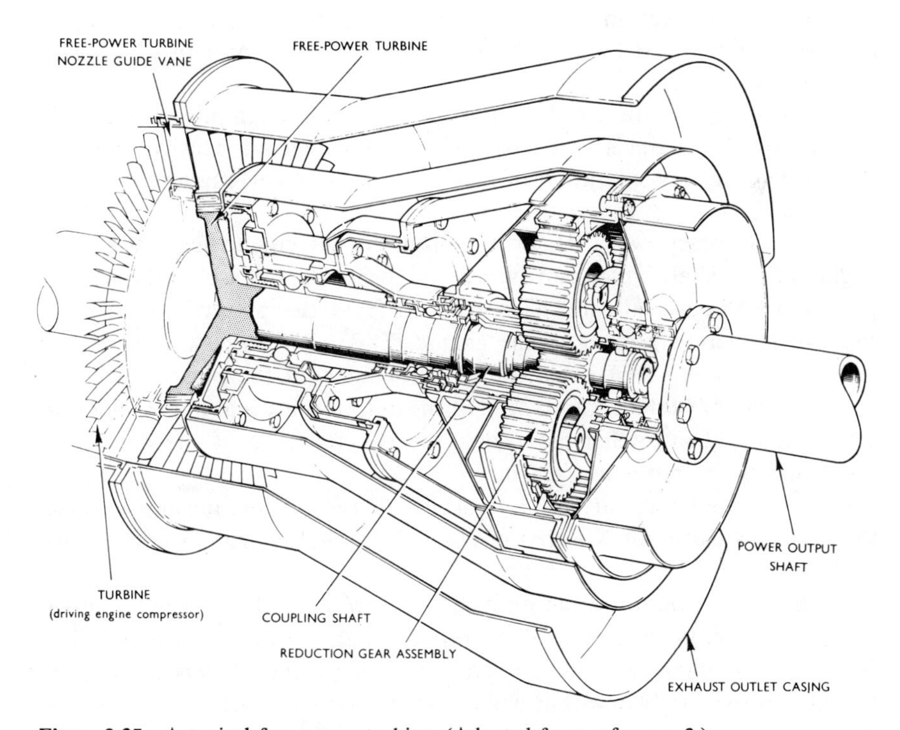

Figure 2.35 A typical free-power turbine. (Adapted from reference 2.)

do exist, which requires a governing system that senses both N_I and N_{II} speeds. Furthermore, the gas turbine engine requires high operating speed to gain high efficiency (i.e., low fuel consumption) so that the power turbine speed of 20,000 to 40,000 RPM must be reduced to adjust it to helicopter rotor speeds of 200 to 400 RPM. This, then, is a ratio of the order of 60 to 1 to 100 to 1—engine turbine rotational speed to helicopter rotor rotational speed. The gear boxes in a helicopter transmission system obviously are critical components of the dynamic system.

After passing through the power turbine, the gas flow has very little energy left. Its velocity is low, although it still has a fairly high temperature. The air must have enough pressure to cause it to flow out the exhaust nozzle. Ideally, then, the exhaust air would be at such a low velocity that it would produce no jet thrust effect. However, in actual operation the jet exhaust velocity does vary considerably over the operating range of the engine. Since jet thrust is a result of the difference in inlet and exhaust velocity of the airflow through the engine, some jet thrust is usually produced and must be taken into consideration in rating the output of the engine (particularly in a turboprop version on a fixed wing aircraft) and in the control of a helicopter. In a hover, in particular, the jet thrust can introduce a force that must be counteracted by an appropriate offset of the rotor thrust to gain equilibrium.

Both shaft horsepower output and specific fuel consumption are greatly affected by the engine's speed of rotation and inlet air density. Inlet air density requires consideration of density altitude in the engine's performance.

The shaft horsepower (SHP) is the output of the engine measured at the engine output shaft which is driven by the power turbine. Usually the output shaft RPM has already been reduced from the power turbine RPM through reduction gearing in the engine. This would typically be on the order of a two- to four-speed reduction. That is, if the power turbine is operating at 24,000 RPM, the speed of the output shaft is about 6000 RPM. This speed is then further reduced to the helicopter rotor speed through the transmission reduction gearing.

In the normal free turbine gas turbine there is a relationship between the rotational speed of N_{II}, that of N_I, and the shaft horsepower as shown in Figure 2.36.

It would be optimum situation if the N_{II} speed could be varied to maintain the maximum efficiency of operation along the optimum power line. In helicopter operation this is not possible, since the N_{II} speed is maintained approximately constant while N_I is varied with fuel flow to give the desired power output. This means that the engine does not operate when

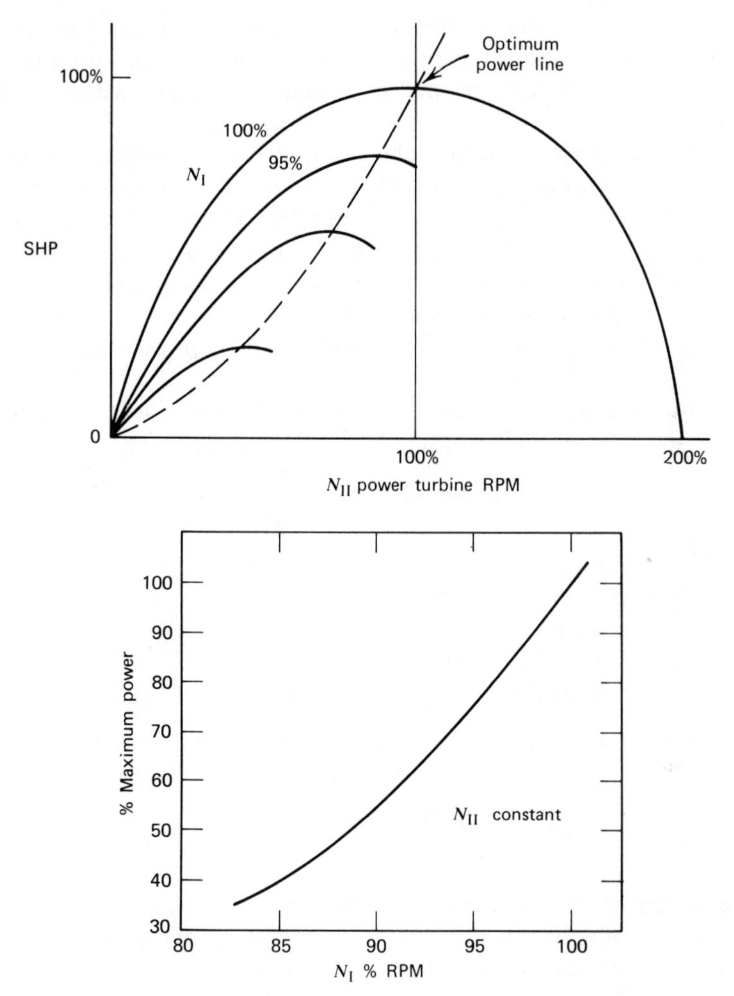

Figure 2.36 N_I and N_{II} effect on power output of shaft turbine engine, (Adapted from reference 13.)

the desired power can be obtained with the minimum fuel flow except at the design condition, which is normal rated power.

The variation of output power with rotational speed can be well seen in Figure 2.36. The power varies with the speed of N_I without regard to that of N_{II}.

It becomes readily apparent that the top 10% of the gas generator speed controls about 50% of the power output. It can be seen that a very small decrease in N_I will mean a significant reduction in power. Thus the few percentage points lost during critical operations when nearly total power is required may be difficult, if not impossible, to regain without loss of altitude.

The effect of airspeed on the engine output is very small for the normal speed ranges under consideration. Therefore, power output can be approximated to be constant with increasing airspeed if speeds in excess of 200 knots are not considered. In reality, power output increases slightly with airspeed. The exact nature of the power variation with airspeed depends on the engine inlet and its efficiency. Realistically, power variation with airspeed should be considered to be constant at all power outputs of the turbine engine.

The output rating of an aircraft or helicopter with forward airspeed is given by the following relationship:

$$\text{ESHP} = \text{SHP} + \frac{T_j V_k}{\eta_p 325}$$

where ESHP = equivalent shaft horsepower (HP)
SHP = shaft horsepower (HP)
T_j = jet thrust (lb)
V_k = vehicle velocity (knots)
η_p = propulsive efficiency (dimensionless)

For example, the T-53-L-9 is rated at 1100 SHP and 124 lb of jet thrust. Assuming that the propulsive efficiency is 0.8 at 100 knots, we have

$$\text{ESHP} = 1100 + \frac{124(100)}{(0.8)(325)} = 1100 + 47.8 = 1147.8 \text{ HP}$$

The jet thrust can contribute significantly to the rating of the engine, although its evaluation is difficult, since pounds of thrust and propulsive efficiency are not readily available to the aviator.

The specific fuel consumption of the gas turbine varies with two primary operating parameters: temperature and power output.

The specific fuel consumption is defined as

$$c_t = \frac{\text{lb/hr}}{\text{ESHP}}$$

As density is decreased, both the fuel flow and ESHP decrease proportionally, so that it can be said that density variations do not by themselves influence specific fuel consumption. However, as altitude is increased, temperature normally decreases. Because the turbine may effect a given thrust output with less fuel at a lower inlet temperature, the specific fuel consumption normally improves or decreases with altitude. If the atmosphere can be considered to be standard, the specific fuel consumption decreases to the tropopause and then remains constant until the efficiency of the compressor begins to break down at sufficiently high altitudes. The standard atmosphere has a temperature decrease up to the tropopause. This is illustrated in Figure 2.37.

Specific fuel consumption also varies quite severely with the power output of the engine. The gas turbine is so designed that it operates most efficiently at high power outputs. This means that the specific fuel consumption is lowest at the higher powers. The engine is designed for normal rated power operation, thus minimizing specific fuel consumption at this particular rotational speed.

Figure 2.38 shows a typical variation of the specific fuel consumption of a small axial-centrifugal gas turbine with N_{I} speed. It can be seen that 100% is the optimum speed for greatest efficiency. The implications of Figures 2.37 and 2.38 are great when considering range and endurance performance.

Gas Turbine Operating Limitations

The gas turbine is a very reliable and troublefree engine. It operates in a continuous cycle, which is conducive to long engine life. The engine is

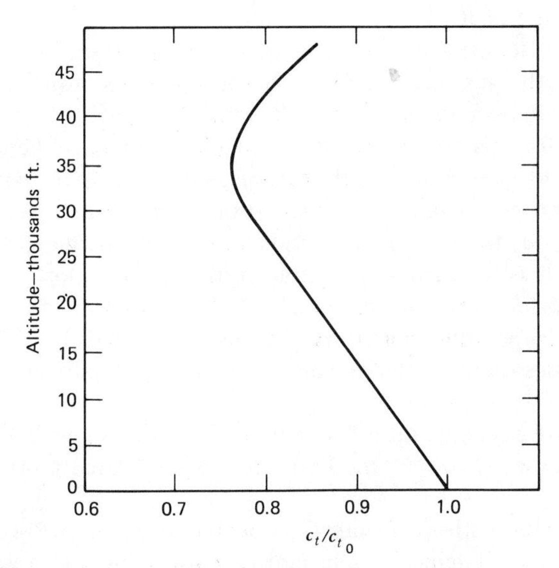

Figure 2.37 Effect of altitude on typical specific fuel consumption.

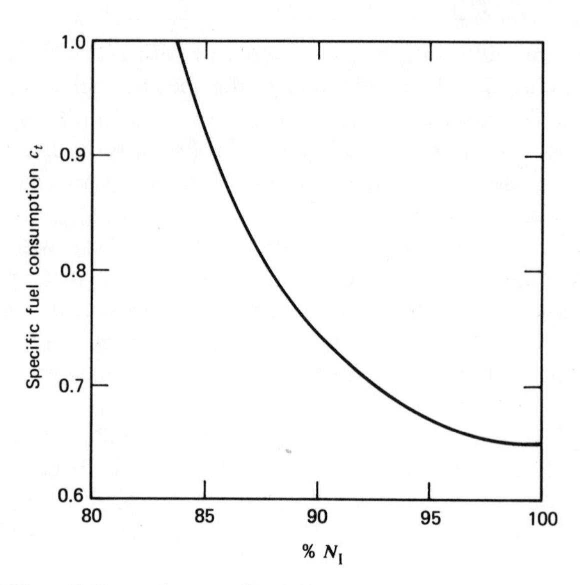

Figure 2.38 Effect of N_I speed on specific fuel consumption.

designed to operate at high power outputs and operates most efficiently at high powers. However, the operating limitations of the engine must be observed meticulously if the engine is to exhibit the long, troublefree life that is expected of it.

Exhaust gas temperature is one of the most important limitations on the operation of the gas turbine. The exhaust gas temperature may be taken at any of a number of positions following the final turbine stage in the engine. It is for this reason that it is difficult to compare the temperatures of various models. In designing the turbine, with the help of an instrumented engine, the proper position at which to take the exhaust gas temperature that will provide the most reliable indication of the turbine temperature is determined. It is the turbine temperature that is of importance and is the true limitation. It is the turbine that puts the lid on the whole engine with its limiting temperature caused by the material of which it is constructed and the stresses on the material caused by the aerodynamic and centrifugal loads.

The exhaust gas temperature is then not a direct, but an indirect reading of the limitation. However, the limitations so indicated must be carefully obeyed.

In conjunction with the exhaust gas temperature, an RPM limitation is established on the engine. It is primarily a stress limitation and is caused by the maximum stress that the turbine can withstand at the operating temperatures. The temperature and speed limitations therefore go together and are listed in the pilot's handbook as a dual limitation.

Of course, an overspeed engine condition breeds overtemperature. In this relation they tend to go together. However, an overtemperature may occur without overspeed, as during an improper start. The overtemperature and overspeed limitations, which are listed together in the pilot's handbook, usually provide starting temperature limitations.

The turbine is under two distinct types of structural stress. It is undergoing creep—a plastic phenomenon caused by stress at high temperatures. It is also subject to fatigue because of the high frequency aerodynamic and structural vibrations occurring in the engine. Both effects are cumulative.

If the temperature is elevated for a period of time, the rate of creep increases. If simultaneously the stress is increased, the rate of creep increases by an order of magnitude. Thus while damage may not be visible to the eye following an overstress and/or overtemperature, there is some shortening of engine life. It is therefore imperative that there be some recording of the limitation that was exceeded so that a judgment may be made as to when the engine must be inspected for creep damage.

A similar situation exists with respect to fatigue damage. An overspeed condition accompanied by overtemperature increases the fatigue environment so much that fatigue damage may increase.

A gross overstress or overtemperature of the turbine section produces visible damage. But the less obvious creep and fatigue damage accumulated through periods of small overstress and overtemperature shortens the turbine's service life, leading to failures before the normal removal and inspection dates.

The magnitude of the overstress produced by the overspeed is not proportional to the overspeed but increases somewhat more rapidly than the overspeed. Therefore a 5% overspeed in rotation produces about a 10% overstress. This large increase in stress with RPM not only shortens the turbine's life, but adversely affects the compressor and other components of the turbine that are sensitive to vibration and fatigue.

The pilot must, therefore, be aware of the various allowable combinations of rotational speed and temperatures for certain periods of time. The limitations fall into categories; some of them may be allowed, some must be reported, some lead to engine removal and inspection, and some require an engine change. Although it may embarrass the pilot to make such a report, particularly when no damage is visible, it is very important that he do so in order to institute the proper safety measures.

Compressor Stall

Various types of compressor stall are possible in gas turbine engines. Their theoretical aspects are so complicated that no exact description of all types of stalls, their causes, and their cures can be made without writing a book on the subject. Stalls may be recognized by compressor pulsations felt through the aircraft structure, sometimes they may be heard, and sometimes they are detected only when the engine fails to accelerate or when it decelerates even though the throttle is not moved. In its mild form a stall gives off no sound or motion detectable by the pilot; a serious stall produces a very loud bang, which can startle a pilot experiencing a stall for the first time.

What makes a gas turbine engine stall? Just as a wing stalls when put into the position of having too high an angle of attack, the compressor stalls when a number, or all, of its blades are subjected to too high an angle of attack. The airflow over the compressor blades and the pressure that it generates then break down, causing the compressor to stop compressing air in its normal way.

Aside from stalls due to a definite engine or accessory malfunction, the usual source of the compressor stall lies in the aircraft and engine inlet duct and the engine and the exhaust duct or nozzle. As shown in Figure 2.39, the air-inlet duct has definite flow characteristics that affect the engine's stall margin to a greater or lesser extent, depending on the duct design and on the flight conditions. In the figure a single compressor blade is shown at an instant of time. The direction of the relative flow (angle of attack) is determined by the vector sum of the velocity due to rotation and the axial flow of air through the compressor. Anything that affects airflow through the inlet must affect the angle of attack.

All compressor blades in a given row of blades have the same angle of attack only when the distribution of air at the face of the engine is perfect. When the distribution is less than perfect, the maldistribution pattern tends to be in the same proportion, back through all of the stages of compression. In all installations to date, there are greater or lesser variations in the airflow at the front of the engine, as shown in Figure 2.3, which cause each blade to change its effective angle of attack as it goes from one position to another around the engine while rotating normally. If the air distribution pattern does not vary too much (about 5% is allowed), the engine operates without stall under normal conditions. However, when the variation in airflow at the front of the engine becomes too great for the engine to handle, a stall results.

The stall process is begun by some change in the pattern of airflow being fed to the engine. The stable angle of attack is changed in some locations if the velocity of the air passing over the moving or stationary blades has

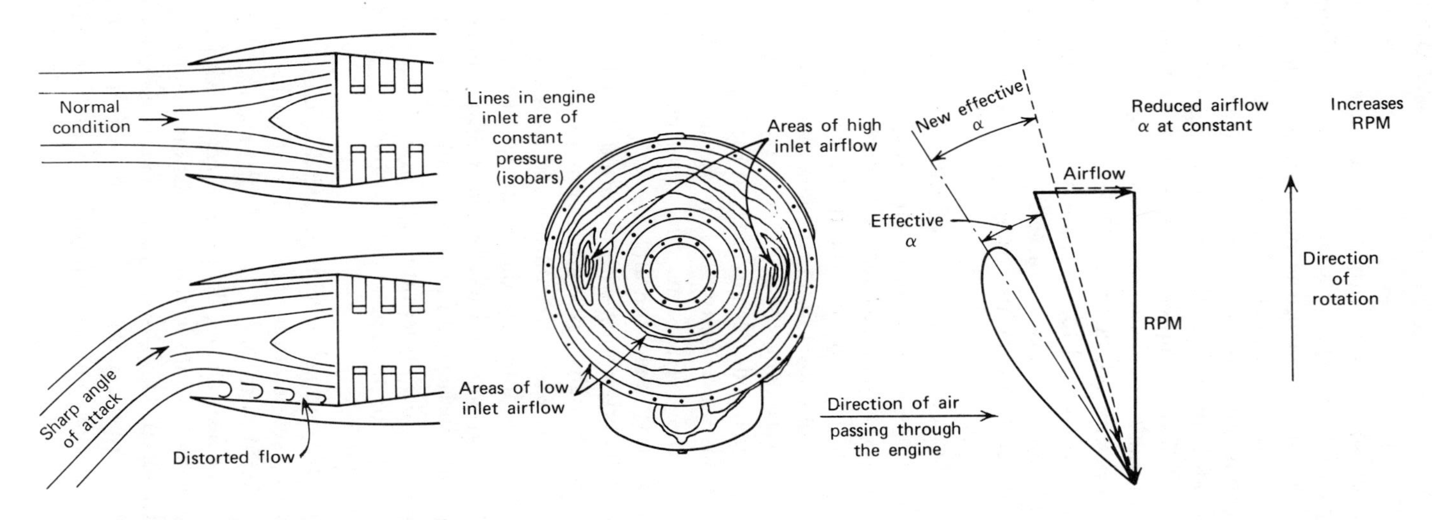

Figure 2.39 Elements of compressor stall.

been decreased, for any reason, without any change in rotational speed, resulting in a new effective angle of attack, as shown in Figure 2.39. If the air velocity becomes low enough, the blade stalls in the same way as an aircraft wing; that is, the angle of attack becomes so large that the blade can no longer exert enough lift and the airflow is badly upset. The complication here is that this can happen over the complete engine-inlet area, and can extend back into all of the compressor stages right up the diffuser, or only to a few blades in one or two rows of compression, or to any degree between these extremes. It is this factor of the large variation in stall-inducing area that makes stalls so hard to understand. Some stalls, in fact, do not make themselves known by noise or surges, but simply result in the engine not being able to accelerate or its losing speed with no change in the throttle position.

Bearing in mind that a decrease in the velocity of the air approaching the compressor blades, when at constant rotational speed, increases the angle of attack of the blades, Figure 2.39 shows, in part, why the velocity of the air to the engine can vary. In an aircraft the engine may be operating normally when in smooth, level flight. If the aircraft should enter an area where the air is very turbulent, the angle of entry of the air into the inlet duct may be sharply changed. Certain areas of the engine face then receive less than the previous air velocity, and, if the maldistribution is severe enough, the engine stalls. The same effect can be obtained by sharply maneuvering the aircraft in smooth air.

In addition to stalls originating with distorted inlet flow, the pilot may occasionally experience stalls associated with the selection of the afterburner in fighter aircraft where afterburner nozzle opening, fuel flow, and combustion coordination influence the back pressure imposed on the engine. He may also experience "off-idle" stalls, called "choo-choo" stalls—a mild transient stall experienced in some installations when the engine is accelerated from idle to the thrust range just above idle. Unless it leads to too slow an acceleration of the engine, the "choo-choo" stall is of no serious consequence to the pilot.

The occasional stalls during acceleration and deceleration are also caused by blade stall. During acceleration, extra fuel is fed to the burners to provide the extra energy needed to accelerate the rotating masses. If inlet conditions cause operation to be near a stall, the process begins with a relatively high internal pressure being built up in the combustion chambers as a result of the extra fuel introduced. This slows down the air coming through the high pressure compressor, to the point where the air velocity and the rotational speed in some part of the compressor no longer match properly, and a stall occurs.

When the throttle is retarded and the engine decelerates, the high pressure rotor slows first because it has the lightest mass. If conditions here are going to produce stall, the slowing of the high pressure compressor, in effect blocks the airflow through the low pressure compressor, and a stall of the low pressure compressor results when the air velocity through it becomes low enough. It should be emphasized here that acceleration and deceleration stalls are unusual because of the automatic acceleration and deceleration schedules built into the fuel control, and that any evidence of either type of stall should call first for an examination of operating conditions and then an examination of the ducts, the engine, and the fuel control to determine what malfunction is causing these stalls.

There are several things that a pilot can do to avoid a stall or to reduce its intensity. Erratic and abrupt throttle movements should be avoided. Rapid throttle advances during periods of high distortion of the air entering the air-inlet duct, such as at low airspeeds, are sometimes the cause of acceleration stalls. Carefully coordinated flying increases the efficiency of the compressor inlet air duct.

The helicopter, because of the nature of the flow through the rotor system, draws debris up from the ground in the form of dust, small rocks, and grass. This material may impinge on the first stages of the compressor and cause the disruption of flow that will culminate in compressor stall.

Dust erosion is a major problem in helicopter operation because of the helicopter's ability to operate from small, unprepared landing sites. If the ground is not dry, the action of the rotor blades quickly dries it and the accompanying activity surrounding the area causes large quantities of dust to form. This dust is circulated through flow patterns of the rotor blades and ingested into the engine where it begins to erode the compressor blades.

The major damage occurs to the trailing edge of the tip of the compressor blades. This damage becomes more severe as the dust progresses through succeeding stages of the blades. The percentage change in the small blades of the final stages of the compressor is much greater than that of the relatively larger blades of the first stages. It is for this reason that the axial-centrifugal compressor increases the resistance of an engine to erosion by sand and dust.

The centrifugal compressor can be considered essentially insensitive to sand and dust erosion. If the last stages of an axial compressor are replaced by a centrifugal compressor, the engine has been found to become approximately 10 times more resistant to sand and dust erosion.

Grass can cause immediate stall by clinging to the first stages of stators and thus disrupting the flow to the following stages. Screens and particle separators on modern helicopters can significantly reduce the magnitude of this problem.

A disruption of the airflow to the inlets of the engine may cause a compressor stall just as does the grass. This disruption may be a result of unusual flow conditions at unusual flight attitudes. The relatively low speed helicopters of the past have a bell mouth intake so that smooth flow is maintained to the engine under all possible conditions. As helicopter speeds increase and the engine intake leading edges become sharper, intake flow conditions may occasionally cause compressor stall.

One way of improving engine acceleration without the onset of compressor stall is through a bleeding system for the excess airflow. Under this type of operation, the engine speed is maintained at a level that provides higher airflow than required for the RPM selected by the fuel flow. The excess air is then bled from the last stage of the compressor or, in the case of the axial-centrifugal compressor, from between the two types of compressors. When rapid acceleration is required, the bleed is closed and the additional pressure is available to match the increased fuel flow. Acceleration is unusually rapid without the danger of stall.

This system, of course, aggravates an already high specific fuel consumption at low power outputs. However, operation at these low power conditions for long periods of time is not normal, and the additional fuel consumption would be expected to be slight.

PROBLEMS

2.1 A helicopter is climbing through 6000 ft indicated altitude (altimeter setting 29.92) and is showing 90 KIAS. The outside air temperature is +20°C. Calculate (*a*) the static pressure, (*b*) the density, (*c*) the true airspeed (use correction of Figure 2.7*a*) and (*d*) angle of climb for a rate of climb of 500 fpm.

2.2 For standard sea level conditions and a true airspeed of 120 knots calculate (*a*) the stagnation pressure, (*b*) the dynamic pressure, and (*c*) the static pressure at a point on the fuselage where the local true airspeed is 60 knots.

2.3 For a fixed-wing aircraft having a wing area of 375 ft^2, a weight of 15,000 lb, and the aerodynamic characteristics of Figure 2.22, calculate for standard sea level conditions (*a*) the lowest speed for $L = W$, (*b*) the angle of attack for level flight at 185 knots, and (*c*) the drag at 185 knots. Assume a zero installation error.

2.4 Estimate the loss in horsepower from a turbo shaft engine rated at 1500 HP at 100% when the N_I speed is reduced to 96%.

Figure 2.40 Courtesy NASA.

Figure 2.41 Courtesy Sikorsky Aircraft Corporation.

DYNAMICS OF HOVERING FLIGHT

3

3.1 INTRODUCTION

This chapter examines the means by which the main rotor system of a helicopter derives lift while hovering in calm air. Hovering in a steady wind is aerodynamically similar to flying in calm air at the same speed (aerodynamic forces depend on the speed and direction of the *relative* wind), and is therefore examined in the chapter on forward flight. (Chapter 4).

Each blade of a rotor is similar to a wing in that it is aerodynamically shaped to be an efficient producer of lift over the aricraft's flight envelope. The blade can be described in terms of the shape of its cross section (chord, thickness, camber, etc.) and the shape of its planform (span, aspect ratio, taper, twist, sweep, etc.). As in a fixed wing, the airfoil shape may change spanwise, and a geometric twist is usually built in, so that the tip sections are "washed out," that is, have lower incidence, toward the tip.

The fundamental difference between a blade of a rotor and a fixed wing is that each section of a rotor blade experiences a significantly different

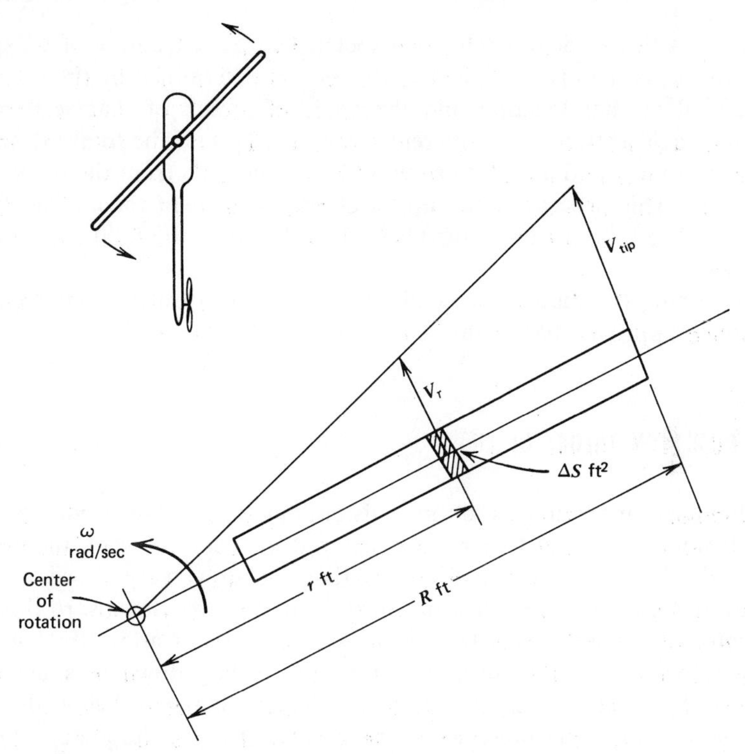

Figure 3.1 Velocity distribution due to rotation.

airspeed (hence dynamic pressure) than its neighboring section at some other span location. This is illustrated in Figure 3.1, where the rotational velocity ω causes a translational velocity V_r at any section directly proportional to the distance of the section from the center of rotation:

$$V_r = \omega r \quad \text{fps} \qquad \text{or} \qquad V_r = \frac{\text{RPM} \cdot r}{9.55} \quad \text{fps}$$

The highest velocity occurs at the tip where r is the largest:

$$V_{\text{tip}} = \frac{\text{RPM} \cdot \text{R}}{9.55} \quad \text{fps}$$

Typical tip velocities range from 350 to 500 knots in hover.

The section of area ΔS ft² is developing lift given by the basic lift equation:

$$\Delta L = \tfrac{1}{2}\rho V_r^2 \, \Delta S C_l$$

where V_r is the particular velocity associated with the location of ΔS spanwise and C_l is the lift coefficient of the section determined by the shape of the airfoil at that location and the angle of attack of that section. In general, each section has a different V_r and C_l. To find the total lift on the blade, one must add all ΔL's produced by all the ΔS's from the blade root to the tip. This process is the subject of "blade element theory" or "strip theory." The total lift of all the blades then becomes the total rotor thrust in hover.

We pursue the discussion of blade element theory after considering a simplified approach based on momentum considerations.

3.2 MOMENTUM THEORY OF LIFT

As discussed in Section 2.6 on propulsion, any device that produces a net aerodynamic force must exert an equal and opposite force on the air. In hover, the net rotor thrust is upward, so that a net downward force is exerted on the airmass. Since the air is unconstrained, it moves downward through the rotor disc, accelerating from some state of rest far above the rotor to some velocity v_i at the rotor, and then proceeding down to some final downwash velocity v_f about one to two rotor diameters below the disc (in free air only—the presence of the ground changes the picture, as we shall see).

Figure 3.2 illustrates momentum theory, showing the ideal velocity and pressure distributions in the airstream. Reality is more complex; the velocity v_i (called the "induced" velocity) actually is not a constant over the entire disc area but varies somewhat from root to tip. Nevertheless, momentum theory does agree suprisingly well with experiment in predicting total rotor thrust and final downwash velocities. Using Bernoulli's equation above and below the disc (but not *through* the disc since energy has been added by the rotor), it can be shown that the final downwash velocity is exactly twice that of the ideal induced velocity:

$$v_f = 2v_i$$

From Newton's second law, the total rotor thrust can be related to the change in velocity of the air per unit time (i.e., acceleration):

$$T_R = \frac{m\,\Delta V}{\Delta t}$$

The mass per unit time flowing through the rotor disc (mass flow rate,

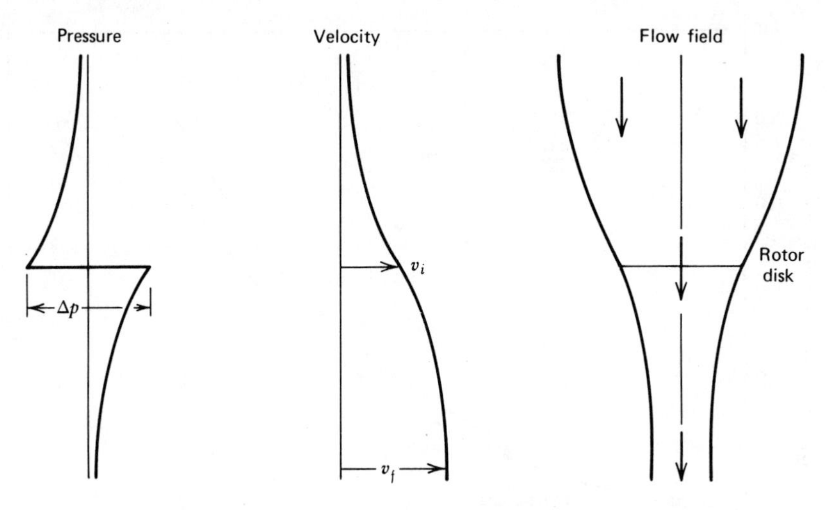

Figure 3.2 Momentum theory for hover out of ground effect.

slugs/sec) depends on the density of the air, the area of the disc, and the velocity through the disc:

$$\frac{m}{\Delta t} = \rho A v_i \qquad \text{slugs/sec}$$

where A is the total disc area ($A = \pi R^2$). Thus

$$T_R = \rho A v_i(\Delta V)$$
$$= \rho A v_i(v_f - 0)$$

And since

$$v_i = \frac{v_f}{2}$$

$$T_R = \frac{\rho A v_f^2}{2}$$

or

$$\boxed{v_f = \sqrt{\frac{2T_R}{\rho A}}}$$

In hover, the total rotor thrust supports the weight, so that $T_R = W$, and

$$v_f = \sqrt{\frac{2W}{\rho A}} = \sqrt{\frac{2DL}{\rho}} \qquad \text{fps}$$

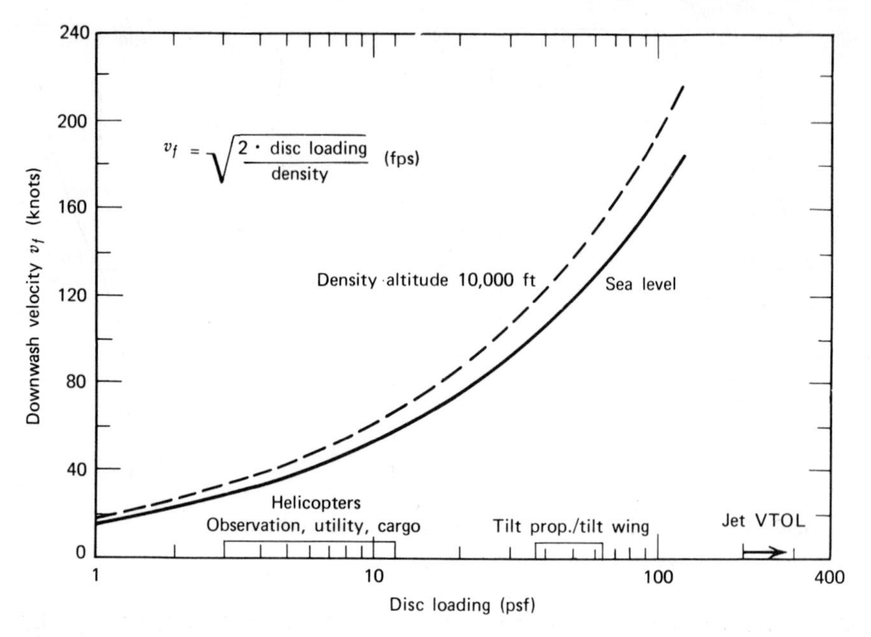

Figure 3.3 Rotor downwash velocity OGE.

where DL is the "disc loading" equal to the aircraft weight divided by the disc area (analogous to "wing loading" for a fixed wing aircraft). The simple relationships above illustrate that rotor thrust in hover may be increased by higher density (lower density altitude), larger disc area (greater rotor diameter), and higher downwash velocities (produced by higher collective pitch setting and/or high RPM). Of particular interest is the dependence of the final downwash velocity on disc loading (the higher the disc loading, the higher the downwash) and on density (the lower the density, the higher the downwash). Figure 3.3 depicts this relationship.

3.3 BLADE ELEMENT THEORY OF LIFT

The momentum theory, though giving an overall picture of the physics of hovering flight, neither provides detailed information about the flow field, nor explains, for example, the exact dependence of rotor thrust on rotor speed or collective pitch setting. Returning to a single section of one blade, we have the picture shown in Figure 3.4. The angle of the airfoil's chordline with the plane of rotation (tip path plane) is called the pitch angle of the

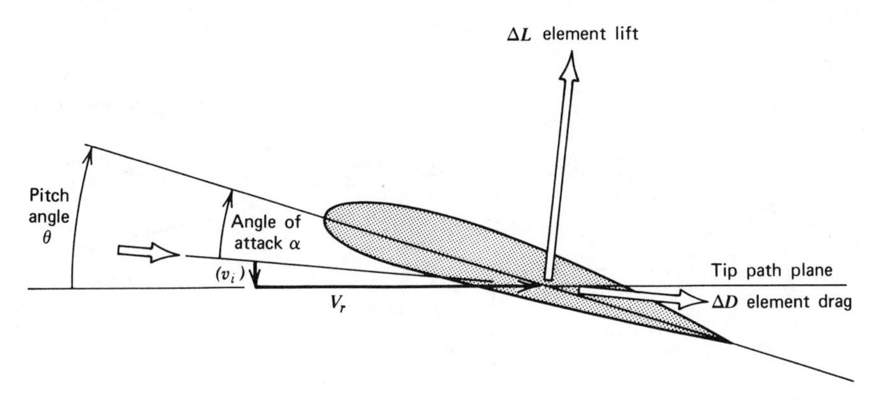

Figure 3.4 Geometry of blade section.

airfoil θ. This is the angle directly controlled by the pilot with the collective pitch control. The angle of attack is always defined as the angle between the chordline and the direction of the relative wind. To find the direction of the relative wind (i.e., where the air is coming from, as the airfoil sees it), it must be appreciated that the air has two velocities relative to the airfoil: the velocity in the tip path plane due to the rotation of the rotor and the induced velocity v_i at right angles to the tip path plane. The resultant relative wind is thus the *vector sum* of these two, as shown in Figure 3.4. It is clear that the pitch angle is larger than the angle of attack in this example.

We must know the angle of attack, since the lift coefficient C_l is proportional to the angle of attack, not the pitch angle (blade stall is also an angle of attack phenomenon, hence the distinction must be made clear). The lift produced by the section is

$$\Delta L = \tfrac{1}{2}\rho V_r^2 \, \Delta S C_l$$

In general, each section has a different V_r (primarily because of the dependence of velocity of rotation on distance from the hub) and a different C_l (because of the changing angle of attack). Figure 3.4 shows that if all sections have the same pitch and approximately the same v_i, the tip sections, have both high velocity and high angle of attack. Consequently, the tips produce a disproportionate amount of lift compared to the inboard sections. This is not only aerodynamically inefficient, but creates large moments about the hub with accompanying large coning angles, as shown in Figure 3.5. Designers therefore keep the blade pitch toward the tip about 8 or 10° smaller than that toward the hub, thus altering the angle of attack distribution and obtaining a more uniform lift distribution.

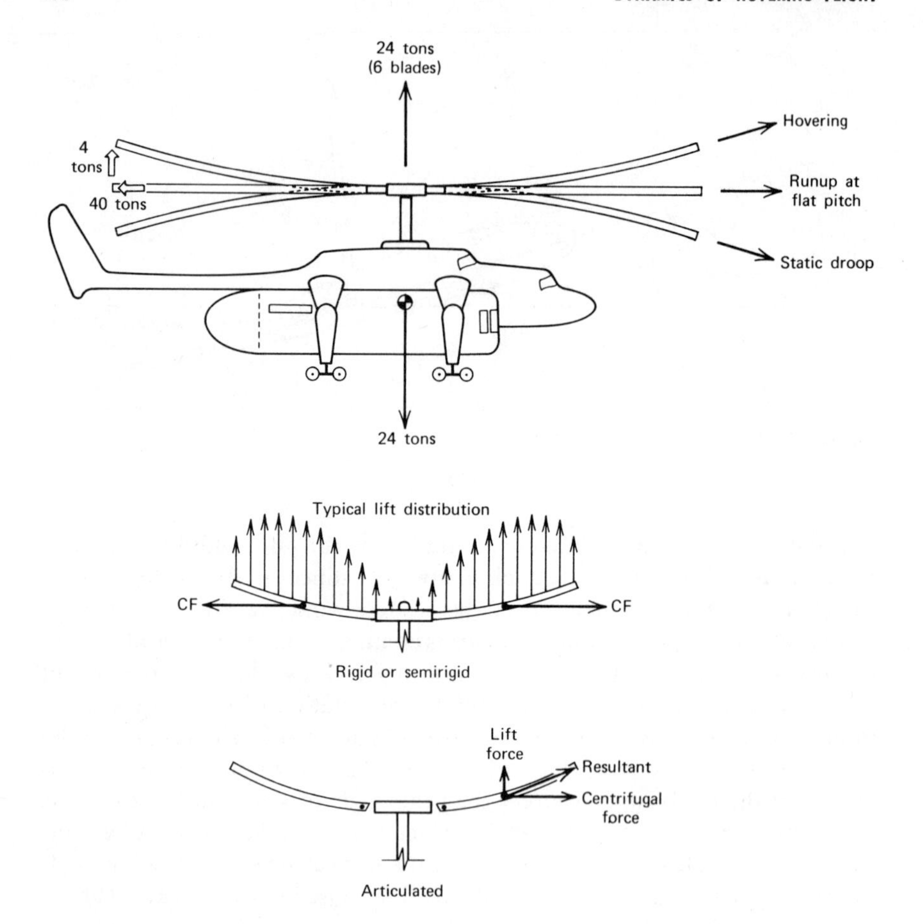

Figure 3.5 Coning of flexible rotor blades.

The total lift is then obtained by adding all ΔL's of all sections of all blades:

$$T_R = \Sigma\,\Delta L = \Sigma\tfrac{1}{2}\rho V_r^2\,\Delta S C_l$$

Performing this addition rigorously requires the use of the integration process in calculus. The result is:

$$T_R = \tfrac{1}{2}\rho\,\frac{V_{\text{tip}}^{\;2}}{3}\,SC_{l_{\text{avg}}}$$

Here S is the total rotor blade area, and $C_{l_{\text{avg}}}$ is the average lift coefficient, accounting for different airfoil shapes and angles of attack spanwise. It is customary, and convenient, to define the ratio of the total blade area to the total disc area as the "solidity ratio:"

$$\text{solidity ratio} = s = \frac{S}{A} \quad \text{(nondimensional)}$$

The solidity ratio then represents the portion of the circular disc occupied by the blades, and is typically 4 to 7%.

The tip velocity, V_{tip}, may be more conveniently expressed in terms of rotational speed as:

$$V_{\text{tip}} = \frac{R \cdot \text{RPM}}{9.55} \quad \text{fps}$$

Also, using $\sigma = \rho/\rho_0$ (density ratio), the expression for total rotor thrust in hover becomes:

$$\boxed{T_R = \frac{\sigma C_{l_{\text{avg}}} \text{RPM}^2 s R^2 A}{230{,}000}} \quad \text{lb}$$

This expression says that the thrust of the rotor will increase directly as the density ratio, average lift coefficient (controlled directly by the collective lever), and the square of the rotor speed increase. The strong dependence on RPM is particularly critical, since, for example, a decay of only 10% of rotor RPM will result in a 19% decrease in lift capability. Figure 3.6 plots this relationship.

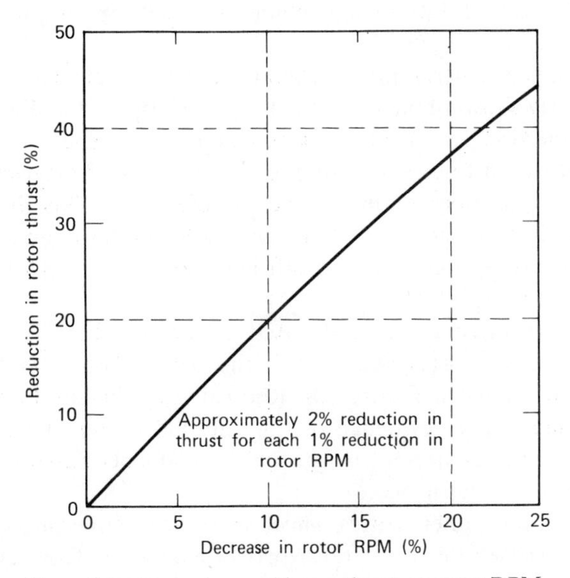

Figure 3.6 Dependence of hover thrust on rotor RPM.

High density altitude (low σ) reduces rotor thrust. Hence to sustain a given weight, a higher $C_{l_{avg}}$ (more collective pitch) is required. A blade section stalls, as does a wing section, when the local angle of attack exceeds the stall angle of the section. Thus there is a maximum $C_{l_{avg}}$, which may define the maximum gross weight for hovering at a given density altitude or, conversely, the maximum altitude at which hovering is possible for a given weight.

As $C_{l_{avg}}$ increases, however, so does the drag due to lift (induced drag coefficient C_{di}). The summation of all the drag forces times their respective radii represents the net requirement for rotor torque, hence power. Since the power available is limited, $C_{l_{max}}$ may be limited in order to prevent RPM decay. Therefore, maximum gross weight and maximum hover ceiling may be defined by power limitations, rather than aerodynamic lifting capability of the rotor.

3.4 HOVERING WAKE GEOMETRY

The idealized straight line flow through the rotor used in the momentum theory (Figure 3.2) is not exactly what happens in fact, although for some purposes the momentum model gives surprisingly good results. The rotor blade tip, as does a fixed wing tip, exhibits a strong rotational vortex, which influences the nature of the entire flow field. These tip vortices are shed down and beneath a fixed wing aircraft. For a hovering helicopter a helical geometry is produced. For a single blade this is seen in the smoke visualization photographs of Figure 3.7.

Figure 3.7*a* is a schleren photograph (one that detects density changes in the flow) clearly showing the helical nature of the tip vortex. Emitting smoke from the blade tip (i.e., in the rotating frame of reference) would produce a similar picture. In Figure 3.7*b* smoke is being emitted externally from the blades (i.e., in the nonrotating frame or reference). This illustrates how surrounding air becomes induced into the vortex pattern and how the wake moves downward and contracts. Both ideas are incorporated in the schematic representation of Figure 3.7*c*.

While the strongest vortex is located at the tip, there is a continuous shedding of weaker vortices all along the blade. This is called a vortex sheet and is depicted in Figure 3.8. Returning to the smoke visualization picture of Figure 3.7*b*, evidence of this internal vortex sheet is indicated by the discontinuities present in the smoke filaments passing through the inner region of the rotor wake.

This continuous inner vortex sheet has been represented in classical theory by a distribution of discrete vortices emanating from evenly spaced

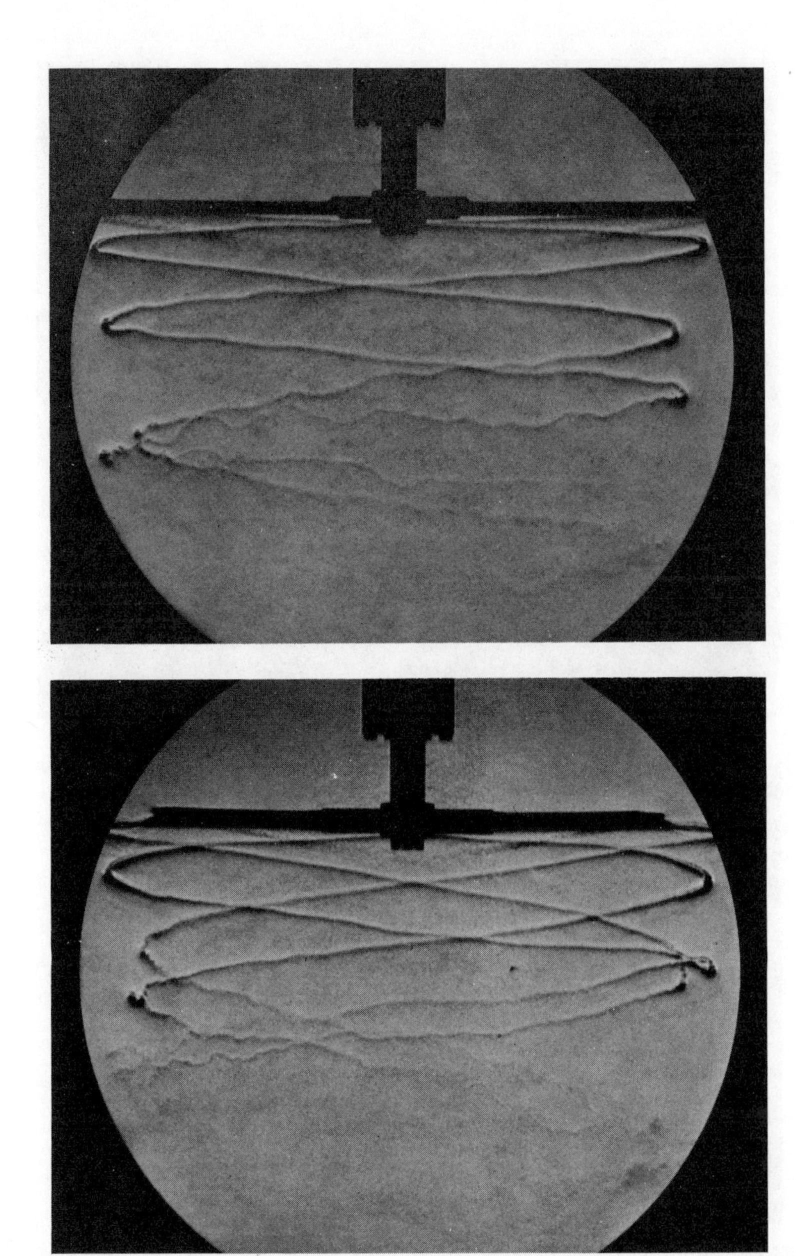

Figure 3.7 Hovering wake structure. (*a*) Schleren photographs of square tipped rotor, $M_T = 0.74$. *Top:* two-bladed rotor; *bottom*: four-bladed rotor. (From reference 92.)

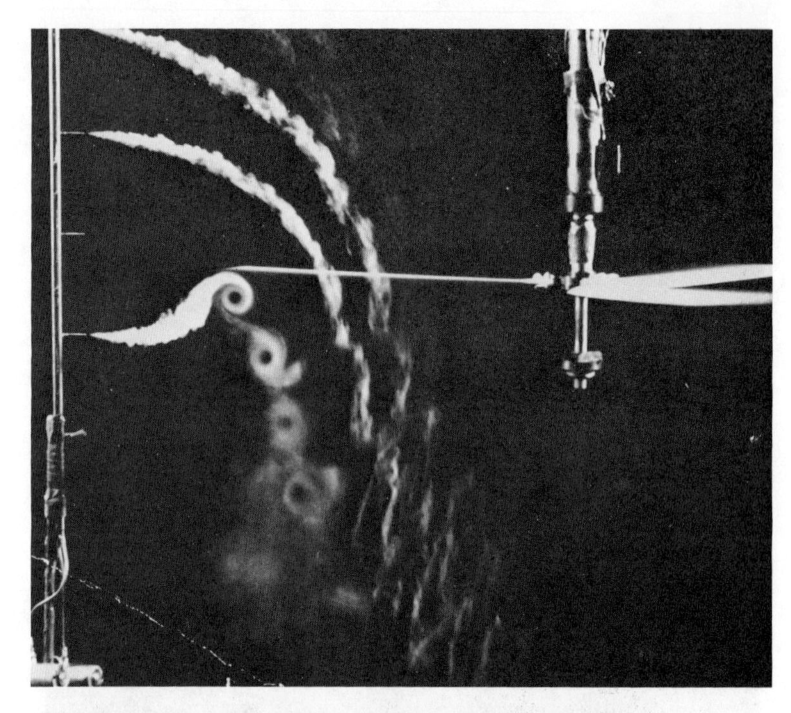

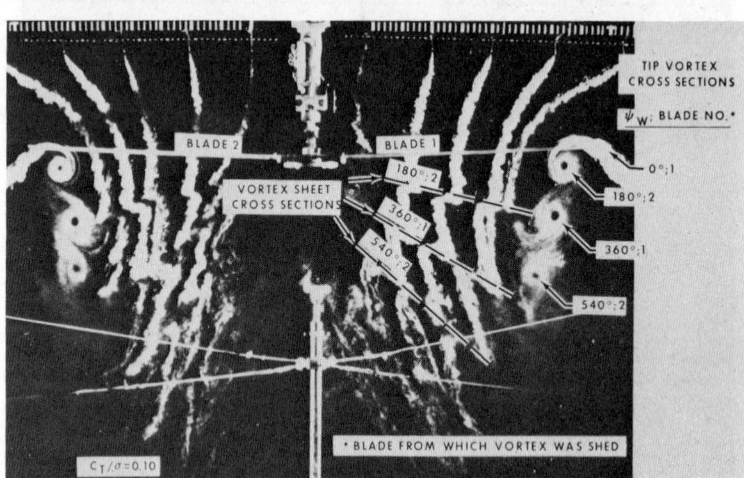

Figure 3.7 (*b*) Smoke-flow visualization of wake vortor system. (From reference 62.)

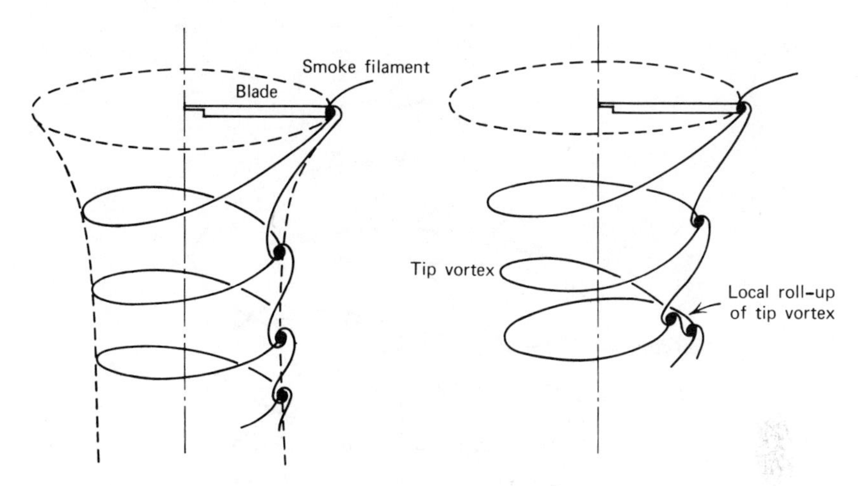

Figure 3.7 (*c*) Idealized tip vortex system motor. *Left:* Stable tip vortex; *right:* unstable tip vortex. (From reference 62.)

locations along the blade span. The difference between this classical wake model and experimental evidence is illustrated in the schematics of Figure 3.9.

The picture is further complicated by the presence of more than one blade, each of which has its own vortex system. The interference of one vortex system with another produces further distortions of the wake.

Finally, at large distances from the rotor, the vortices become unstable and dissipate with time, as they do behind a fixed wing aircraft (observe this in contrail breakup of high altitude jet aircraft).

3.5 DRAG, TORQUE, AND POWER

While producing lift, a blade section is also producing drag. This drag force, acting at some distance from the center of rotation, causes a torque that tends to retard the rotational motion of the blades, as shown in Figure 3.10. This torque must be overcome in order to maintain the rotational speed. The engine supplies sufficient power to the mast to overcome the total torque, caused by all the elemental torques of each section of each blade. To calculate the power required to do this, we must know the relationship between power and torque:

$$\text{power} = \text{torque} \cdot \text{angular velocity}$$

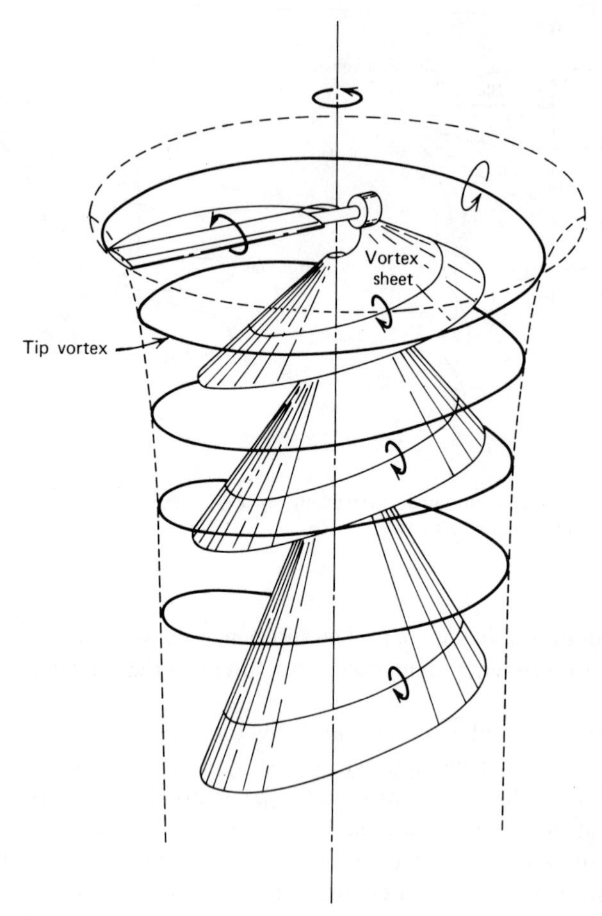

Figure 3.8 Schematic or rotor wake structure. (From reference 62.)

Thus a given power may be delivered at high torque and low RPM or low torque at high RPM. For the same rotational speed, torque becomes a direct measure of power. If power is to be expressed in horsepower, torque in foot-pounds, and angular velocity in revolutions per minute, we have:

$$\boxed{P = \frac{T \cdot \text{RPM}}{5255}} \quad \text{hp}$$

Thus the power required to overcome the drag of just one section is

$$\Delta P = \frac{\Delta D \cdot r \cdot \text{RPM}}{5255} = \frac{\frac{1}{2}\rho V_r^2 \, \Delta S C_d \cdot r \cdot \text{RPM}}{5255}$$

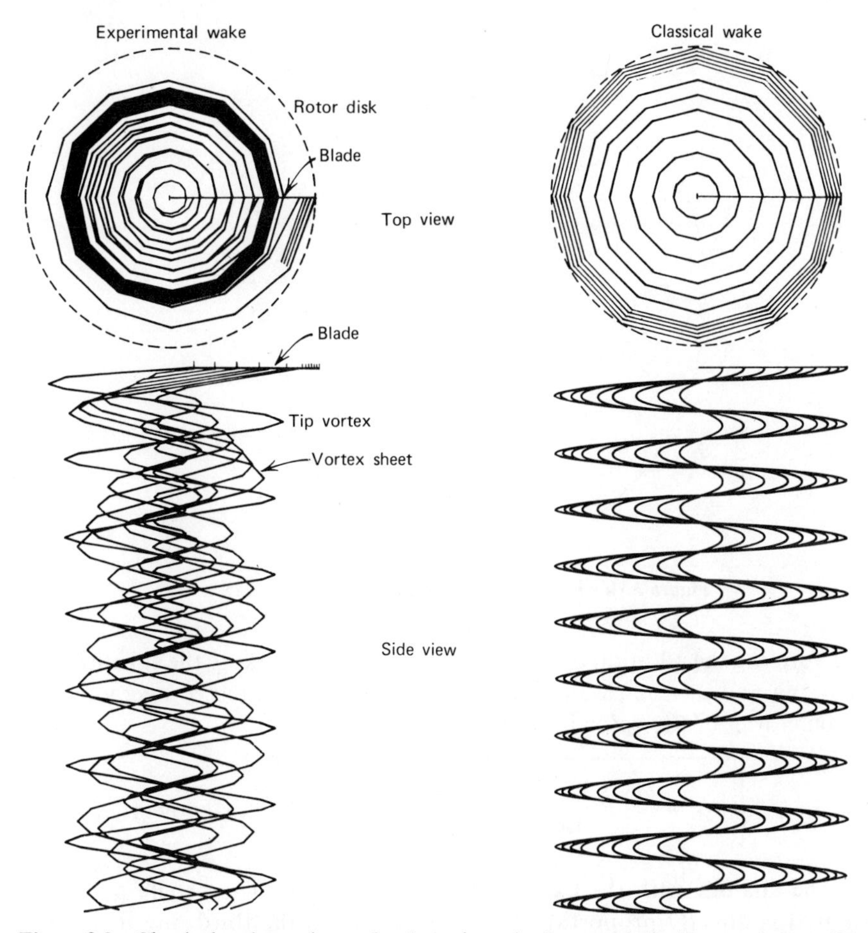

Figure 3.9 Classical and experimental wake trajectories for one blade. (From reference 62.)

Again, each section has a different V_r, C_d, and r; hence care must be taken in the summation process. Of particular interest is the drag coefficient of the section, which may be broken into its profile drag and induced drag contributions:

$$C_d = C_{d_{pr}} + C_{d_i}$$

Here the profile drag of the blade section is associated with pressure and skin friction drag at zero lift, and the induced drag coefficient represents the additional drag existing when the section is producing lift.

Taking the profile drag first, we obtain

$$\Delta P_{pr} = \frac{(\frac{1}{2}\rho V^2 \, \Delta S C_{d_{pr}}) \cdot r \cdot \text{RPM}}{5255}$$

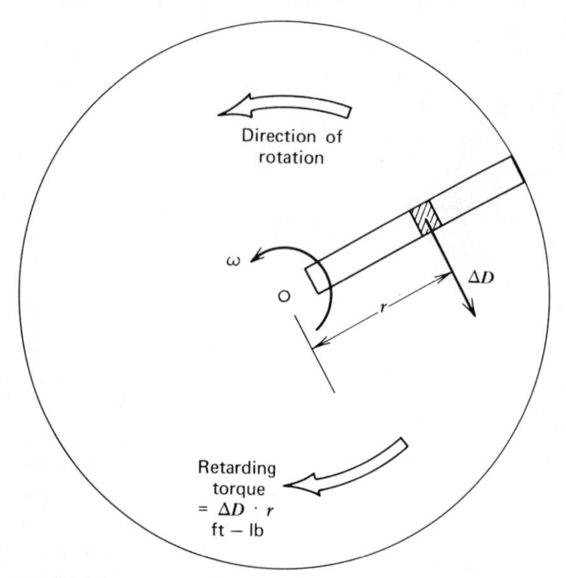

Figure 3.10 Production of torque.

Performing the addition over all blade sections and making the substitutions $S = sA$ and $\rho = \sigma\rho_0$, we obtain the total power required to overcome the profile drag of the rotor in hover:

$$\boxed{P_{pr} = \frac{\sigma(C_{d_{pr}})_{\text{avg}}\ \text{RPM}^3\ sR^3A}{1.61 \cdot 10^9}} \qquad \text{profile horsepower}$$

The analogy with the fixed wind case is obvious. The profile power required is directly proportional to density and to the third power of rotational speed.

The necessary power to overcome induced drag can be obtained more directly by using the momentum theory developed previously. As for fixed wing aircraft, the power can be expressed as the product of a force times the velocity (in the direction of the force) with which the body moves relative to the air:

$$\text{power} = \frac{\text{force} \cdot \text{velocity}}{550} \qquad \text{hp}$$

In the case of induced drag, the force is the rotor thrust, which in hover is equal to the aircraft weight. The velocity is the induced velocity at the rotor disc, v_i. Thus

$$P_i = \frac{W \cdot v_i}{550}$$

But from our previous discussion of momentum theory, we know that

$$v_i = \sqrt{\frac{W}{2\rho A}} \qquad \text{(ideal)}$$

Therefore

$$P_i = \frac{W}{550}\sqrt{\frac{W}{2\rho A}}$$

Substituting $\rho = \rho_0\sigma$ and $A = \pi R^2$, we obtain

$$\boxed{P_i = \frac{W^{3/2}}{67R\sigma^{1/2}}} \qquad \text{ideal induced horsepower}$$

Again, the *induced* portion of the total power required goes up as weight goes up and as density goes down. The way in which P_i varies with weight and density is not exactly the same as in the fixed wing case.

The ratio of this ideal induced power to the actual total power required is called the hovering figure of merit, and it gives some insight into the efficiency of the helicopter in hover:

$$\text{hovering figure of merit: } M = \frac{P_i}{P_{\text{tot}}} = \frac{W^{3/2}}{67R\sigma^{1/2}P_{\text{tot}}}$$

Astonishingly, almost all helicopters exhibit hovering figures of merit in a narrow range between 0.5 and 0.6. For a given helicopter the higher the gross weight the higher the induced power, while profile power remains constant. Thus induced power becomes a larger fraction of the total, leading to a higher figure of merit. Somewhat surprisingly, then, a helicopter operates more efficiently when hovering at maximum gross weight than at any other weight (or course, the magnitude of the power required is highest at that weight).

Thus the total hover power required is

$$P_{\text{req}} = P_{pr} + P_i$$

$$\boxed{(P_{\text{req}})_{\substack{\text{hover}\\ \text{OGE}}} = \frac{\sigma(C_{d_{pr}})_{\text{avg}}\text{RPM}^3 s R^3 A}{1.61 \cdot 10^9} + \frac{W^{3/2}}{67R\sigma^{1/2}}}$$

Note that the effect of rotational speed is felt only in the profile portion, while the effect of weight is felt only in the induced portion. Increasing the density altitude decreases profile drag while increasing induced drag. Typically in hover, the induced power is 65 to 75% of the total. Thus the combination of high gross weight and high density altitude demands the most power to be delivered to the rotor. Figure 3.11 is a typical chart from

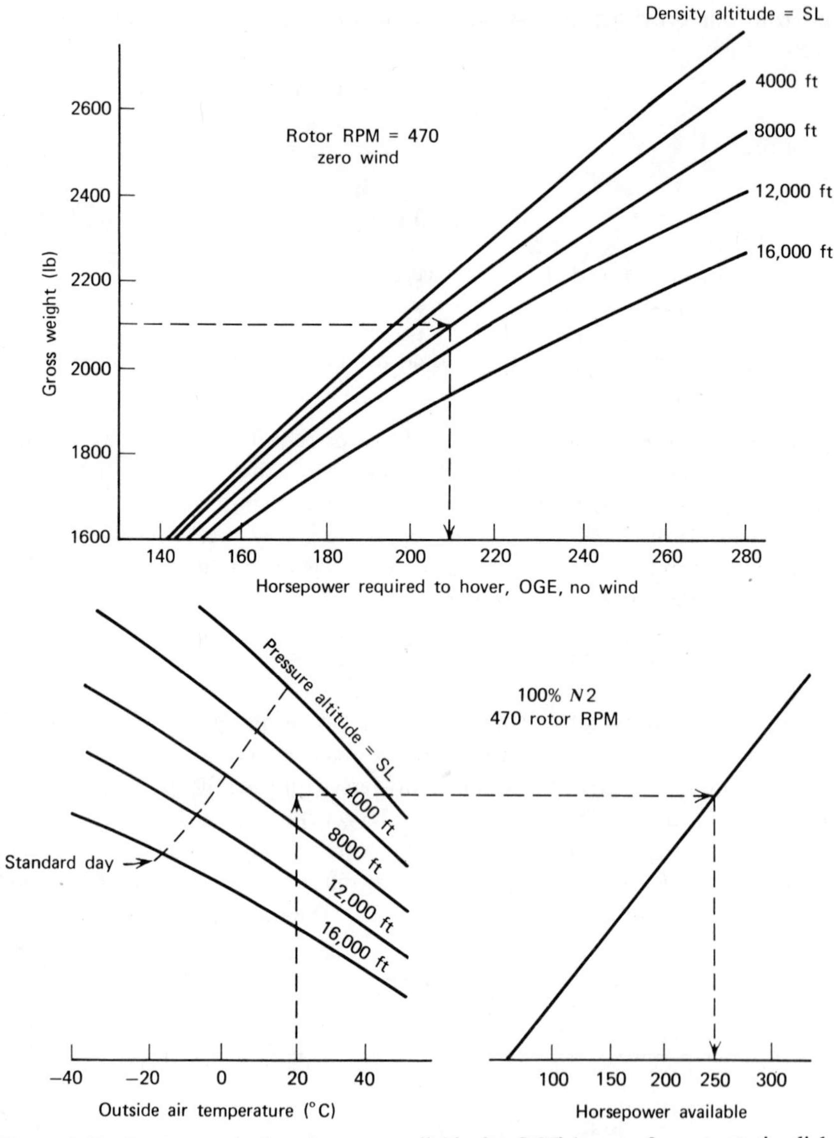

Figure 3.11 Power required and power available for OGE hover of representative light observation helicopter. (U.S. Army data.)

the pilot's manual of a light observation helicopter, illustrating power required (these charts also include some small power for driving the tail rotor).

The hovering performance of the helicopter depends on the difference between the power available and that required. Though the power available does not depend on aircraft weight, it certainly depends on density, being almost directly proportional to it. Thus at a high density altitude the power available is low and the power required is high. The implications for the maximum gross weight that can be lifted in a given set of conditions are clear.

A direct indication to the pilot of the power being developed in his torquemeter. This instrument is in fact a pressure measuring device, which senses oil pressure at some convenient location in the transmission system. It is not a *direct* reading of torque (ft-lb) or of power (HP). However, for every installation there is usually some calibration factor relating torquemeter reading (psi) and power. One installation might require a multiplications of 3.3 to get horsepower (e.g., 75 psi · 3.3 = 247.5 HP), while a different model helicopter may have a completely different calibration factor. The performance charts in the pilot's manual give torquemeter readings, since they are what the pilot has to deal with.

Figure 3.12 illustrates the hovering performance of the helicopter whose power characteristics were given in Figure 3.11.

3.6 GROUND EFFECT IN HOVER

We have not yet considered the effect of the presence of the ground. When the rotor is operating in proximity to the ground (for practical purposes,

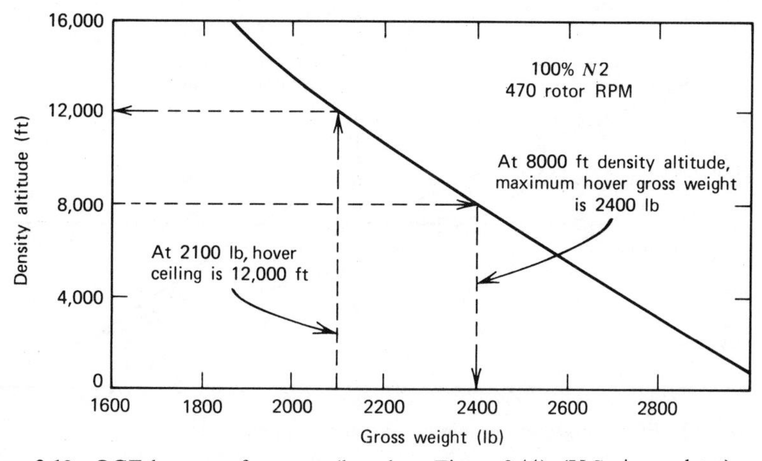

Figure 3.12 OGE hover performance (based on Figure 3.11). (U.S. Army data.)

at a height less than one rotor diameter), the downwash field is altered from its free air state. As we know, in subsonic flow any distrubance in the flow field is felt to some extent everywhere else in the field. Thus the flow direction and magnitude around the rotor are altered by the presence of the ground, being more severe the closer. the rotor is to the ground.

At the surface there obviously cannot be any flow in the vertical direction. Thus the vertical velocity v_f previously assumed is now reduced to zero. Correspondingly, the induced velocity at the rotor disc, v_i, is retarded. Figure 3.13 illustrates the effect of this on a given airfoil section. The basic effect is an increase in the local angle of attack that the section sees. There are two basic consequences: (1) the lift vector becomes larger and (2) the lift vector tilts further forward, toward the vertical. Both effects increase the net aerodynamic force acting to support the weight. Thus for the same expenditure of power more weight can be lifted in ground effect than out

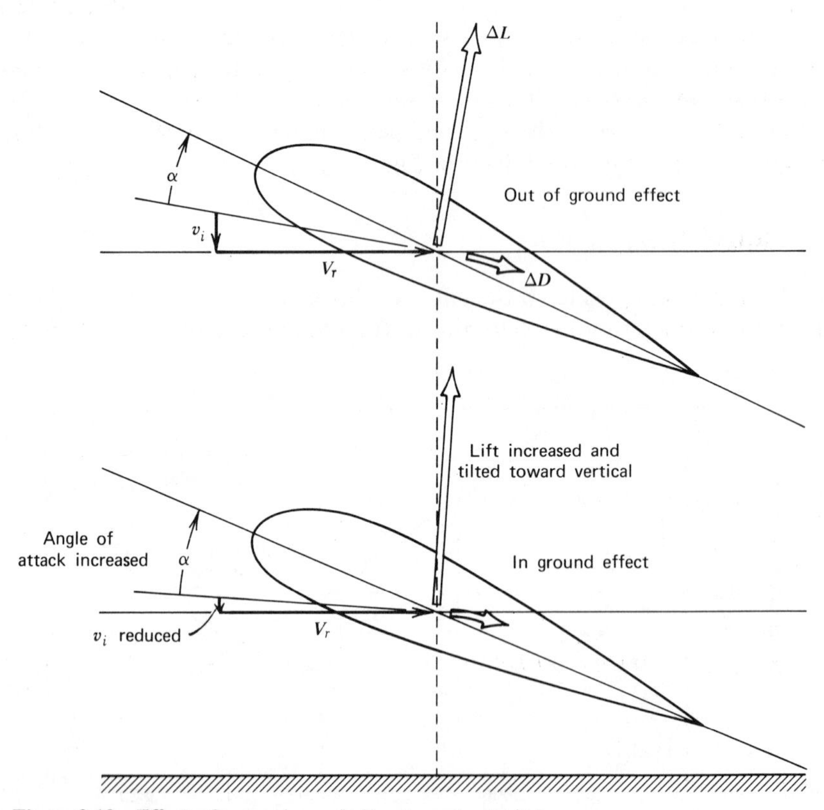

Figure 3.13 Effect of ground proximity at constant pitch.

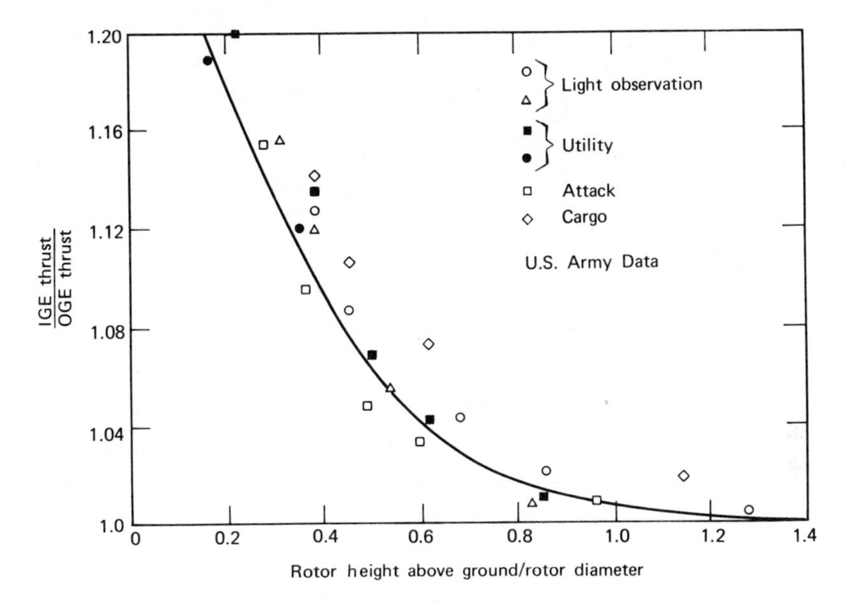

Figure 3.14 Increased lift capability in ground effect. (From reference 63.)

of it. Figure 3.14 shows how much extra lifting power can be obtained, as a function of rotor distance above the ground. At a rotor hub height equal to one rotor radius an increase of approximately 7% in lifting capability is experienced.

However, since usually the pilot wishes to support a given weight, he must, when in ground effect, reduce the pitch angle of the blade so that the total vertical component equals the weight. The induced drag then, of course, is also reduced, and so is the induced power required. Because in hover the induced power is approximately 75% of the total, the reduction in ground effect may be substantial. Figure 3.15 illustrates the size of the effect for our earlier helicopter. Note that the large potential benefits of ground effect are not usually obtainable, since the rotor seldom can get closer to the ground than about one third a rotor diameter. Also, since the induced velocity at the rotor disc is reduced, the severity of the tip vortex system is diminished.

For a helicopter of given weight the rotor produces the same total lift (equal to the weight) whether hovering IGE or OGE. Thus the average pressure difference, ΔP, across the disc is the same in either case. The concept of a "bubble of high pressure air" beneath the helicopter is inaccurate and sometimes misleading, even though it serves as a convenient analogy when explaining the phenomena to a layman. The pressure distribution along the

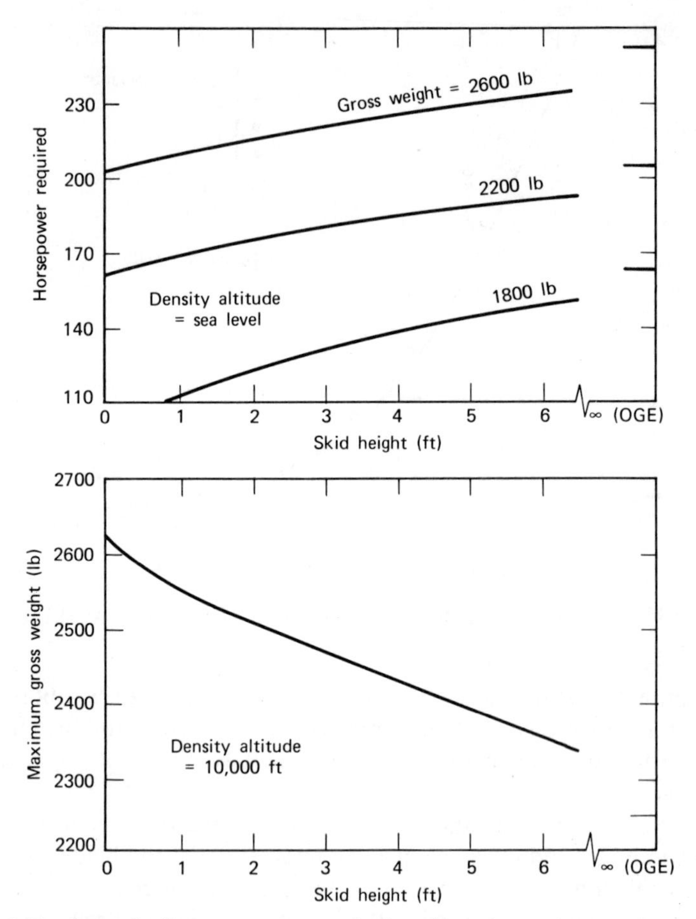

Figure 3.15 Ground effect on power required and maximum hover gross weight for representative light observation helicopter. (U.S. Army data.)

ground naturally is different from the pressure distribution on a horizontal plane the same distance below the rotor if no ground is present. But the entire flow field is changed—flow velocities, flow directions, and pressures. The idea of a finite volume of air at a pressure higher than the ambient atmosphere is an unnecessary simplification of the real case. Also, the concept of a cushion of denser air is entirely false. There is essentially no increase in air density beneath the helicopter compared to anywhere else in the flow.

It should also be noted that the curves apply to hovering over firm, flat terrain. Over water, energy is absorbed from the airstream in producing wave motion, and over tall grass, energy is used in producing horizontal drag forces on each blade of grass. Consequently, when compared to hovering over hard surfaces *at the same rotor height* (above the water surface or from the *base* of the grass), the ground effect is *smaller* than is indicated in the operator's manual.

The horizontal flow velocities, which are produced by the ground deflecting the airstream below the rotor 90°, can be significantly higher than the downwash velocity, V_f, calculated by the simple momentum model. This phenomenon is discussed and examples are given in Section 6.8. Ground effect in forward flight is examined in Section 4.5.

PROBLEMS

3.1 (*a*) What is the tip speed of a 44 ft diameter rotor in hover at 330 RPM? (*b*) What is the tip Mach number under standard sea level conditions? (*c*) What is the tip Mach number at 10,000 ft density altitude?

3.2 A heavy lift helicopter has two 60 ft diameter rotors, each with five blades having a constant chord of 2.5 ft. Calculate, for a gross weight of 50,000 lb at sea level, (*a*) the solidity ratio, (*b*) the disc loading, and (*c*) the OGE hovering wake velocity.

3.3 For the helicopter of Example 3.2, calculate the profile and induced power required, for an RPM of 210 and an average profile drag coefficient of 0.02. If an additional 120 HP is required for the tail rotor, transmission losses, and so on, what would be the figure of merit?

3.4 Using the performance charts in the Appendix, construct a graph of OGE hovering ceiling as a function of gross weight. Repeat for the IGE ceiling at a 2 ft skid height.

Figure 3.16 Courtesy Bell Helicopter Company.

DYNAMICS OF FORWARD FLIGHT

4

4.1 INTRODUCTION

The development of lift on a rotor is not so easily appreciated in forward flight as in hover, since for each blade section the magnitude and direction of the relative wind are continually changing. That is, we now have an unsteady aerodynamic field, rather than the steady one experienced when hovering in calm air. That is illustrated in Figure 4.1. In addition to the velocity V_r due to rotation, each element feels an additional velocity V, due to the forward speed of the helicopter. The net velocity vector experienced by a blade section is the *vector sum* of $\mathbf{V}$ and $\mathbf{V}_r$. When the blade is at the 90° azimuth position ("advancing blade") the two velocities add arithmetically to produce the highest airspeed felt by the section. Conversely, at the 270° azimuth position, the two velocities subtract arithmetically to produce the lowest airspeed. At other azimuth positions, the vectors $\mathbf{V}$ and $\mathbf{V}_r$ are not collinear; hence their vector sum results in a relative wind that is not perpendicular to the leading edge. This "yawed"

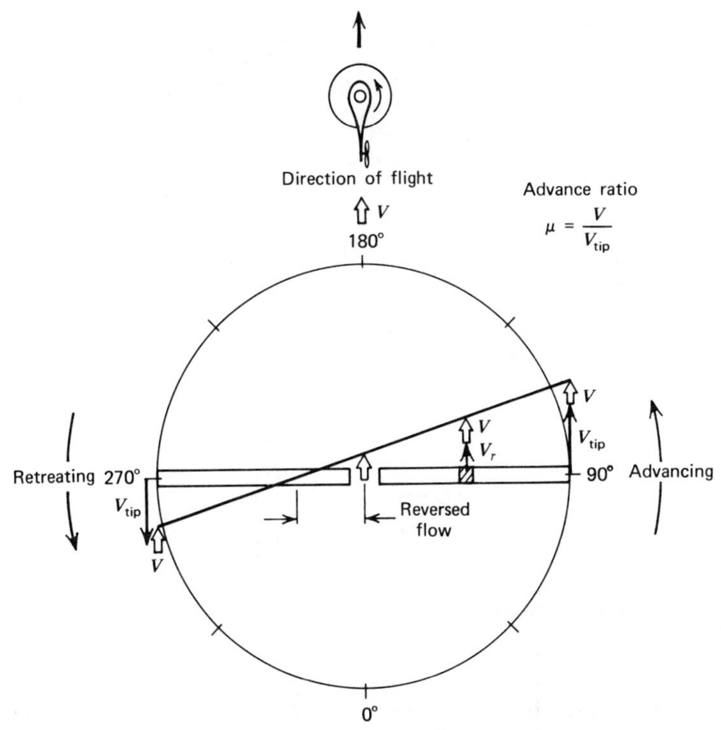

Figure 4.1 Velocity distribution in forward flight.

condition is similar to a swept wing in forward flight, and proper account of the different aerodynamic characteristics must be taken in performance prediction.

It can also be seen that on the retreating blade near the root (and for other azimuths at about 270°) an area of reversed flow exists, that is, the relative wind moves from trailing edge to leading edge. Obviously, this part of the blade is not an efficient lift producer. For a fixed blade pitch setting, a large lift dissymmetry will exist because of the higher average airspeed on the advancing than on the retreating side. In very early helicopters, whose blades were rigidly attached to the hub (and were very rigid themselves), uncontrollable left rolling tendencies limited forward flight.

The obvious solution is to somehow reduce the angle of attack on the advancing side and increase it on the retreating side, thus compensating for the velocity asymmetry. This can be done by reducing the pitch of each blade as it traverses the advancing side and increasing it on the retreating side. This "cyclic feathering" is performed on some helicopters, but the

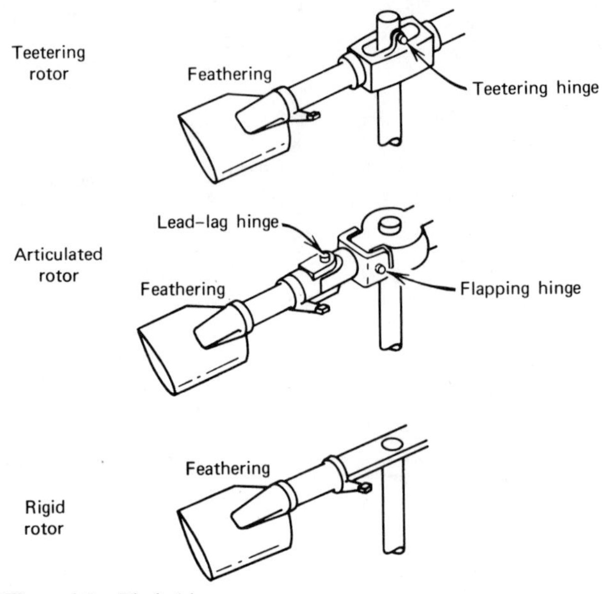

Figure 4.2 Blade hinge systems.

vast majority employ flapping hinges (either a single "teetering" hinge on a two-bladed rotor or independent flapping hinges in multibladed rotors—Figure 4.2).

4.2 BLADE FLAPPING

To understand flapping, and its implications for rotor control, it must first be realized that an unrestrained hinge (no dampers) is unable to sustain a moment, that is, $\Sigma M_{\text{hinge}} = 0$. Thus an increase in lift on the advancing side results in a moment that is *not* immediately transmitted to the hub, hence the fuselage. What happens is that the blade begins to flap up in response to the increased moment being felt. What is the result of this flapping-up motion on the advancing side?

Consider again the picture of a blade section at the time it is on the advancing side. Figure 4.3 shows that as a result of an additional *up* flapping velocity (the blade flaps up so that the relative wind moves downward), the angle of attack is *decreased.* This decreases the lift generated on the advancing side. A similar *increase* in angle of attack on the retreating side is accomplished by allowing the blade to flap *down.* Compared to zero

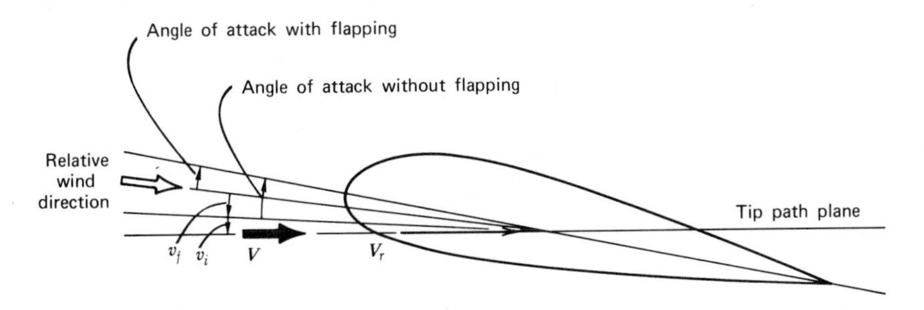

Figure 4.3 Decrease in angle of attack on advancing because of upflapping. V, helicopter forward speed; V_r, velocity due to rotation; v_i, induced velocity; v_f, flapping velocity.

flapping, upflapping reduces the angle of attack, and downflapping increases the angle of attack.

The entire flapping behavior of a single blade is complex. The lifting forces (hence the flapping moments) are changing continuously around the disc. Moreover, as a blade moves up, the increased moment due to the centrifugal forces tends to oppose the motion, trying to restore the blade to its original unflapped position. That is, the centrifugal forces act like a spring which exerts a restoring force on a mass, proportional to its distance from its static, or trim, position. It is well known that a mass on a spring oscillates at its "natural" frequency and that the period of this oscillation depends on the "stiffness" of the spring and the size of the mass. Likewise, a blade subjected to sinusoidal flapping moments as it moves around the disc tends to oscillate up and down at its natural frequency. It can be shown that the natural period of flapping oscillation, for a freely hinged blade, *is exactly equal to once per blade revolution.* That is, there is one complete flapping cycle for each traverse of the rotor disc.

In such a resonant motion, there is a definite relationship between the flapping *velocities* and the flapping *displacements.* Figure 4.4 shows that the maximum upward and downward velocities occur at the 90° and 270° positions respectively, and the maximum upward and downward displacements at the 180° and 0° positions. Because of the flapping displacements, the entire rotor disc is tilted backward with respect to the rotor mast. This "blowback" effect is easily observed in a wind tunnel when the tunnel velocity is increased and the rotor shaft is maintained at right angles to the flow. *Whenever the angle between the rotor shaft and the tip path plane is not 90°, flapping is taking place* regardless of the helicopter's attitude with respect to the earth.

To fly forward from hover, the pilot must of course initially tilt the tip path plane forward (we discuss the means in Chapter 5) so that a component

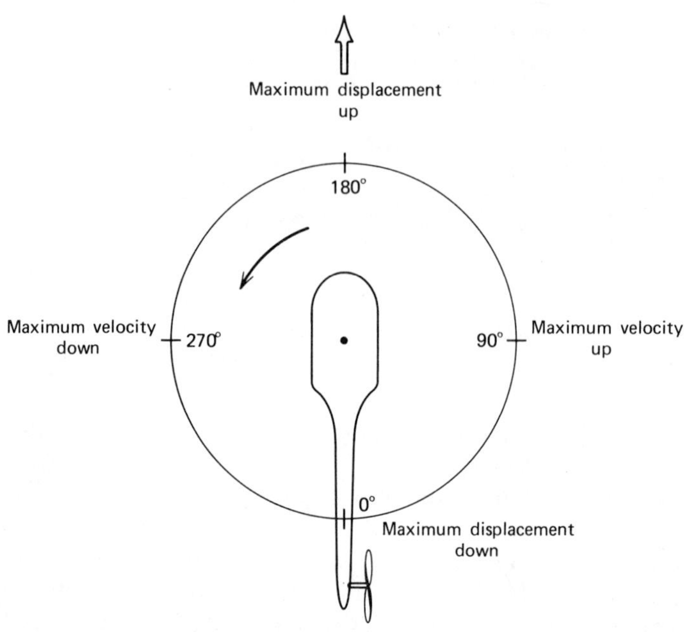

Figure 4.4 Flapping behavior in forward flight.

Azimuth Position	Flapping Velocity	Flapping Displacement
0°	Zero	Maximum down
90°	Maximum up	Zero
180°	Zero	Maximum up
270°	Maximum down	Zero

of the total lift is in the horizontal. The aircraft then accelerates from rest. Once a velocity develops, the tip path plane tends to blow back as explained above. Consequently, the pilot finds that he must *further* push forward on the stick to maintain his acceleration.

The tilting of the rotor disc because of velocity changes has obvious effects on the pitching tendencies of the aircraft. When a headwind gust occurs, the resulting flapping behavior tends to make the disc blow back, which causes the total lift vector to move ahead of the center of gravity, which in turn causes a noseup pitching moment on the fuselage. This effect enters our discussion of stability and control later.

The so-called "rigid rotor" helicopters do not have flapping hinges. However, their blades are so flexible that structural bending in the flapping sense takes place, having a similar effect on lift equalization. In fact, about

90% of a typical rigid rotor's "stiffness" comes from centrifugal forces. Thus while the natural frequency of flapping is not exactly once per revolution, it is usually only slightly higher.

In either case, the flapping motion is automatic and natural for a rotor blade in forward flight. No control inputs are required to initiate or maintain this mode of motion. It should also be noted that no gyroscopic effects are needed to account for blade flapping, although the analogy with a gyroscope is often used in elementary texts to explain the 90° phase shift between cause and effect.

4.3 RETREATING BLADE STALL

The ability of flapping to equalize lift has a fundamental limitation associated with the stalling of blade sections. This phenomenon limits the maximum forward speed capability of wingless helicopters. Clearly, the increase of angle of attack on the retreating side, as forward speed increases, eventually causes stalling, with an associated dramatic loss of lift and a large lift dissymmetry.

It should be mentioned that for very short periods the stalling angle of attack measured in a steady flow wind tunnel can be exceeded without loss of lift. This "dynamic" lift condition results from the finite time it takes for the boundary layer to change its separation point on the airfoil. This phenomenon allows fighter pilots to momentarily pull more *G*'s than they could sustain for longer periods. Since the retreating blade is at high angles of attack only momentarily, the section does not stall in the conventional sense at the specified "static" stall angle of attack. Nonetheless, at some point a dramatic loss of lift is experienced on the retreating side. This occurrence is accompanied by dramatic drag increases and an immediate requirement for more power. In some cases it may be the lack of power that limits the maximum forward speed rather than the loss of lift itself.

Consider a blade section on the retreating side (Figure 4.5) that is flapping downward (relative wind is upward). The forward flight velocity, V, now acts opposite to the rotational velocity, V_r. As the forward flight speed increases, so does the flapping velocity. Both effects can be seen to increase the local angle of attack on a retreating blade section. Eventually, a stall occurs.

Since the pitch angle may vary spanwise, it is not immediately clear which section of the retreating blade stalls first. Figure 4.6 illustrates a typical angle of attack distribution for a flapping rotor in forward flight. The largest positive angles of attack are shown to occur in a zone bounded by

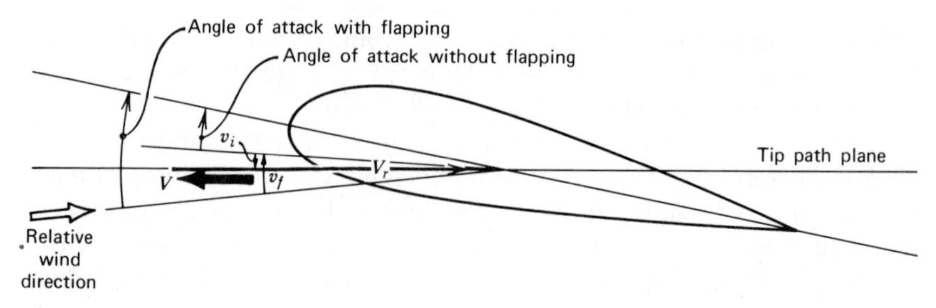

Figure 4.5 Increase in angle of attack on retreating side because of V, helicopter forward speed; V_r, velocity due to rotation; v_i, induced velocity; v_f, flapping velocity.

azimuths of 270° to 300° and at radii from 70 to 100% of blade radius (for untwisted blades the angle of attack is maximum at the tip).

When stalling finally occurs, the loss in lift around the 270° position results in a large downward flapping displacement around the 0° position, thus tilting the disc back and causing the fuselage to pitch up. Correct pilot technique for dealing with retreating blade stall is discussed in Section 6.7.

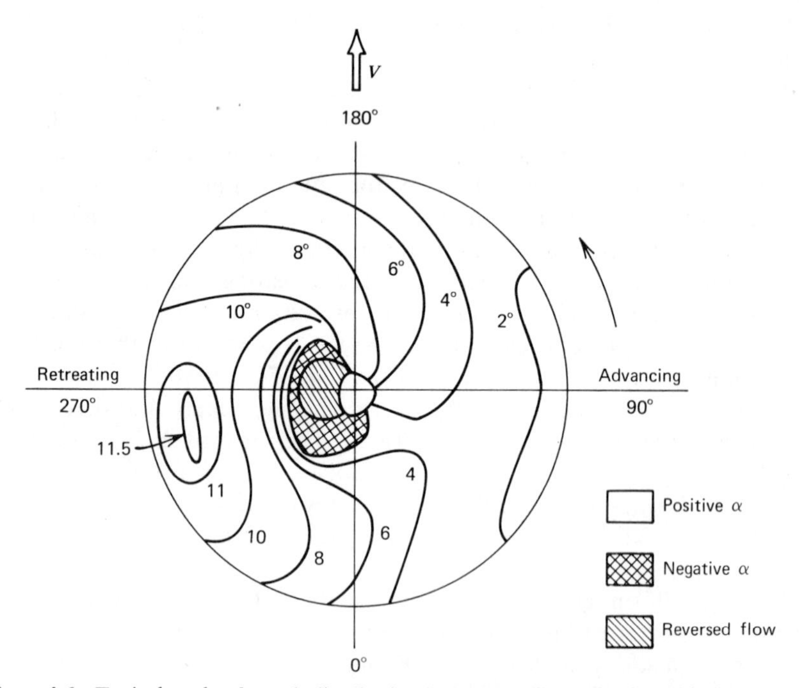

Figure 4.6 Typical angle of attack distribution in forward flight of twisted blade.

4.4 POWER REQUIRED

The induced and profile drag both are different in forward flight than they are in hover, as can be expected from the changes in airspeed and angle of attack felt by each blade section. Furthermore, the parasite drag of the fuselage (previously zero in hover) must now be added:

$$P_{\text{tot}} = P_{\text{pr}} + P_i + P_p$$

A simple model for the *induced* power may be obtained for speeds above about 30 knots by considering the disc to be a circular wing. This can be done since, from afar, the flow field and downwash distribution appear similar to a fixed wing aircraft supporting the same weight and having a span equal to the rotor diameter. Thus:

$$P_i = \frac{D_i V}{550} = \frac{C_{D_i} q S V}{550} \quad \text{HP}$$

$$= \frac{C_L^2 q S V}{550 \pi e A R}$$

But

$$C_L = \frac{W}{qS} \quad \text{and} \quad q = \tfrac{1}{2}\rho V^2$$

$$\therefore P_i = \frac{W^2}{550 \cdot \frac{1}{2}\rho V \pi e A R S} \quad \text{HP}$$

However, $SAR = b^2$, and for a rotor $b^2 = (2R)^2 = 4R^2$. Substituting this, as well as $\rho = \sigma\rho_0$, we obtain

$$\boxed{P_i = \frac{0.122 W^2}{\sigma V R^2 e}} \quad \text{induced horsepower above 30 knots}$$

The dependence on weight has gone from $W^{3/2}$ in hover to W^2, and the dependence on density ratio from $1/\sqrt{\sigma}$ to $1/\sigma$. From hover to 30 knots, then, the induced power expression is changing rapidly, and is too complex for analysis here. Figure 4.7 shows the dependence on forward speed over the total flight envelope. Of particular note is the rapid fall-off of induced power for moderate speed changes from hover.

The span efficiency factor e has the same meaning for rotors as for wings. Experimental data indicate that a value of 0.91 is typical at the higher speeds.

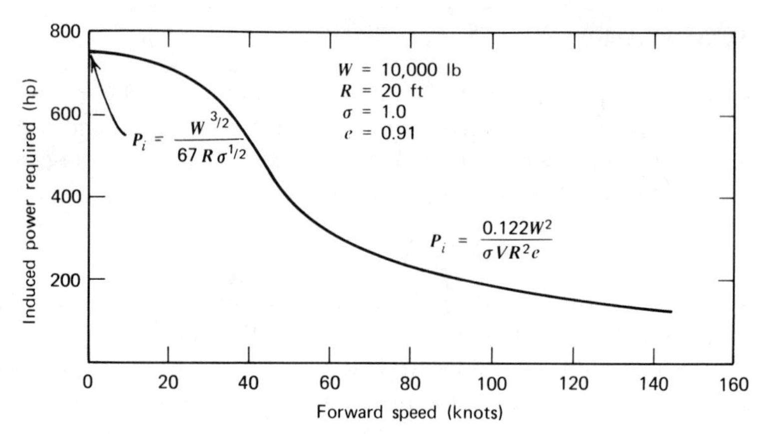

Figure 4.7 Induced power required.

The profile power required in forward flight differs from that in hover by reason of three main effects:

1. There is an overall increase in the magnitude of the relative wind over the rotor (V^2_{avg} effect), causing higher drag.
2. The different angle of attack distribution over the rotor disc (see Figure 4.6) causes a higher average drag coefficient.
3. "Compressibility" effects on the high speed advancing side cause an additional wave drag effect.

The first of these effects has been calculated from theory to be a simple function of how fast the helicopter is traveling compared to the rotational speed of the tip, that is, advance ratio:

$$\text{advance ratio} = \mu = \frac{V}{V_{tip}}$$

The advance ratio goes from zero in hover to values less than 1 in forward flight (for $\mu = 1$, $V = V_{tip}$, and the entire retreating blade would be in reverse flow at the 270° position).

The second effect is also a function of μ, since the angle of attack distribution continues to distort as μ increases. A correction factor, C_μ, is applied to the hover value to account for this effect. Designers have theoretical and empirical values for C_μ.

The third effect arises from shock wave formation near the blade tips on the advancing side, and is referred to as a compressibility effect. Some helicopters experience Mach numbers in excess of the section critical Mach number (M_{crit}) at farily low speeds. A 48 ft diameter rotor, turning at

324 RPM while the helicopter has a forward velocity of 100 knots TAS, experiences the following local Mach number on the advancing tip (standard sea level conditions):

$$M = \frac{V_{\text{tip}} + V}{a} = \frac{\frac{24(324)}{9.55} + 100(1.69)}{1116.9} = 0.88$$

The critical Mach number (at which shock waves first appear on the upper surface and the drag coefficient rises steeply) of many airfoil sections is below this value. Therefore, additional wave drag is experienced, with accompanying increases in required power to maintain RPM. The power penalty for this effect is shown in Figure 4.8 for a cargo helicopter. The tip Mach number was varied by changing temperature (which changed the speed of sound) and not by changing RPM. The effect is somewhat masked by improved gas turbine efficiency at low temperatures. If this were not the case (or if Mach numbers were changed by RPM instead of temperature) more dramatic impact of compressibility would have been noted. Even so, the power increment at maximum gross weight and 0.72 Mach number is 8.5% of the maximum installed power in the aircraft, which is considerable. At higher density altitudes, where the average angle of attack is higher

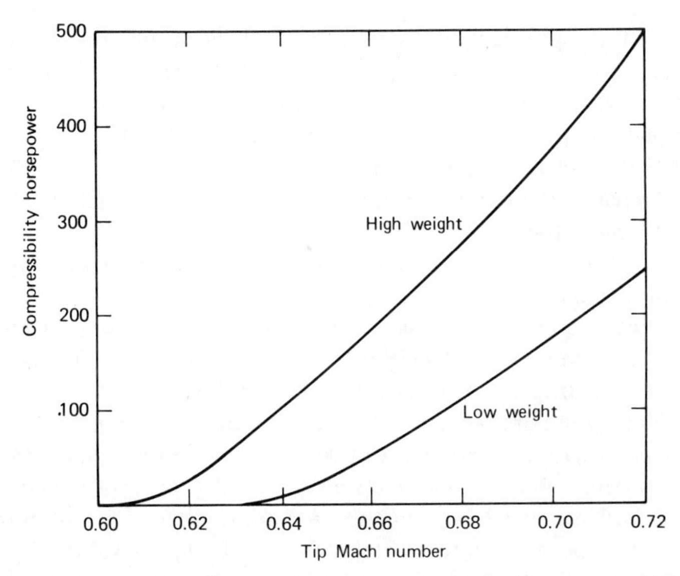

Figure 4.8 Compressibility effects on hovering power required for a cargo helicopter at standard sea level. (U.S. Army data.)

(and speed of sound lower) compressibility effects alone may account for 20% of the total power required.

As noted in Section 2.5, swept back tips and thinner airfoil sections near the tip improve this situation.

The total profiile power in forward flight can be expressed as

$$P_{\text{pr}} = (P_{\text{pr}})_{\text{hover}} \cdot (1 + 4.65\mu^2) \cdot C_\mu \cdot C_c$$

where $1 + 4.65\mu^2 \rightarrow V^2_{\text{avg}}$ effect

$C_\mu \rightarrow \alpha_{\text{avg}}$ effect

$C_c \rightarrow$ compressibility effect

Here the 4.65 factor is an empirical one, and will change from rotor to rotor. *The net result is a gradual, steady increase of profile power as forward speed is increased.*

The parasite ("flat plate") power results from increasing drag on the fuselage as speed is increased. As in the case of fixed wing parasite drag,

$$P_p = \frac{D_p V}{550} = \frac{\frac{1}{2}\rho V^3 f}{550}$$

$$P_p = \frac{\rho V^3 f}{1100} \quad \text{HP}$$

where f is the equivalent flat plate area (*not* the projected frontal area). This area varies greatly, depending on the configuration of the aircraft, as shown in Table 4.1. Note that simply removing cargo doors may increase the flat plate area (hence the parasite power) by as much as 20%. Adding two XM159 19-round rocket pods to each wing of the normally clean AH-1G increases the parasite drag by 66%, making it similar to the clean UH-1C in this respect.

The net result of all three power contributions is shown in Figure 4.9 for a sample case.

The dominant effect of induced power at low speed causes an initial reduction in power required as speed increases from hover. At high speed, where induced drag contributes little, the combined effects of increasing profile and parasite drag lead to an increase in the power required. Between the extremes there is a minimum in the power required curve. For most helicopters, this point occurs at an advance ratio of approximately 0.14 (i.e., at a forward speed 14% of the tip rotational speed). The power required at this speed is approximately 60% of the hover value.

The helicopter's performance capabilities (maximum speed, angle of climb, rate of climb, horizontal acceleration, etc.) depend on the difference

Table 4.1 Equivalent Flat Plate Drag Areas of Four U.S. Army Helicopters

Aircraft	Configuration	Equivalent Flat Plate Drag Area (ft^2)
Hughes OH-6A	Clean	4.50
	Rear doors removed	5.75
	All doors removed	5.80
Bell OH-58	Clean	12.00
	Rear doors removed	13.00
	All doors removed	13.60
	XM27E1 Minigun	13.20
Bell UH-1C	Clean	20.00
	Cargo doors removed	23.25
Bell AH-1G	Clean	11.75
	One XM159 rocket pod Inboard each wing	14.85
	One XM159 rocket pod Outboard each wing	14.95
	Two XM159 rocket pods each wing	19.45

Source. U.S. Army Data.

between the power available and the power required. Any variable (weight, density altitude, temperature, etc.) that affects either P_{av} or any component of P_{req}, alters the aircraft's performance.

4.5 FORWARD FLIGHT PERFORMANCE

Maximum Level Speed

While the maximum achievable speed in level forward flight is often limited by controllability (notably the effects of retreating blade stall), another restriction may be the lack of available power. The high speed intersection of the two curves (Figure 4.10) defines V_{max}. Increasing density altitude lowers P_{av} and may or may not increase P_{req}, depending on the speed. Generally, the reduction in P_{av} is dominant, and V_{max} (true) decreases. Increasing weight increases P_{req} without changing P_{av} and again V_{max} is reduced. Naturally, higher speeds than V_{max} may be obtained by diving, providing either controllability or structural problems are not limiting.

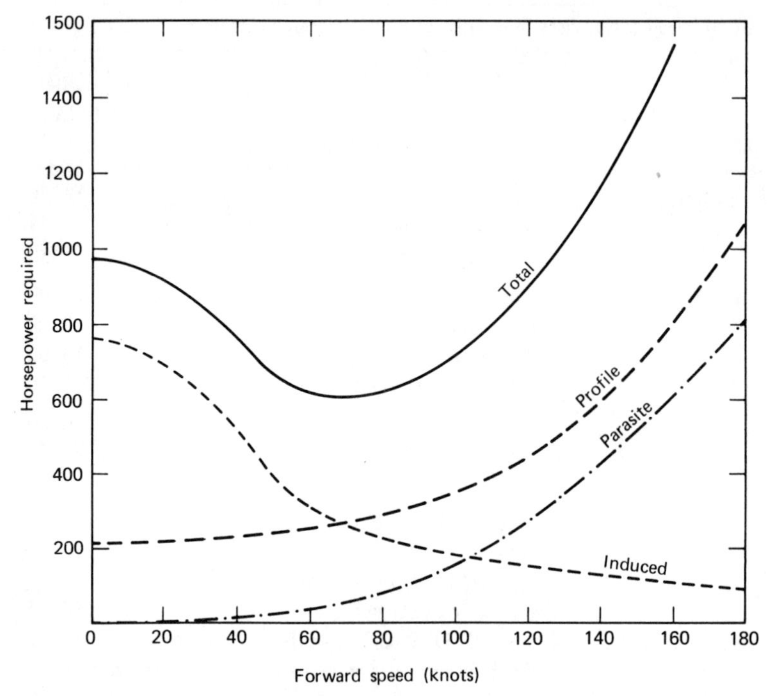

Figure 4.9 Power required in forward flight. $W = 10{,}000$ lb; $R = 20$ ft; $e = 0.91$; $s = 5\%$; RPM $= 320$; $M_{crit} = 0.75$; $f = 15$ ft^2; standard sea level, OG*F*.

Maximum Angle of Climb

For obstacle clearance, maximum angles of climb may be required. Clearly, if the power available exceeds the power required to hover out of ground effect, a 90° climb angle is possible (at least until the resulting density changes affect the picture). If P_{av} is less than P_{req} for hover (but greater than the minimum P_{req}), what speed will result in the maximum angle of climb? Recall that the climb angle in forward flight (no wind) is given by

$$\sin\gamma = \frac{\text{rate of climb}}{\text{airspeed}} \qquad \text{(same units top and bottom)}$$

The rate of climb for a helicopter, as for a fixed wing aircraft, is related to the excess power. Thus to maximize angle of climb we need to know the point at which excess power, divided by airspeed, is maximum. In general, this point occurs at a forward speed *less* than that of minimum P_{req}. The recommended airspeeds for obstacle clearance are usually given in the pilot's manual.

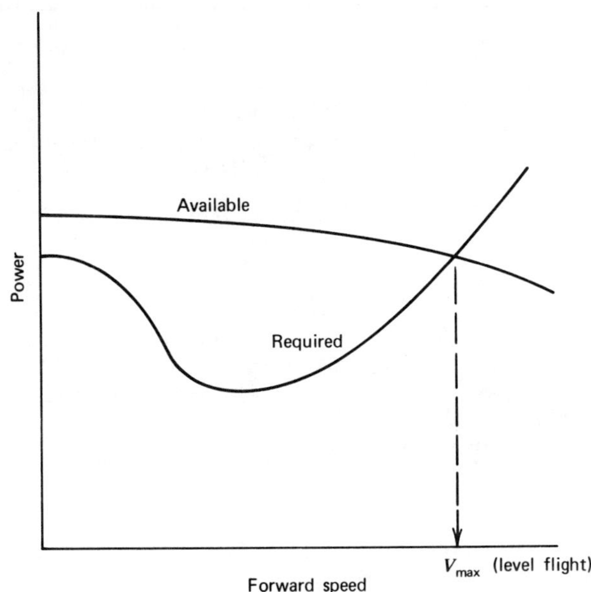

Figure 4.10 Maximum level flight speed.

Maximum Rate of Climb

As stated earlier, the maximum rate of climb occurs at the speed where the excess power ($P_{av} - P_{req}$) is a maximum. Since P_{av} is relatively unaffected by velocity, the maximum rate of climb is when P_{req} is minimal. This point is located roughly $\mu = 0.14$. As density changes, the relative contribution of parasite, profile, and induced power also changes, and the minimum shifts, usually to slightly lower speed. Also, to maintain a constant TAS as density altitude increases, indicated airspeed must be reduced. As density altitude increases during the climb, P_{av} decreases, and so then does the rate of climb.

Figure 4.11, adapted from the flight manual of a utility helicopter, illustrates these effects.

Ceiling

For a given aircraft weight, the excess power decreases with increasing density altitude to the point where there is zero excess power even at the speed for minimum power required. By definition this is the absolute ceiling of the aircraft. Higher altitudes cannot be sustained, although they may be

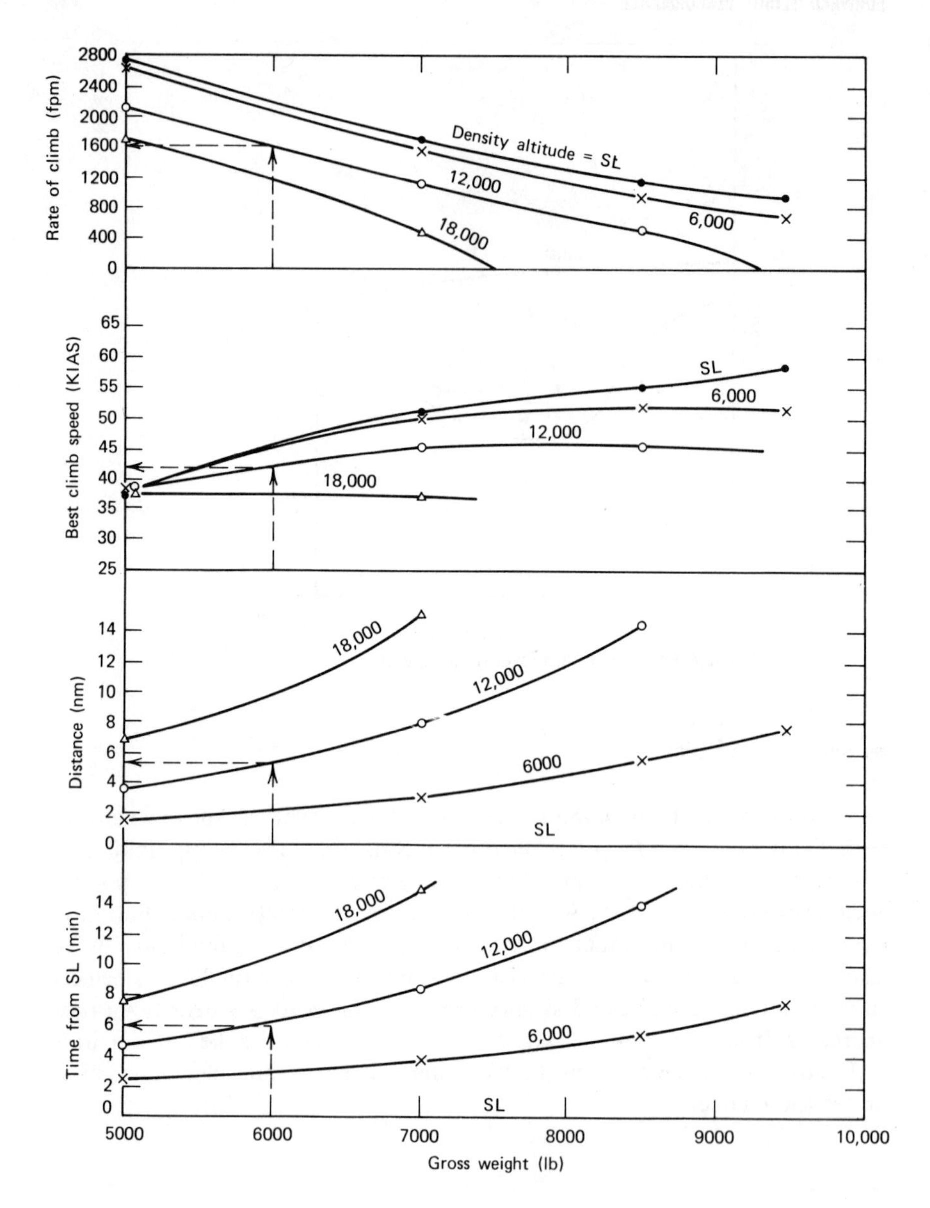

Figure 4.11 Climb performance—typical utility helicopter.

achieved momentarily by "zoom" maneuvers. Service ceiling and combat ceiling (maximum rate of climb of 100 and 500 fpm respectively) obviously occur at lower altitudes. The effect of increased gross weight is to increase P_{req} at all speeds, hence to lower the altitude at which these rates of climb can be achieved.

Transition from Hover—Translational Lift

So far our discussion of performance has dealt with "equilibrium" conditions—the velocity vector is constant, the rate of climb is constant, and so on. We have not yet considered roll, pitch, or yaw capability. The transition from a hovering condition to, say, a steady climb, involves a transient condition in which accelerations are experienced and rapid changes in rotor aerodynamic states occur.

Consider a helicopter hovering in ground effect at a 2 ft skid height (Figure 4.12). As we have seen, the power setting required is less than an

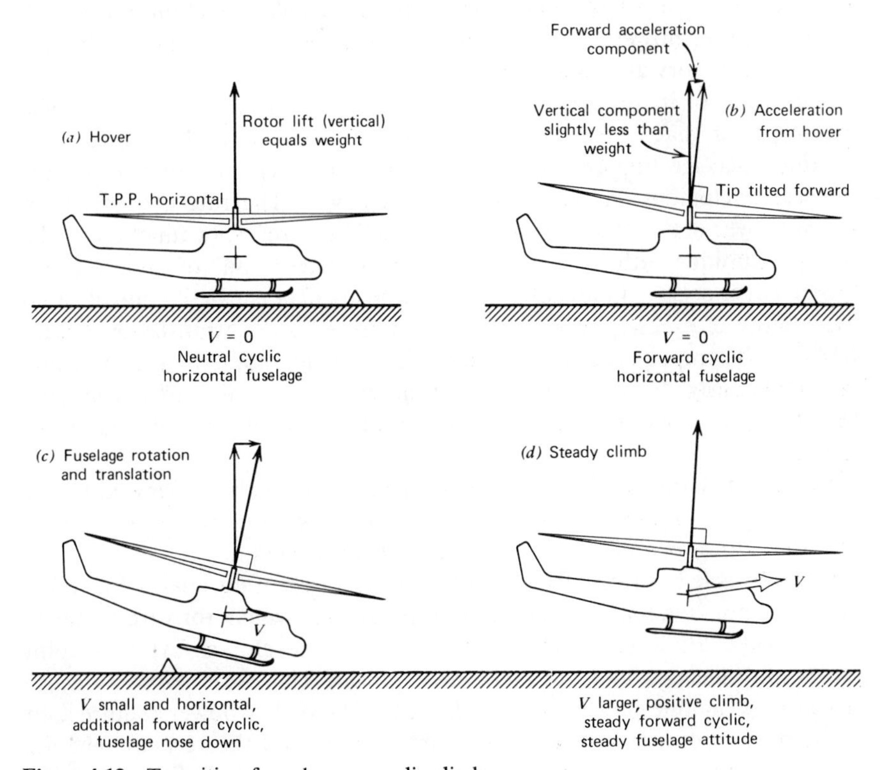

Figure 4.12 Transition from hover—cyclic climb.

OGE hover. Suppose that the pilot pushes slightly forward on the stick, tilting the tip path plane slightly forward, but does not change collective pitch. The initial effect is twofold:

1. A small horizontal component of the rotor thrust vector now exists.
2. The vertical component of rotor thrust, supporting weight, is slightly reduced.

As a result of the first effect, the helicopter *begins* to accelerate forward. As a result of the second, the helicopter *begins* to accelerate slightly downward. The initial direction of flight is forward and slightly downward. This has mistakenly been described as falling off the leading edge of the "ground effect bubble." A second or so later, the helicopter will have lost some altitude but gained some forward speed. The loss in altitude simply increases the ground effect, thus minimizing the altitude loss. If done very slowly, it is possible to transition some helicopters (at light weights) by the use of cyclic control alone without measurable altitude loss (as measured at the center of gravity). Note that ground effect does not disappear in forward flight. Since induced power becomes a smaller fraction of the total power picture, however, ground effect will appear to the pilot to be less significant in forward flight than in hover.

The result of increased forward speed is a drop in power required. The excess power that now exists can be used to establish a climb rate or to continue accelerating (or some of both). Continued acceleration causes increased velocities and even more excess power. The rate of increase of excess power depends on the acceleration of the aircraft (a function of the pilot's technique with forward cyclic) and the "steepness" of the power required curve as speed increases. The combined effect is usually one of rapid availability of excess power—commonly referred to as "translational lift." It should be emphasized that translational lift is not something that occurs instantaneously. It occurs in a short time because the aircraft is changing velocity rapidly over the area where the power required curve changes most dramatically.

The rapid change in the flow state of the rotor is easily recognized by the accompanying changes in rotor vibration frequency and magnitude, which give the pilot a cue of the translational lift phenomenon.

Best obstacle clearance from a hovering start (assuming that OGE hover power is not available) involves a technique in which forward flight is established IGE until translational lift is well developed. At this point increased collective and aft cyclic are applied. The excess power due to increased available power adds to that due to reduced power required. In addition, the rotor thrust vector is tilted back toward the vertical. The net result is a rapidly increasing flight path angle and rate of climb.

4.6 DESCENDING FLIGHT

When a helicopter is descending, the aerodynamic flow state through the rotor is not the same as in level flight at the same speed. This is particularly true in pure vertical descents when the rotor is thrusting in a direction directly opposite to the direction of flight. Traditionally, four different flow states have been identified for descending flight: normal thrusting state, vortex ring state, autorotative state, and windmill break state. Figure 4.13 is an idealized representation of these states for a purely vertical descent.

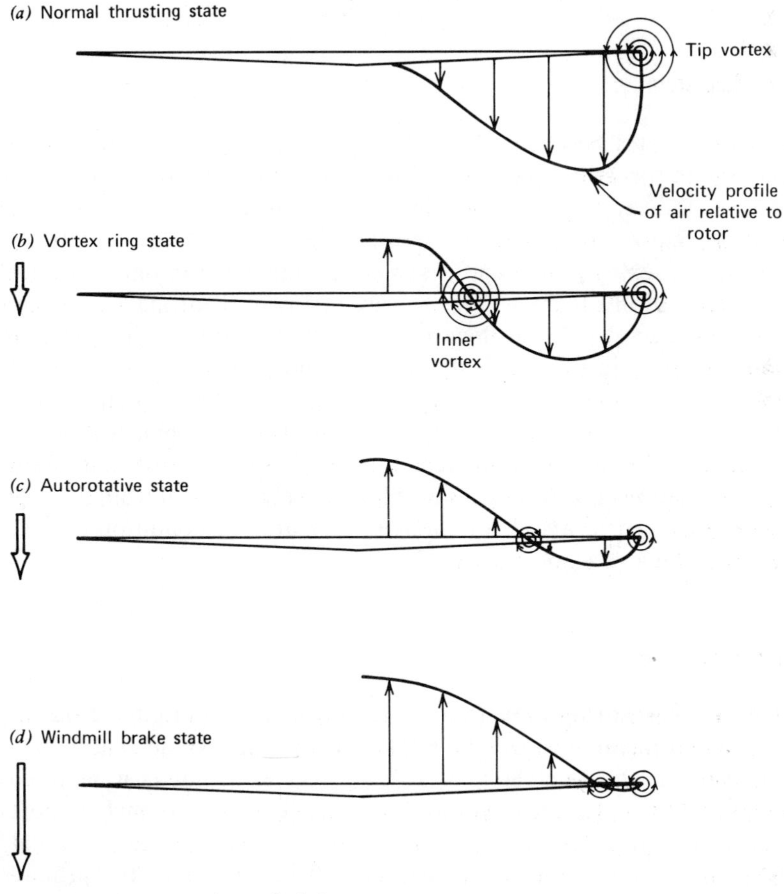

Figure 4.13 Flow states in vertical descents.

Normal Thrusting State

For hovering, and fairly low rates of descent, the velocity of the air induced through the disc exceeds the rate of descent itself, and an induced velocity profile similar to that shown in Figure 4.13*a* is obtained. In this state all flow through the rotor is downward (relative to the rotor), but not necessarily of equal magnitude because of the nonuniform conditions of speed and angle of attack from root to tip. Thrust is quite steady, and a constant requirement for power from the engine is required to maintain RPM. This condition exists from hover to descent rates up to approximately 70% of the ideal hovering induced velocity:

$$(v_i)_{\text{hover}} = \sqrt{\frac{DL}{2\rho}}$$

Vortex Ring State

For descent rates between 70 and 150% of $(v_i)_{\text{hover}}$, a condition of large variations in thrust is experienced (±30%), with accompanying increased vibration and tendencies to produce even higher rates of descent. This condition, known to pilots as "settling with power," is more formally called the vortex ring state and is somewhat like flying in one's own wake. As can be seen in Figure 4.13*b*, the high rate of descent has overcome the normal downward induced flow on inner blade sections. The flow is thus upward, relative to the disc in these areas and downward elsewhere. This produces a secondary vortex ring in addition to the normal tip vortex system. The result of this set of vortices is unsteady, turbulent flow over a large area of the disc, with an accompanying loss of thrust and excessive thrust fluctuations even though power is still being supplied from the engine. Pilots are warned to avoid situations that create this condition (i.e., steep descents at high rates of descent).

Autorotative State

Beyond the vortex ring state, things settle down again in terms of the intensity of the turbulent, unsteady flow. There is some rate of descent in vertical flight, between 150 and 180% of $(v_i)_{\text{hover}}$, where no power is required to maintain RPM. This state of autorotation is, of course, extremely important in cases of engine failure when one wishes to produce thrust, equal to weight, in order to effect controlled equilibrium flight to the ground at reasonable rates of descent. In essence, potential energy is being used up at a rate just sufficient to provide the power requirement in vertical flight. The details of how this is accomplished must focus on the local flow condition over various sections of the blades, which is examined at length in Section 6.2. Suffice it to say at this point that the autorotative flow state is the *boundary* between conditions where power must be delivered to the rotor to prevent RPM decrease and where power must be extracted from the rotor to prevent speed increase.

Windmill Brake State

If we somehow cause the rotor to descend at rates in excess of approximately 180% of $(v_i)_{\text{hover}}$, it is necessary to brake the system in order to maintain RPM. In this state, all the flow is "up" relative to the rotor, and energy may be extracted from the system. This is the state in which windmills operate, extracting energy from the flow of the air past them. This is not a normal operating state for any helicopter, although there is a transient condition experienced during cyclic flare following an autorotative approach to landing when the RPM increase is purposely accepted to increase the rotational kinetic energy in the rotor which is then available to arrest the rate of descent to almost zero for landing.

The above descriptions have been simplified, and those wishing a more thorough explanation should consult reference 100. Also, the flow states have been described for vertical flight only. In descents at forward airspeed, similar states may exist, but the rates of descent at which they occur and the symptoms of their existence to the pilot are different. Figure 4.14 summarizes the situation.

In the figure, showing horizontal speed versus vertical speed, straight lines emanating from the origin are lines of constant descent angle (γ). Given any two of the variables (V_v, V_h, and γ), the third is determined. Superimposed on this grid are flow state regions for a typical helicopter. Several interesting conclusions can be drawn from this figure.

First, the vortex ring state can be completely avoided by descending on flight paths shallower than about 30° (at any speed). Furthermore, for steeper approaches it can also be avoided at sufficiently slow or sufficiently fast speeds. What is happening in both cases is that the turbulent wake created by the vortex systems is not remaining in the vicinity of the rotor and causing difficulty. At very shallow descent angles, the wake is shed mostly *behind* the helicopter. At steep angles, it is *below* the helicopter at slow rates of descent, and *above* the helicopter at high rates of descent.

Next, it is clear that the rate of descent at which autorotation is achieved depends on airspeed. It is large at low airspeed, decreases to a minimum at

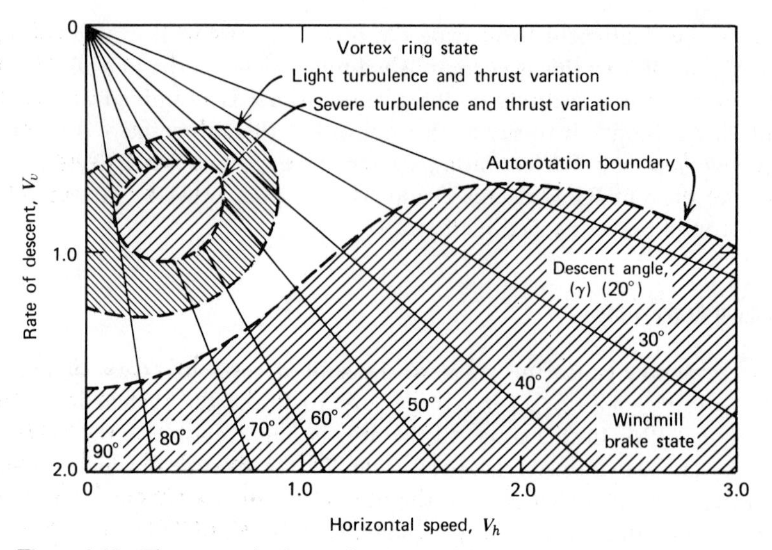

Figure 4.14 Flow states in descending forward flight. (From reference 100.)

some intermediate speed, then increases again at high speed. The speed appropriate to the minimum rate of descent and the variables that affect this speed are obviously of great importance to the pilot. These questions are discussed thoroughly in Section 6.2.

Lastly, for maximum glide distance in autorotation, one should achieve the shallowest possible flight path angle. This occurs at the intersection of the autorotation boundary and a straight line drawn from the origin tangent to the boundary. Note that this is a higher speed than that for minimum descent rate.

4.7 MANEUVERING FLIGHT

Maneuverability is the ability to change the direction of flight or to accelerate linearly within the constraints imposed by available power and energy. The fundamental limitation on maneuverability is the rotor's maximum thrust capability. Traditionally, helicopters have not needed high degrees of maneuverability in their normal missions, but the advent of the armed helicopter has placed increasing emphasis on this aspect of flight. Consequently, even light observation and utility helicopters are now being required to meet increasingly stringent maneuver requirements.

For a change to occur in the aircraft's velocity vector, either in magnitude or in direction, an unbalanced force must exist in the appropriate direction.

Moreover, according to Newton, the rate of change of the velocity vector is proportional to the magnitude of the unbalanced force and inversely proportional to the aircraft's mass. But where does the unbalanced force come from in order to perform the intended maneuver?

Level Acceleration

Consider the requirement to accelerate from hover to high forward speed in a straight line at a constant altitude. To accelerate at 10 ft/sec^2 (0.311 G) and have the vertical component of the rotor thrust vector remain equal to the aircraft weight (i.e., constant altitude), the disc must be tilted forward 17.3° and the magnitude of the rotor thrust must be increased 5% (Figure 4.15). Similarly, to accelerate sideways from rest at the same rate, the disc must be tilted sideways and the thrust must be increased by exactly the same amount.

As the speed builds up, the increased drag on the fuselage requires further disc tilt and further increases in rotor thrust to maintain the same level of acceleration. If this is not done, the acceleration decreases, reaching zero at some steady state velocity. The maximum translational acceleration capability of a helicopter at constant altitude and rotor RPM is clearly restricted by rotor thrust capability and any limitation on disc tilting.

Level Turning

Consider a constant speed, constant altitude right-hand turn as depicted in Figure 4.16. In forward flight, any unbalanced force purely perpendicular

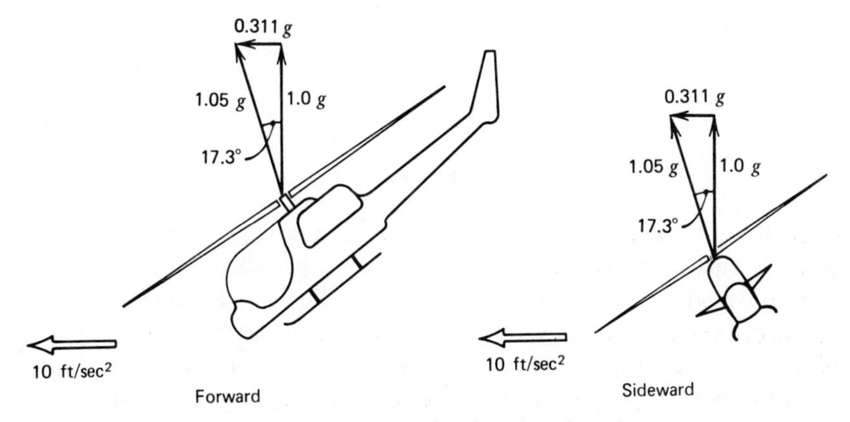

Figure 4.15 Thrust vectoring for linear acceleration (from hover).

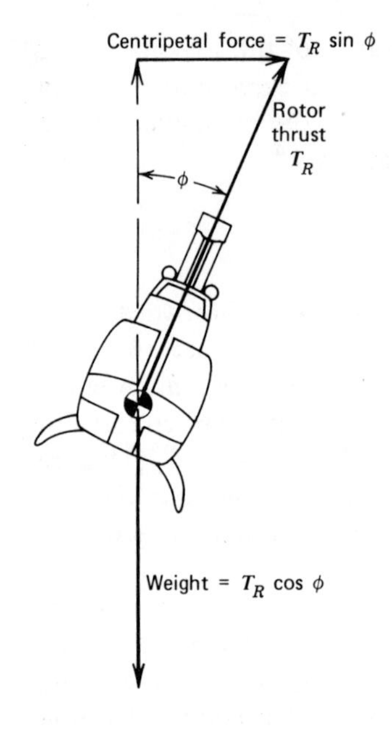

Figure 4.16 Effect of turning in forward flight.

Bank Angle ϕ	Load Factor N_Z	Increase in T_R (%)
0	1.000	—
15	1.036	3.6
30	1.154	15.4
45	1.414	41.4
60	2.000	100

to the velocity vector changes the orientation of that vector at a rate proportional to the magnitude of the unbalanced force. Tilting the disc 17.3° in this case, and at the same time increasing thrust by 5% to keep the vertical component constant, results in the required centripetal force component. From the geometry of the situation depicted in Figure 4.16 it can be seen that

$$\cos \phi = \frac{W}{T_R}$$

and that

$$N_z = \frac{T_R}{W} = \frac{1}{\cos \phi}$$

Thus there is a unique relationship between bank angle and normal load factor in this maneuver. It can again be seen that some maximum bank angle exists above which the requirement for increased thrust cannot be met at the conditions present (speed, altitude, temperature, etc.). Furthermore, increased thrust means increased induce drag on the blades, hence increased induced power required. The power required curves for an attack helicopter are shown in Figure 4.17.

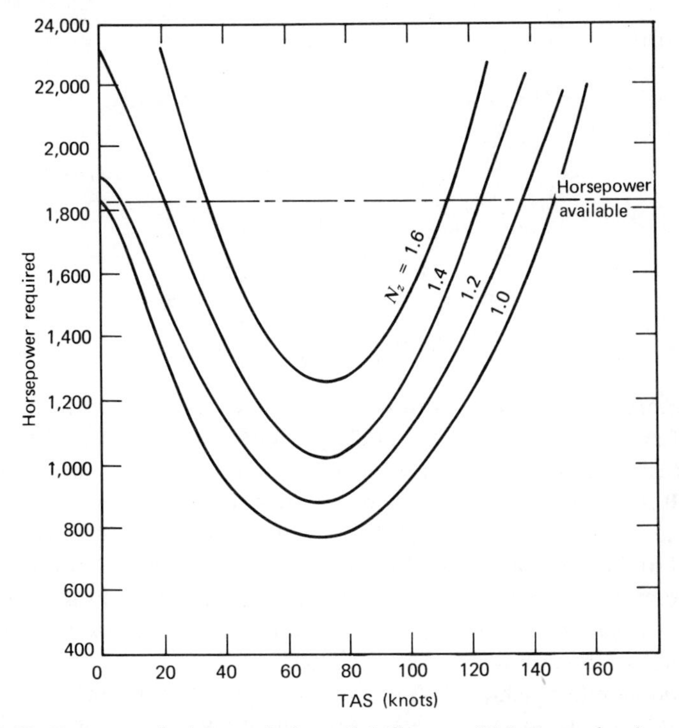

Figure 4.17 Power required for typical attack helicopter. (U.S. Army data.)

From our discussion of rotational motion in Chapter 1, the centripetal force is related to radius of turn by

$$\text{CF} = \frac{W}{g} \cdot \frac{V^2}{R_T}$$

Figure 4.17 shows that CF $= T_R \sin \phi$ in this case, so that

$$T_R \sin \phi = \frac{W}{g} \cdot \frac{V^2}{R_T}$$

Manipulating this equation, together with those above, yields the following two important relationships for horizontal equilibrium turning:
turn radius:

$$R_T = \frac{V_k^2}{11.26\sqrt{N_z^2 - 1}} \qquad \text{ft}$$

rate of turn:

$$\text{ROT} = \frac{1091\sqrt{N_z^2 - 1}}{V_k} \qquad \text{deg/sec}$$

Since $N_z = 1/\cos\phi$, these expressions can alternately be written as

$$R_T = \frac{V_k^2}{11.26 \tan\phi}$$

$$\text{ROT} = \frac{1091 \tan\phi}{V_k}$$

The expressions relate quantitatively what is experienced in flight— at constant speed, increasing bank angle (or load factor) reduces turn radius and increases turn rate; at constant bank angle, increased speed increases turn radius and decreases turn rate. Figure 4.18 plots these relationships. Using the figure, 40° of bank (1.3 G) at 80 knots produces a turn radius of 677 ft and a turn rate of 11.4 deg/sec. It will be noted that there are an infinite number of speed-bank angle combinations that yield the same turn rate. In our example, the same turn rate can be achieved at 120 knots if the pilot increases bank angle to 52° (1.63 G).

The simple relationship of $N_z = 1/\cos\phi$ is strictly true when ϕ is defined as the tilt of the rotor thrust vector (and the flight path angle $\gamma = 0$). The variable readily apparent to the pilot is his *fuselage* bank angle, which is what he sees relative to the actual horizon (or to the artificial horizon indicator). There is usually some trimmed attitude of the fuselage, which results in a misalignment of the thrust vector with the vertical body axis of the fuselage. This effect is not significant in horizontal turns, and the simple relationship may still be used where ϕ stands for fuselage bank angle.

The expressions for turn radius and rate are only true for coordinated turns (ball in the middle, no side forces). If, for example, the pilot uses right pedal to aid a right-hand turn at low airspeed, he causes a sideslip angle to develop that in turn causes aerodynamic side forces on the fuselage. These add to the horizontal component of rotor thrust, thus increasing the centripetal force. Turn rate is thus increased and turn radius decreased. The expressions developed and Figure 4.18 do not account for uncoordinated flight.

In hover, "turning" is accomplished by yawing the aircraft with directional control. Since the forward velocity vector is zero, changing its direction has no meaning. Thus the expressions are also not appropriate to the special case of hovering.

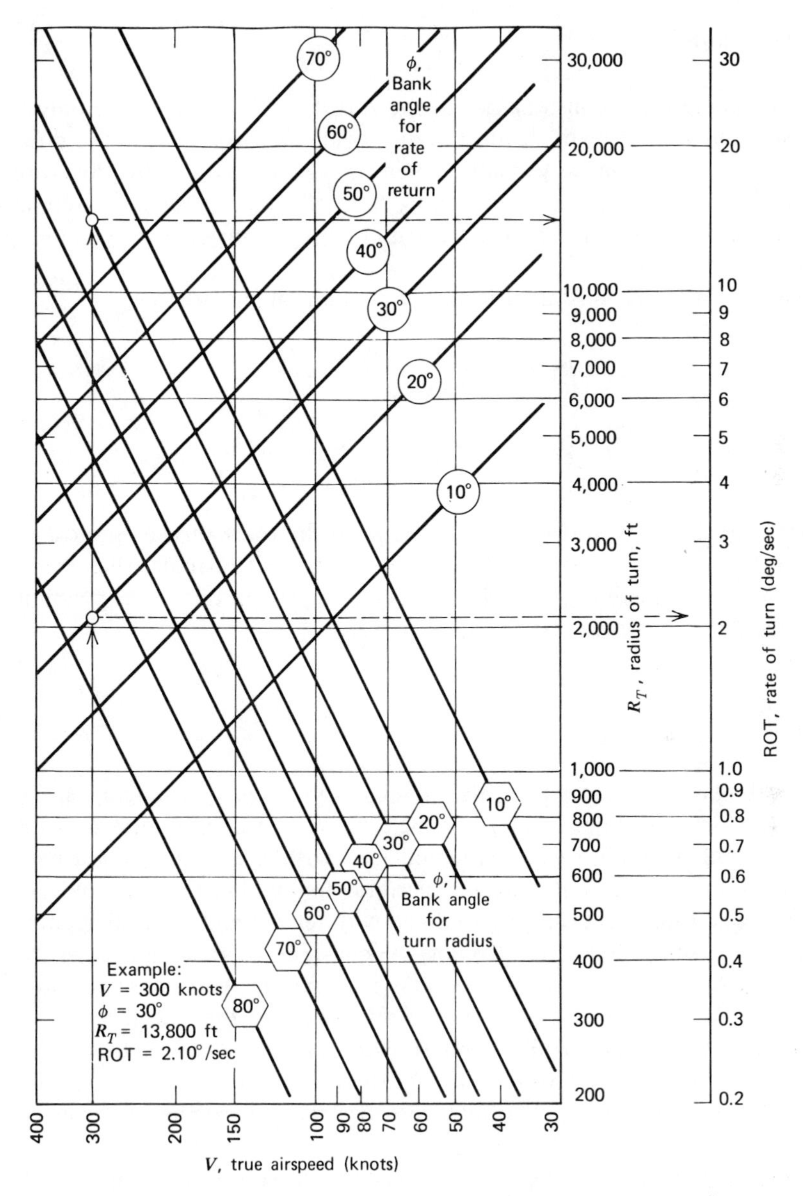

Figure 4.18 General turning performance (constant altitude, constant speed).

Climbing Turns

In a climbing turn (constant speed) the thrust vector is tilted not only to the side but also forward. It must now provide an extra force in the direction of flight to balance the component of weight in that direction (previously zero). At a given load factor, the helicopter turns on a smaller radius (and at a faster turn rate) when climbing than when not climbing at the same speed.

The turning relationships for steady climbing flight become

$$R_T = \frac{V_k^2 \cos^2 \gamma}{11.26 \sqrt{N_z^2 - \cos^2 \gamma}}$$

$$\text{ROT} = \frac{1091 \sqrt{N_z^2 - \cos^2 \gamma}}{V_k \cos \gamma}$$

Descending turns are identical, except that the rotor thrust vector is inclined somewhat backward from the flight direction to balance the component of weight tending to accelerate the aircraft. The turning expressions for negative γ are identical to those above.

Looping

Vertical plane maneuvers usually involve continuously changing speed, altitude, pitch attitude, flight path angle, pitching velocity, and radius of curvature of the flight path. For simplicity, consider a circular flight path, executed in the vertical at constant speed (assuming that the helicopter has the physical force requirements to do so without encountering any control restrictions—most helicopters do not). At constant R_T and V it is clear that the centrifugal force must also be constant. At the bottom of the loop (Figure 4.19) weight acts opposite to this force, at the 3 and 9 o'clock positions it acts perpendicular to the force, and at the top of the loop it acts with the force. It is therefore clear that there is an ever-changing requirement for the component of rotor thrust directed toward the center of the circle.

Simultaneously, the component of rotor thrust parallel to the flight path must change to accommodate changing weight components in this direction. Changes in both the magnitude and the direction of the rotor thrust vector are required to accomplish the maneuver, as illustrated in Figure 4.19*a*. Note that for the incremental 2 G loop shown, the rotor must produce up to three times the aircraft's weight and the disc must be tilted as

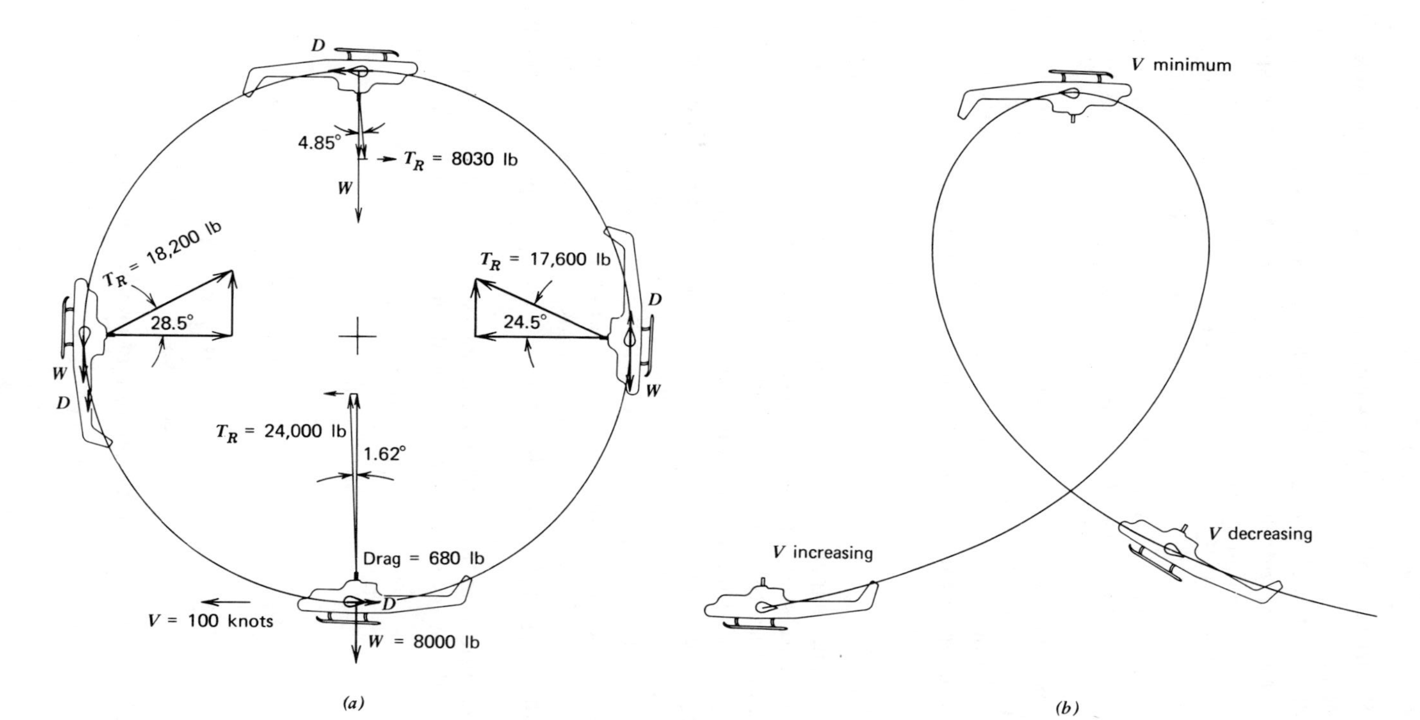

Figure 4.19 Looping maneuvers. (*a*) Circular: constant speed and parasite drag, constant centripetal force, constant turn radius, and changing T_R and disc tilt. (*b*) Noncircular: varying speed and parasite drag, varying centripetal force, varying turn radius, and varying T_R and disc tilt.

much as 28.5° forward and 24.5° backward. This is usually not possible for most helicopters.

Recall that the thrust increases demanded by maneuvering flight are accompanied by disproportionate increases in power to maintain speed. Furthermore, high speed maneuvering is condusive to retreating blade stall. For these reasons most helicopters are rather limited in their vertical plane maneuvers.

The few helicopters that have demonstrated loops to date have flown noncircular flight paths at varying speeds, such as those shown in Figure 4.19*b*.

Loops, rolls, and split-s turns have been occasionally demonstrated by some helicopters. Aerobatics of this type, however, have not been a normal part of the helicopter mission, including training missions and should not be attempted in aircraft not specifically cleared for such maneuvers.

General Maneuvering

A perfectly general maneuver involves simultaneous climbing (or descending), turning, and accelerating (or decelerating). Such maneuvers are usually difficult to analyze, but some insight is gained into general maneuver capability by considering energy concepts.

The energy state of a helicopter at any given flight condition is its potential, kinetic, and rotor rotational energies. With the exception of certain portions of the autorotation maneuver, RPM (hence rotor rotational energy) must be held to within rather strict limits to prevent undesirable control problems and loss of rotor thrust. Thus, for simplicity, we confine changes of the energy state solely to changes in kinetic or potential energy, or both.

Work is performed in transferring from one energy level to another. The *rate* at which this work is performed is, by definition, power. Thus

$$\text{power} = \frac{\Delta E}{\Delta t} = \frac{\Delta \text{PE}}{\Delta t} + \frac{\Delta \text{KE}}{\Delta t}$$

But

$$\text{PE} = Wh \qquad \text{and} \qquad \text{KE} = \frac{WV^2}{2g}$$

$$\therefore \text{power} = W\frac{\Delta h}{\Delta t} + \frac{W}{2g}\left(\frac{\Delta(V^2)}{\Delta t}\right)$$

However, $\Delta h/\Delta t$ is no more than the rate of climb. Likewise,

$$\frac{1}{2}\,\frac{\Delta(V^2)}{\Delta t}$$

can be shown by differentiation to be $V \cdot a$.

$$\therefore \frac{\text{power}}{W} = \text{rate of climb} + \frac{\text{velocity} \cdot \text{acceleration}}{g}$$

What is the source of the power required to climb, accelerate, or do both? It is simply the difference between the power supplied by the engine and the power required at the altitude-airspeed-G flight condition in question. Excess power can be used to increase airspeed, increase altitude, turn, or for combinations of all three.

If no excess power is available ($P_{av} = P_{req}$), there can still be energy *trades*. For example, acceleration can be accomplished by descending, and turning can be accomplished by either descending or decelerating.

Returning to Figure 4.17, the power required to execute a 1.6 G level turn at 140 K exceeds the power available. Nonetheless, the turn can be accomplished by allowing the aircraft to decelerate. At 118 knots (1.6 G) the power required has been reduced to that available, and no further deceleration (loss of kinetic energy) is required.

PROBLEMS

4.1 (*a*) Calculate the true airspeed of the advancing tip of a 48 ft diameter rotor rotating at 298 RPM when the helicopter itself is flying at 95 KTAS. (*b*) What is the Mach number on the advancing side for 10,000 ft (standard conditions)? (*c*) What is it for the retreating side? (*d*) What is the advance ratio?

4.2 At an instant of time a given rotor blade section has a pitch angle (relative to the tip path plane) of 15° and a TAS of 550 fps. If the sum of the induced and up-flapping velocities is 60 fps (as in Figure 4.3), what is the angle of attack?

4.3 The induced power required curve for a 10,000 lb helicopter is shown in Figure 4.7. For 100 knots forward speed calculate: (*a*) the induced power required if the weight is increased 25%, (*b*) the density altitude is increased to 10,000 ft, and (*c*) both occur simultaneously.

4.4 For the helicopter shown in Figure 4.9, with a constant 800 HP available: (*a*) What is the minimum and maximum speeds possible OGE? (*b*) At what speed would you expect maximum rate of climb to occur? (*c*) Discuss how the situation might change for IGE conditions.

4.5 For the helicopter of Figure 4.9 estimate the total power required in hover and at 100 knots for the following simultaneous changes: $W = 12{,}500$ lb, $f = 20$ ft^2, density altitude $= 10{,}000$ ft.

4.6 Consider the attack helicopter of Figure 4.17 in a 45° bank level turn at 90 KTAS. Calculate (*a*) the turn radius, (*b*) the turn rate, (*c*) the normal load factor, and (*d*) the horsepower required to sustain the turn without losing speed or altitude.

4.7 For the helicopter of Figure 4.17 with 1400 HP available and a weight of 9000 lb, calculate (*a*) the available rate of climb at 80 KTAS and (*b*) the available longitudinal acceleration in level flight at 80 KTAS.

4.8 Using the performance charts of the Appendix, calculate the ratio of power required to fly at 25 knots forward, compared to hover (OGE) for the following: (*a*) sea level, $W = 2000$ lb, (*b*) 14,000 ft density altitude, $W = 2000$ lb, and (*c*) sea level, $W = 2700$ lb.

Figure 4.20 UTTAS Mock-up. (Courtesy Sikorsky Aircraft.)

HELICOPTER STABILITY AND CONTROL

5

5.1 INTRODUCTION

Stability and control are as important in successful helicopter flight as the more easily appreciated concepts of performance that have been discussed in the two preceding chapters. A large rocket engine mounted on a unicycle may have outstanding speed and acceleration, but it cannot, for lack of adequate stability and control, effectively utilize this inherent performance capability. Many helicopters are limited in various portions of their flight envelope by stability and/or control considerations.

A helicopter is in a state of *equilibrium* when the vector sum of all forces and all moments is equal to zero. In equilibrium there is no acceleration either in the translational or rotational sense, and the aircraft remains in its steady flight condition. If the equilibrium is disturbed by a gust or a deflection of the controls, the aircraft experiences acceleration caused by an unbalance of force and/or moment. The magnitude of the translational acceleration is proportional to the unbalanced force (according to Newton's second law), and the magnitude of the rotational acceleration is proportional to the unbalanced moment.

Static Stability

The *static stability* of a helicopter is defined by the direction and magnitude of the initial tendency to return to equilibrium conditions following some disturbances from equilibrium. For example, if a helicopter in equilibrium forward flight is hit by a sudden upgust, the angle of attack of each blade section experiences an increase. The angle of attack of the entire disc may also be said to be increased by the upgust. The static stability of the aircraft, *with respect to angle of attack*, is determined by the initial pitching behavior of the aircraft in response to the sudden increase in angle of attack. If the aircraft initially pitches down (i.e., nosedown moments are created in response to increased angle of attack), the angle of attack moves back toward its original undisturbed value. This behavior is said to be *statically stable*, or the aircraft is said to exhibit *positive static stability* with respect to angle of attack. If the aircraft pitches up, thus further increasing angle of attack *negative static stability* (unstable behavior) is evident. Zero initial pitching moment is called *neutral static stability*.

Stability is always discussed with respect to a stated motion variable. In our example the motion variable is angle of attack. Different kinds of stability may exist with respect to different motion variables. Most helicopters exhibit negative static stability with respect to angle of attack, but positive static stability with respect to airspeed, as we see later. Stability can also be discussed with respect to motions about any aircraft axis. For example, it is usual to discuss a helicopter's directional stability in terms of what the aircraft does in yaw, following a disturbance in sideslip angle.

Dynamic Stability

The term "static" is applied in static stability since the resulting motion is not considered. Only the *initial tendency* to return to equilibrium conditions is considered in static stability. *Dynamic stability* concerns itself with the resulting motion in time. If the helicopter is disturbed from equilibrium, the time history of the resulting motion indicates the dynamic stability of the system. In general, the system demonstrates positive dynamic stability if the amplitude of motion decreases with time. The various conditions of possible dynamic behavior are illustrated by the time history plots of Figure 5.1.

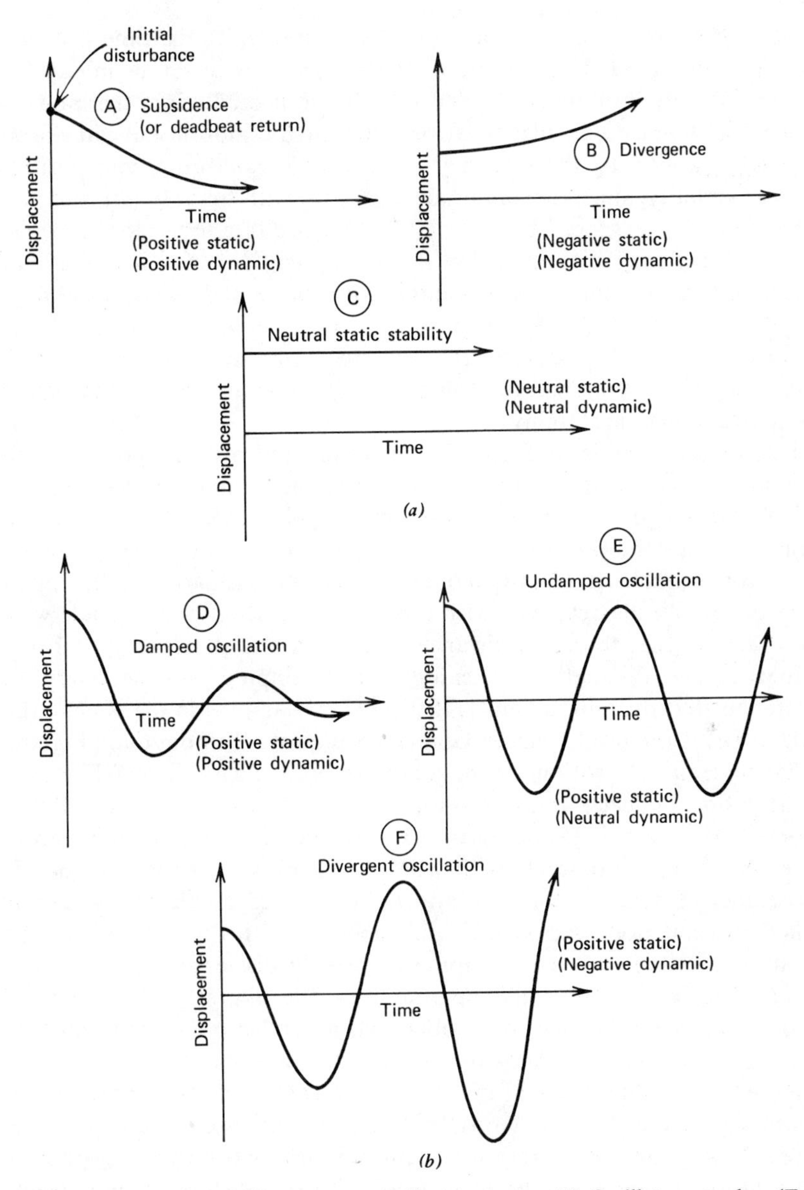

Figure 5.1 Dynamic stability. (*a*) Nonoscillatory modes. (*b*) Oscillatory modes. (From reference 6.)

The nonoscillatory modes shown in the figure depict the time histories possible without oscillatory motion. If the system is given an initial disturbance and the motion simply subsides without oscillation, the mode is termed "subsidence" or "deadbeat return." Such a motion indicates positive static stability by the tendency to return to equilibrium and positive dynamic stability, since the amplitude decreases with time. In (*B*) is shown the mode of "divergence" by a noncyclic increase of amplitude with time. The initial tendency to continue in the displacement direction is evidence of static instability and the increasing amplitude is proof of dynamic instability. Part (*C*) illustrates the mode of pure neutral stability. If the original disturbance creates a displacement that remains constant thereafter, the lack of tendency for motion and the constant amplitude indicate neutral static and neutral dynamic stability.

The oscillatory modes of Figure 5.1 depict the time histories possible with cyclic motion. One feature common to each of these modes is that positive static stability is demonstrated in the cyclic motion by tendency to return to equilibrium conditions. However, the dynamic behavior may be stable, neutral, or unstable. In (*D*) the mode of a damped oscillation is illustrated where the amplitude decreases with time. The reduction of amplitude with time indicates that there is resistance to motion and that energy is being dissipated. The dissipation of energy—or "damping"—is necessary to provide positive dynamic stability. If there is no damping in the system, the mode of (*E*) is the result—an undamped oscillation. Without damping, the oscillation continues with no reduction of amplitude with time. While such an oscillation indicates positive static stability, neutral dynamic stability exists. Positive damping is necessary to eliminate the continued oscillation. For example, an automobile with worn shock absorbers (or "dampers") lacks sufficient dynamic stability, and the continued oscillatory motion is neither pleasant nor conducive to safe operation. In the same sense, the aircraft must have sufficient damping to rapidly dissipate any oscillatory motion that would affect the operation of the aircraft. When natural aerodynamic damping cannot be obtained, a synthetic damping must be furnished to provide the necessary positive dynamic stability.

Figure 5.1 also illustrates the mode of a divergent oscillation. This motion is statically stable, since it tends to return to the equilibrium position. However, each subsequent return to equilibrium is with increasing velocity such that amplitude continues to increase with time. Thus dynamic instability exists. The divergent oscillation occurs when energy is supplied to the motion rather than dissipated by positive damping. The most outstanding illustration of the divergent oscillation occurs with the short period pitching oscillation of an aircraft. If a pilot unknowingly supplies control functions which are near the natural frequency of the airplane in pitch, energy is added to the system, negative damping exists, and the "pilot induced oscillation" results.

In any system, the existence of static stability does not necessarily guarantee the existence of dynamic stability. However, the existence of dynamic stability implies the existence of static stability.

Any aircraft must demonstrate the required degrees of static and dynamic stability. If the aircraft were allowed to have static instability with a rapid rate of divergence, it would be very difficult—if not impossible—to fly. The degree of difficulty would compare closely with learning to ride a unicycle. In addition, positive dynamic stability is mandatory in certain areas to preclude objectionable continued oscillations of the aircraft.

The forces and moments that move a helicopter originate in two sources —*aerodynamic* and *inertial*. All surfaces exposed to the airstream, especially the lifting surfaces of the main rotor blades, tail rotor blades, and fixed tail surfaces, contributed incremental forces and moments about the aircraft's center of gravity. In any dynamic motions these contributions are always changing. Inertial forces are not so readily appreciated—but in many helicopter motions they play a dominant role. Chief among these is the gyroscopic moments associated with the main rotor. These moments are not aerodynamic, and would occur in a vacuum. Because of these effects, for example, a helicopter executing a pitch-up maneuver tends to roll right and a helicopter executing a right rolling maneuver tends to pitch down. This inertial *cross-coupling* plays an important role in dynamic stability and controllability, as we shall see.

Control

Control of helicopter is its ability to respond to control inputs and achieve the desired condition of flight. Adequate control must be available to perform takeoffs, hover, landing, and all other maneuvers required by the mission. *Control power* or *control authority* refer to the maximum moment that can be generated on the aircraft by application of the cockpit controls. *Control sensitivity* refers to the moment generation capability *per unit of control displacement* (e.g., per inch of cyclic stick movement). Both control parameters are important and are discussed in flying qualities documents.

There is important contradiction between stability and controllability, since adequate controllability does not necessarily exist with adequate stability. In fact, a high degree of stability may tend to reduce the controllability of the aircraft. The general relationship between the two is illustrated in Figure 5.2, where different degrees of static stability with a ball placed on various surfaces are shown.

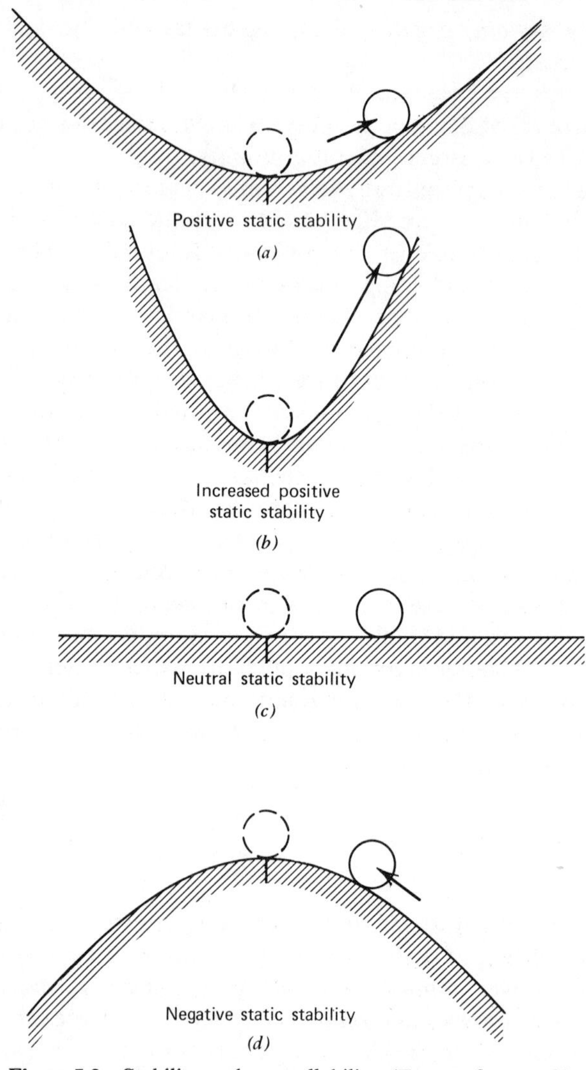

Figure 5.2 Stability and controllability. (From reference 6.)

Positive static stability is shown by the ball in a trough; if the ball is displaced from equilibrium at the bottom of the trough, there is an initial tendency to return to equilibrium. If it is desired to "control" the ball and maintain it in the displaced position, a force must be supplied in the direction of displacement to balance the inherent tendency to return to equilibrium. The same stable tendency in an aircraft resists displacement from trim by pilot effort on the controls or atmospheric disturbances.

The effect of increased stability on controllability is illustrated by the ball in a steeper trough. A greater force is required to "control" the ball to the same lateral displacement when the stability is increased. In this manner, a large degree of stability tends to require more control moment. It is necessary to achieve the proper balance between stability and controllability during the design of a helicopter.

The effect of reduced stability on controllability is illustrated by the ball on a flat surface. When neutral static stability exists, the ball may be displaced from equilibrium and there is no stable tendency to return. A new point of equilibrium is obtained, and no force is required to maintain the displacement. As the static stability approaches zero, controllability increases to infinity and the only resistance to displacement is a resistance to the motion of displacement—damping. For this reason, the lower limits of stability may be set by the upper limits of controllability. If the stability of the helicopter is too low, control deflections may create exaggerated displacements of the aircraft.

The effect of static instability on controllability is illustrated by the ball on a hill. If the ball is displaced from equilibrium at the top of the hill, the initial tendency is for the ball to continue in the displaced direction. In order to "control" the ball to some lateral displacement, a force must be applied opposite to the direction of displacement. This effect would be appreciated during flight of an unstable aircraft by an unstable "feel" of the aircraft. If the controls were deflected to increase the angle of attack, the aircraft would be trimmed at the higher angle of attack by a push force to keep the aircraft from continuing in the displacement direction. Such control force reversal would evidence the airplane's instability; the pilot would be supplying the stability by his attempt to maintain the equilibrium. An unstable aircraft can be flown if the instability is slight with a low rate of divergence. Quick reactions coupled with effective controls can allow the pilot to cope with some degree of static instability. Since such flight requires constant attention by the pilot, only slight instability can be tolerated.

5.2 TRIM

An aircraft is said to be trimmed if all moments in pitch, roll, and yaw are equal to zero. Thus trim is a necessary, but not sufficient, condition for equilibrium. Strictly, an aircraft may be in trim and may be rotating about one or more of its axes if that rotation is occurring at a constant rate. Usually, however, we speak of trimming the aircraft for zero rotational rates. Pilots often use the word trim to mean the attainment of an equilibrium condition "hands off." This requires, in addition to the zero moment, zero control force. While the external set of forces on the aircraft determine whether the aircraft is in equilibrium, the internal flight control system mechanism determines whether the condition can be achieved with zero control force.

Hover Trim

Consider the balances of external forces required to achieve equilibrium in a zero wind hover (Figure 5.3). It can be seen that several conditions must be met simultaneously for total equilibrium to exist:

1. The vertical component of rotor thrust must balance aircraft weight.
2. The rotor thrust must be tilted to the left so that its horizontal component balances the tail rotor thrust to the right (otherwise right drift would result). This can be accomplished with slight left cyclic stick or a preset tilt in the rotor hub.

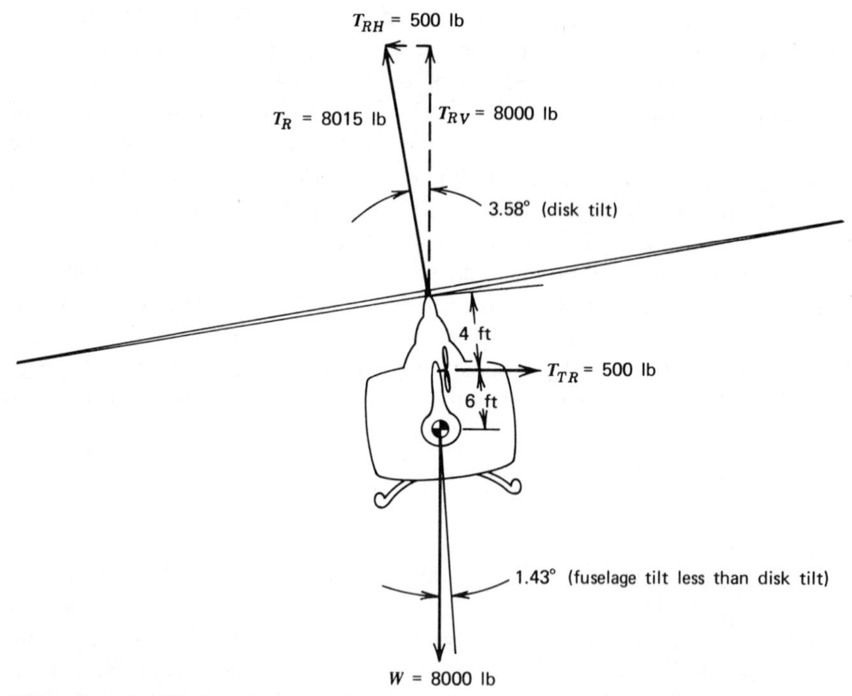

Figure 5.3 Equilibrium hover conditions. $\Sigma F_V = 8015 \cos(3.58°) - 8000 = 0$; $\Sigma F_H = 8015 \sin(3.58°) - 500 = 0$; $\Sigma M_{CG} = 500(6) - 500(10) + 8000\,[10 \sin(1.43°)] = 0$.

3. Since, for the configuration shown, the horizontal component of rotor thrust acts above the line of action of the tail rotor thrust (and is of equal magnitude) a resultant left rolling moment would exist if the center of gravity were vertically below the rotor hub. By hovering with the fuselage in a slightly left roll attitude the vertical component of lift balances the left rolling tendency.

4. The longitudinal center of gravity (CG) position must be in line with the rotor thrust line (this determines the equilibrium pitch attitude in hover). For an aft center of gravity a noseup attitude is required, a nosedown attitude and for a forward center of gravity.

5. The main rotor torque (tending to yaw the fuselage to the right) is balanced by the tail rotor thrust acting through its long moment arm to the center of gravity.

Now all forces and moments are balanced, and the helicopter is hovering in its "trimmed" attitude. Note that by positioning the tail rotor sufficiently high (close to rotor hub height) the left rolling tendency is minimized and the helicopter requires little or no bank for equilibrium. Also, the trimmed attitude is dependent on gross weight as well as the center of gravity position. If the gross weight is increased, more rotor torque is required, necessitating more tail rotor thrust (i.e., more left pedal input). This increases the amount of disc tilt (i.e., more left cyclic stick) to balance sideforces. The rolling tendency likewise increases with the buildup of the two sideforces (for the case of the main rotor hub above the tail rotor hub). Hence more bank to the left is required to displace the center of gravity to the right of the vertical rotor thrust component, thus restoring roll equilibrium. Any lateral displacement of the center of gravity also causes a change in the fuselage trimmed roll attitude.

In hover in a right crosswind several additional effects determine the trim attitude and the required control displacements:

1. The main rotor torque decreases (as in forward flight) requiring less tail rotor thrust (less left pedal) and less disc tilt (less left stick).

2. The main rotor "blows back," in this case to the left, requiring more right cyclic stick (into wind) to keep it in its place.

3. Aerodynamic sideforces on the fuselage tend to drift the aircraft left, requiring additional right stick.

4. Aerodynamic sideforces on the tail boom and vertical stabilizer tend to weathercock the aircraft to the right (into wind) requiring left pedal increases.

As can be appreciated, these effects each influence both the required stick and rudder positions and the equilibrium flight attitude. For a given steady wind, however, there is some combination of control positions for which all forces and all moments are balanced, and trim is again achieved.

Forward Flight Trim

In forward flight, especially at high speed, strong aerodynamic forces on the fuselage and tail surfaces influence the requirements for trim. The vertical tail, for example (or any tail surfaces that have vertical components), is capable of exerting sideforces when a local sideslip condition exists at the tail. This may be had by purposely setting the vertical tail at some angle of incidence relative to the longitudinal aircraft axis or by flying the entire helicopter in a slight sideslip (say, one quarter of a ballwidth at 100 knots). Sideforces to the right produce a left yawing moment, which decreases the need for tail rotor thrust.

Longitudinal trim can be a problem at high forward speed. Since a large forward horizontal force is required to overcome parasite drag, the disc is tilted forward appreciably. This creates a nosedown moment about the center of gravity. The aircraft assumes excessive nosedown attitudes at high speed unless some other restoring moment is provided. Horizontal tail surfaces do this by supplying an aerodynamic downforce proportional to fuselage angle of attack. Thus as speed is increased the nosedown tendency caused by forward rotor tilt is partially compensated for by noseup moments created by the horizontal surfaces (Figure 5.4). On some helicopters "sync-elevators" are provided, where a horizontal surface attached to the fuselage is geared to rotate with stick movement. This gives download control somewhat independent of fuselage angle of attack, thus permitting (assuming proper gearing between surface and stick) relatively level fuselage trim attitudes throughout the speed envelope. For sync-elevators not to create unwanted nosedown pitching moments during maneuvering, they are often fitted with a spoiler on their upper surface or have negative camber.

The stability and control characteristics are both measured from a given trimmed condition. If the aircraft is not trimmed, its free flight behavior following a disturbance is affected by the out-of-trim condition as well as the aircraft's basic stability, and the true character of the latter is masked.

Trimmability and stability are necessarily tied together. Theoretically an unstable aircraft cannot be trimmed, since the slightest atmospheric disturbance will cause it to continuously depart from the original condition. Conversely, a stable configuration may be difficult to trim because of peculiarities in the flight control system, including friction, breakout, backlash, and insensitive or oversensitive trim systems.

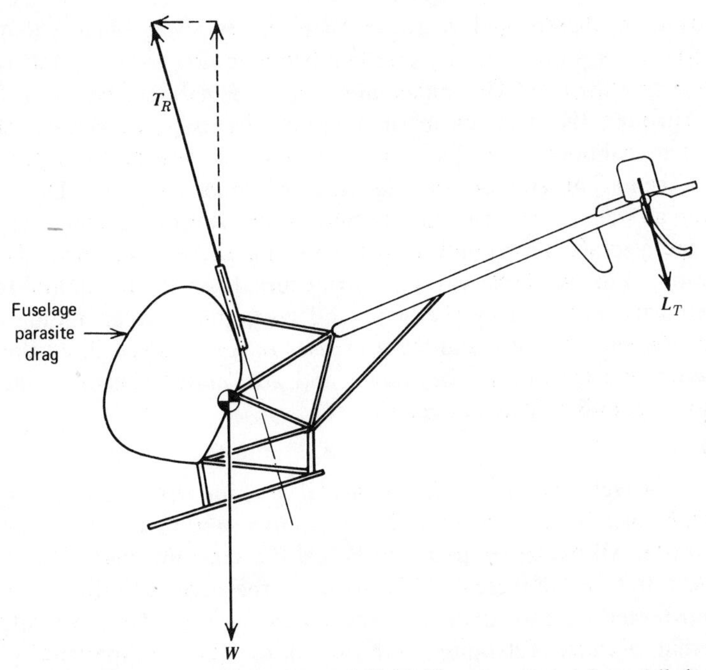

Figure 5.4 Balance of moments in forward flight. Noseup moment from tail download helps to balance nosedown moment from rotor thrust, thus allowing more level fuselage attitude.

5.3 STATIC STABILITY

Longitudinal Static Stability

Longitudinal static stability is usually discussed in terms of the pitching moments caused by changes in rotor angle of attack and forward airspeed from the trimmed condition. Both effects manifest themselves to the pilot in the altered longitudinal cyclic stick position that is required to accomplish these changes without retrimming. The helicopter's overall static stability in a given flight condition, though influenced by many aerodynamic factors, is dominated by what happens in the main rotor.

Airspeed Stability. Consider first the effect on the rotor of a change in forward airspeed (the helicopter is assumed to be initially trimmed at some constant forward airspeed). An increase is forward airspeed (caused by a headwind gust, for example) immediately increases the dynamic pressure for advancing blades and decreases that for retreating blades; that is, it adds to the rotational velocity on the advancing side and subtracts from it on the retreating side. The immediate result is a dissymmetry of lift condition. Through the mechanism of flapping, discussed previously, the tip path plane is blown back. The rotor thrust vector now acts in front of the aircraft center of gravity, and the fuselage rotates noseup. The noseup rotation as well as the thrust tilt are both in the direction required to decelerate the aircraft, thus tending to negate the airspeed increase. This, by definition, is in the stable sense. Any downloads on the horizontal tail are momentarily increased by the headwind gust, thus further adding to the stable characteristic. For sudden decreases in forward speed, by the same reasoning, the aircraft pitches down and accelerates—again a stable response. Figure 5.5*a* summarizes this effect.

Angle of Attack Stability. Next consider a sudden change in rotor angle of attack, such as that encountered in an upgust or in a sudden collective pitch input. All blades simultaneously feel the same increase in local angle of attack. In terms of increased lift, however, the advancing side experiences a much larger increase than does the retreating side. To appreciate this, recall that, because of flapping, both sides of the disc are experiencing equal lift before the gust. The advancing side is at a low angle of attack but high airspeed; the opposite is true for the retreating side. Thus a given change in the angle of attack produces a much larger percentage increase on the advancing side than on the retreating side. Hence the coefficient of lift is disproportionally increased on the advancing side while airspeed is unaffected. Again, we have the lift dissymetry that causes blowback and a noseup moment. This time the motion is unstable, since its direction is such as to increase the angle of attack even further, thus aggravating the situation. Figure 5.5*b* summarizes this effect.

The fuselage and tail also contribute to the angle of attack stability. Most fuselages by themselves are unstable. At increased angles of attack, noseup aerodynamic pitching moments are created. The opposite is true of the horizontal tail. Increased angle of attack at the tail increases the lift forces (or decreases the downloads), thus causing a nosedown moment and a stabilizing effect. The relative strengths of these contributions obviously vary with the helicopter and as a function of airspeed. At low airspeed the contributions of the fuselage and tail are negligible. At high forward speed some helicopters gain sufficient stability from the horizontal tail to overcome the unstable tendencies of the rotor.

In quantitatively assessing these effects, proper account must be taken of interference. The flow velocities and directions in the tail region differ from

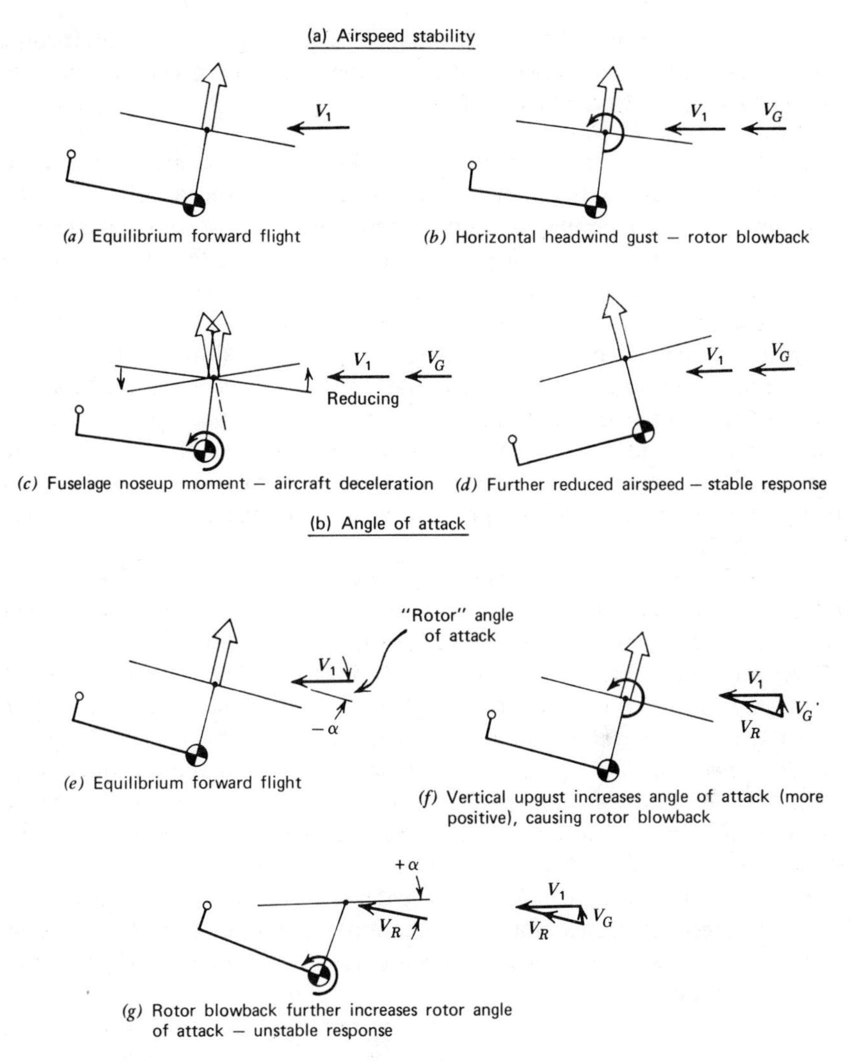

Figure 5.5 Airspeed and angle of attack stability.

those at the rotor. Flow interference, especially from the main rotor wake at low airspeed, is extremely important to overall longitudinal static stability. In particular, care must be taken in positioning the horizontal tail so that it does not find itself in a low dynamic pressure region or in severely turbulent conditions. In some cases the degree of static stability is very nonlinear. For example, stable tendencies may be evident for small disturbances from trim and unstable tendencies for large ones. In multirotor helicopters, especially tandems, aerodynamic interference between the two rotors can cause destabilizing effects.

Overall Static Stability. Overall static stability can be conveniently measured by determining the stick displacement versus speed behavior. The helicopter is first trimmed at a constant airspeed in, say, in straight and level flight. Next, the pilot purposely moves the longitudinal cyclic control in such a way as to ultimately achieve a new equilibrium speed, say 10 knots above the previous one. He does not change collective setting or use the longitudinal trim control. The steady state stick position in the second condition is compared to that in the first. In the case of increasing airspeed a more forward position of the cyclic control indicates positive longitudinal static stability, and a further aft position would be unstable. In either case the *initial* movement of the stick would be forward to initiate the speed increase. It is the final, or equilibrium, position of the stick that measures static stability.

Figure 5.6 gives flight test results for a twin rotor helicopter. Notice that at 42 knots trim speed the helicopter is strongly unstable in the longitudinal static sense, as evidenced by a more forward stick position required to fly slower and vice versa. (*Note.* The figure does not indicate the direction of the stick *force* for this condition.) At 111 knots trim speed, this helicopter is nearly stable. Negative static stability is an undesirable feature from the pilot's viewpoint. It requires constant attention to maintain speed and attitude, and dramatically increases pilot workload. At moderate instability the aircraft can be flown, but the accompanying high pilot workload detracts from mission effectiveness.

Also shown in Figure 5.6 are the changes with airspeed of the pitch attitude, lateral stick position, and directional pedal position. A change in one of the last two variables indicates a degree of "cross-coupling," which is discussed later.

Lateral-Directional Static Stability

The three important characteristics of helicopter lateral-directional static stability are (1) dihedral effect, (2) directional static stability (weathercocking), and (3) sideforce.

Dihedral Effect. Borrowed from fixed wing nomenclature ("geometric" dihedral) and in the case of helicopters better expressed as "effective dihedral," this term refers to the rolling moments generated as a result of

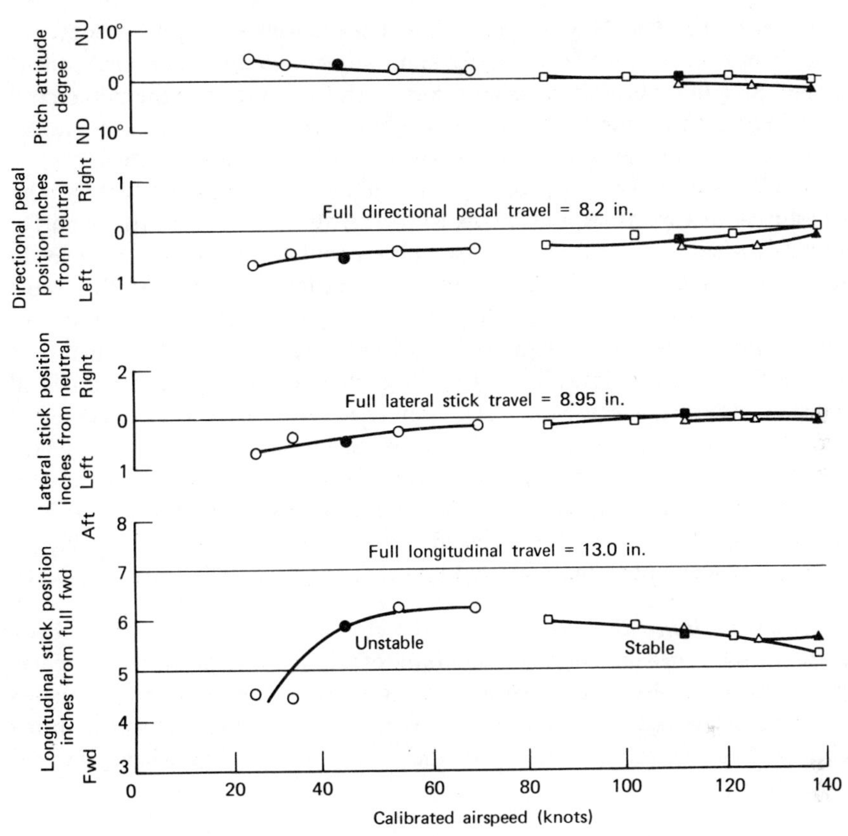

Figure 5.6 Static longitudinal collective-fixed stability: cargo helicopter. (U.S. Army data.)

sideslip. For hover in calm air, sideslip angle is not defined, and it is convenient to discuss hovering dihedral effect in terms of rolling moments due to sideward velocity. Traditionally, a right sideslip angle (relative wind from the right) defines the positive direction, and a right rolling moment is also said to be in the positive direction. A helicopter exhibits a positive dihedral effect if, in a right sideslip, it tends to roll left ("out of wind"), that is, requires lateral cyclic input "into wind." The magnitude of the effect is measured by the lateral control displacement per unit sideslip angle.

We saw that, in hover, both the disc and the fuselage had to be banked to the left to account for the tail rotor force to the right. In forward flight the same balance is necessary, but it may now be achieved by flying wings level and assuming a right sideslip. The right sideslip causes sideforces on the fuselage that, at the correct sideslip angle, just balance the tail rotor thrust at that speed. Thus, in general, it is not possible to fly a helicopter in equilibrium flight without a steady bank angle, sideslip angle, or both. If sideslipping flight is elected, as it usually is, the magnitude of the "inherent" sideslip angle must increase as gross weight increases, since the latter creates more rotor torque and thus a requirement for more tail rotor thrust.

A sideward velocity, whether produced by pure sideward flight or by sidesliping at forward speed, tends to tilt the disc away from the wind for exactly the same reasons that the disc blows back in response to changes in forward airspeed. This creates a left rolling moment, that is, in the stable direction. Vertical tail surfaces generate large sideforces in sideslips—especially at high speed. If the center of pressure of the vertical surface is above the center of gravity, a further contribution to positive dihedral effect is obtained (negative if the center of pressure is below the center of gravity). Similarly, if the center of pressure of the sideforces on the fuselage is below the center of gravity, a negative dihedral contribution is obtained, as shown in Figure 5.7. For good flying qualities a moderate degree of positive effective dihedral is necessary, that is, there must be right lateral cyclic displacement to maintain bank angle in right sideslips and vice versa.

Directional Static Stability. Static directional stability, or weathercock stability, is a measure of the magnitude of the restoring yawing moments generated by sideslip. It has three main sources: (1) aerodynamic moments on the fuselage, (2) sideforces on the vertical tail, and (3) tail rotor thrust changes with sideslip. The first of these is generally destabilizing for the

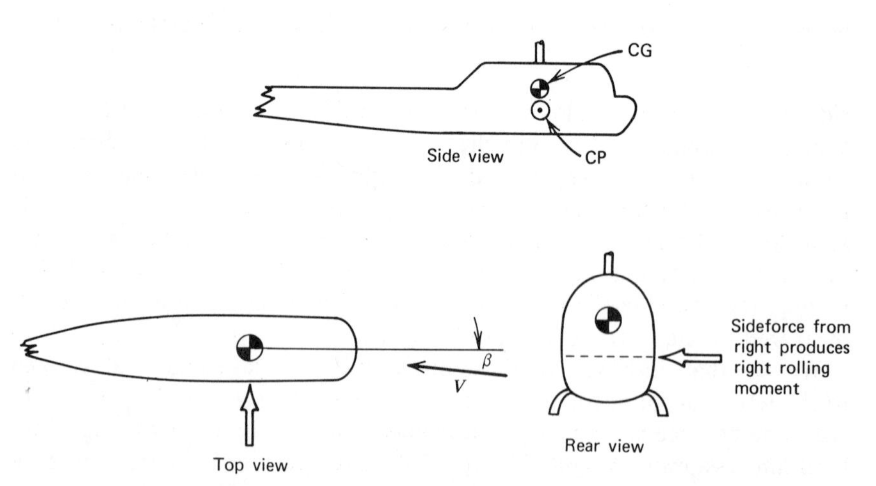

Figure 5.7 Unstable dihedral effect due to fuselage sideforces. (From reference 5.)

same reason as with respect to longitudinal static stability. The second is stabilizing, and in fact is the main reason for a vertical tail. A right sideslip produces sideforces from the right on the vertical tail. Since the tail is behind the center of gravity, a right yawing moment is produced tending to negate the initial disturbance. The third is also stabilizing. An increment of lateral velocity from the right reduces tail rotor thrust while one from the left increases thrust. This restoring moment is the major source of static directional stability in single rotor helicopters, especially at low speed where the vertical tail is ineffective.

The fuselage configuration and flight path sometimes combine to mask the tail rotor from the free stream and make it rather insensitive to small angles, as shown in Figure 5.8.

Sideforces. Sideforces on the helicopter determine the bank angle required to hold a specific sideslip angle at constant increasing forward speed. The higher the airspeed, the larger the bank angle required.

The sideforce characteristic is very important for a number of reasons, not the least of which is the effect on directional stability. When two aircraft have the same static directional stability but one has zero sideforce per unit of sideslip and the other produces a very large value of sideforce for a very small sideslip, the aircraft with zero sideforce *appears* to have a significantly higher static directional stability in forward flight. This is evident during lateral cyclic—only turns at equal bank angles. The aircraft with the zero sideforce characteristic quickly slips into a large sideslip while the other never develops a sideslip of more than a few degrees. Since the static directional stability was said to be equal, the static yawing moment for equal bank angles is must greater for the low sideforce aircraft simply because of

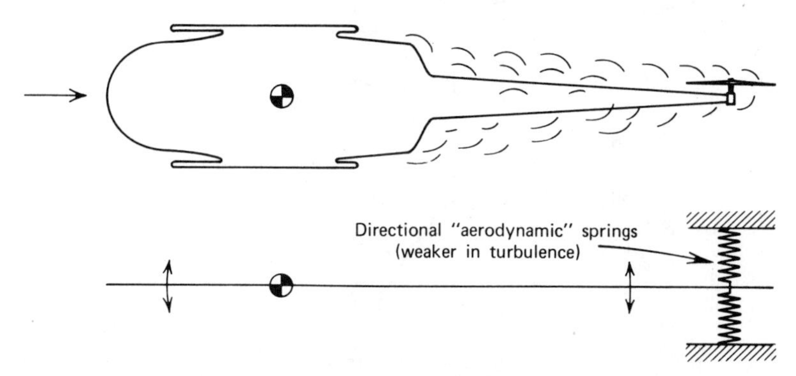

Figure 5.8 Loss of directional stability due to fuselage/tail rotor interference. (From reference 5.)

its larger sideslip angle. Sideforce characteristics are very important to slow speed operations and should not be lightly passed over.

Summary of Effects. Figure 5.9 shows the results of a static lateral-directional test done on an attack helicopter. It is fairly typical of single rotor helicopters in this weight class. Several points should be noted:

1. Lateral stick position—aricraft is stable at both speeds (more so at higher speed), requiring right stick to hold right sideslip.

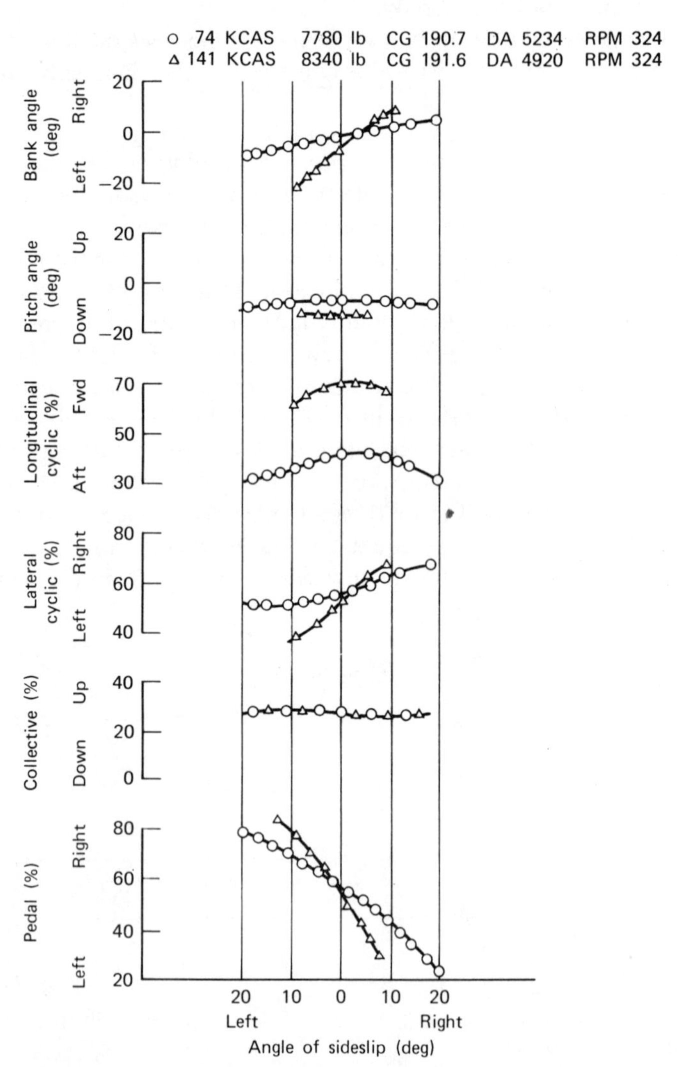

Figure 5.9 Static lateral-directional stability for an attack helicopter. (U.S. Army data.)

2. Directional control position—positive directional stability evident by requirement for more left pedal to hold increasing right sideslip and vice versa. Again, a higher degree of stability exists at the higher speed. Note that at 141 KCAS, 10° of sideslip leaves only a 20% directional control margin for further maneuvering and turbulence control. A critical condition is often present at high power settings (hover and V_{max} at maximum gross weight and a high density altitude) with right sideslips. Figure 5.10 illustrates this effect for a typical utility helicopter.

3. Roll attitude—increasing right sideslip requires increasing right bank as expected. At the same sideslip angle more bank is required at the higher speed because of the higher sideforces pıeviously discussed.

4. Longitudinal cyclic position—note first that at zero sideslip the trim position is fuıther forward at the higher speed, as you would expect from an aircraft with positive static stability. In both cases more aft stick is required when a steady sideslip is developed in either direction. A possible reason for this is that the horizontal surfaces lose some of their downforce capability in the sideslip flow field, thus requiring more back stick to provide the noseup moment to hold a constant pitch attitude.

5.4 DYNAMIC STABILITY AND CROSS-COUPLING

We have discussed trimmed flight and static stability. In static stability, we saw, a motion variable initially tends to revert toward its original trim value after being disturbed from that value. However, positive static sta-

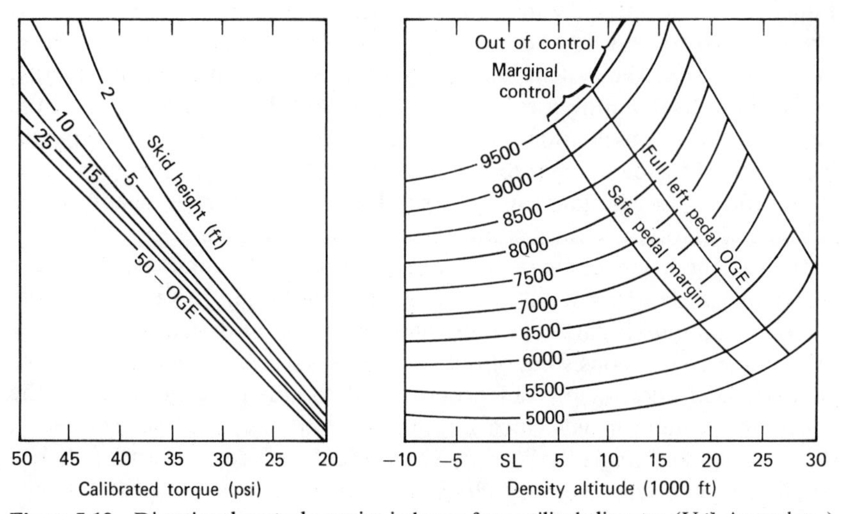

Figure 5.10 Directional control margins in hover for a utility helicopter. (U.S. Army data.)

bility with respect to all important variables, about the appropriate axis, is not sufficient to ensure a well-behaved aircraft. Once the motion is in progress, additional forces and moments come into play that influence the subseqeuent motion. One of the most important of these is damping.

Damping

Damping is present whenever a force is produced on a body proportional to the velocity of that body. Positive damping is said to exist when the force is in a direction opposite to the motion, that is, opposite to the velocity vector change. In a simple mass and spring system, the spring exerts a force on the mass proportional to the distance of the mass from its equilibrium position. Such "springlike" forces and moments are evident in a helicopter and contribute to its static stability (e.g., yawing moment proportional to sideslip angle). A mass on a spring, once disturbed from its equilibrium state, oscillates up and down at some "nautral" frequency depending on the stiffness characteristics of the spring. When the mass is at maximum travel, both the restoring spring force and the acceleration are maximum (although velocity is zero). As the mass passes through the equilibrium point, and spring, forces again build up, tending to bring the mass back to center. The dynamic interplay between these two forces, spring and inertia, determines the character of the motion. In this case it is (in the absence of any other external forces) a constant amplitude oscillation similar to that in Figure 5.1*e*, that is, it exhibits positive static and neutral dynamic stability.

If we now add a damper, such as a piston in a cylinder of fluid, an additional force influences the motion. The force contributed by the damper is proportional to velocity and is always in a sense opposite to the direction of motion. Thus the system must do positive work, hence expend energy, in fighting this damping force. The result is twofold: (1) a decrease in the amplitude of the oscillation with time and (2) a decrease in the apparent frequency. If the damping forces are large in comparison to the inertia and spring forces, oscillation can be prohibited altogether. A deadbeat, or subsidence, motion is then attained, as shown in Figure 5.1*a*.

Just as there are aerodynamic spring forces and moments, there are aerodynamic damping forces and moments. Returning to our directional stability example, Figure 5.11 illustrates the origin of directional damping in a simple system consisting of only a vertical surface behind the center of gravity. Sideforces on the tail proportional to sideslip angle provide the restoring spring moment. Once a rotational *rate* has developed, however, the local sideslip angle, as seen by the vertical surface, is changed. When rotating in one direction, say clockwise looking from above, the change

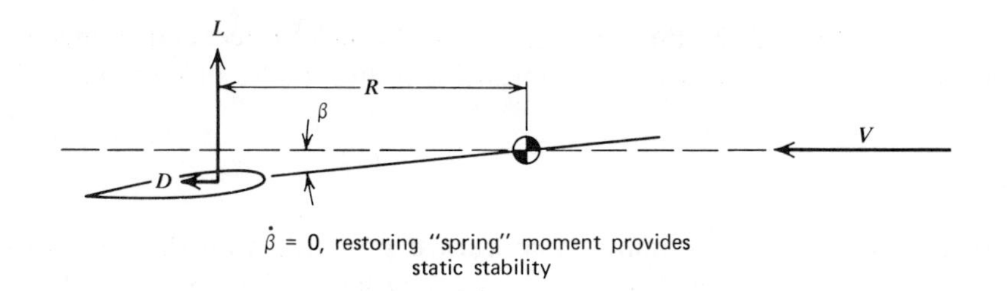

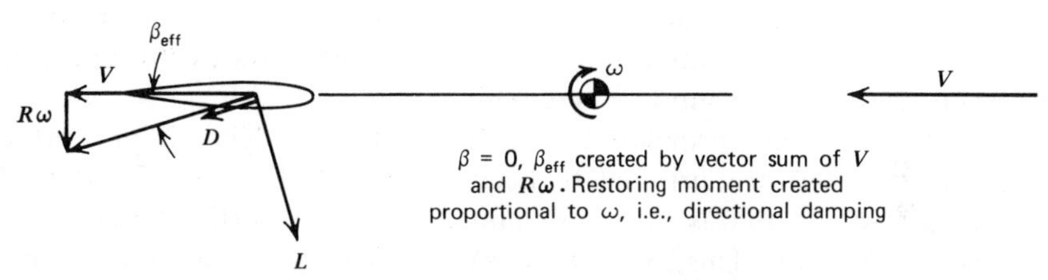

Figure 5.11 Origin of directional damping due to vertical tail.

is in such a direction as to add an additional moment, over and above that due to sideslip angle, opposite to the motion. At the extremes of displacement, rotational rates are momentarily zero, as is the damping contribution. Static moments are of course maximum at this point, tending to rotate the system back to the equilibrium. As the tail swings through zero sideslip angle, the situation is reversed—we have zero spring force and maximum damping. Depending on the values of mass, sideforce per unit sideslip, and sideforce per unit yaw rate, a damped oscillation may result.

Our example involves a single degree of freedom—sideslip. In most aircraft, especially in helicopters, there are many possible degrees of freedom. Moreover, motion of one flight variable may induce motions in another. Such interactions and cross-coupling tend to form distinct *modes* of motion. For example, a pure yawing mode strictly never exists. Yawing motions, involving changes in sideslip, cause corresponding changes in rolling moments. Thus a combined lateral-directional mode of motion is present, especially at forward airspeed and to a lesser extent in hover.

In general, there are six "rigid body" degrees of freedom for the fuselage: translation along all three body axes (up-down, right-left, fore-aft) and rotation about these axes (pitch, roll, yaw). The rotor itself has some additional independent degrees of freedom, including collective coning, longitudinal cyclic flapping, lateral cyclic flapping, and rotational speed. The pilot judges the flying qualities of the helicopter in terms of the first six, and is only indirectly concerned with the blade motions themselves. Of course, it is the blade motions that determine the major forces and moments. on the fuselage. Let us examine typical helicopter modes of motion.

Longitudinal: Hover

Longitudinal dynamic stability is concerned primarily with three motion variables: up-down translation, fore-aft translation, and pitching. In a zero wind hover, up-down motion comes closest to being "decoupled" than it does in any other flight condition. That is, there is an independent "plunging mode" involving primarily heaving up and down with very little interplay with fore-aft motion or pitching.

This mode has no springlike force, that is, no aerodynamic or inertial force is generated proportional to height itself (OGE). There is vertical damping, however, that is, an aerodynamic Z-force proportional to the *rate* of ascent or descent. This force comes mainly from the rotor and to some extent from aerodynamic forces on the fuselage. When the helicopter starts to translate up, for example, in response to an increment of upward collective, the vertical rate of ascent causes each blade element to "see" a reduced angle of attack—the same idea as in upflapping (on the advancing side only) in forward flight. Thus the total rotor thrust is reduced as a result of the upward motion itself. This reduction tends to negate the original thrust increment that initiated the motion. Figure 5.12 illustrates the subsequent motion, showing the gradual attainment of a new steady state rate of vertical climb. Note that no overshoot or oscillation can develop in this mode, since there are no spring forces in this direction.

When the helicopter is hovering in ground effect there *is* a spring force. As discussed in Chapter 3, at fixed power an increase in thrust is experienced closer to the ground and to vertical displacement, which can provide an aerodynamic spring. Hence an oscillatory plunge mode is possible in ground effect which, if not well damped, may cause difficulty for the pilot in precise height control.

In hovering flight, vertical damping is closely related to height control and gust response. In the latter case an incremental updraft results in an increase in angle of attack of all the blade elements. The resultant increase in thrust accelerates the helicopter upward until the rate of climb equals the updraft velocity, at which time the *relative* velocity is zero, the damping force is zero, and no further acceleration occurs. The time it takes to reach the new velocity is purely a function of the magnitude of the vertical damping force. If the damping is large, lower accelerations over a longer time are experienced. This is good from the standpoint of gust response. We like to have low accelerations (hence low forces felt by the occupants)

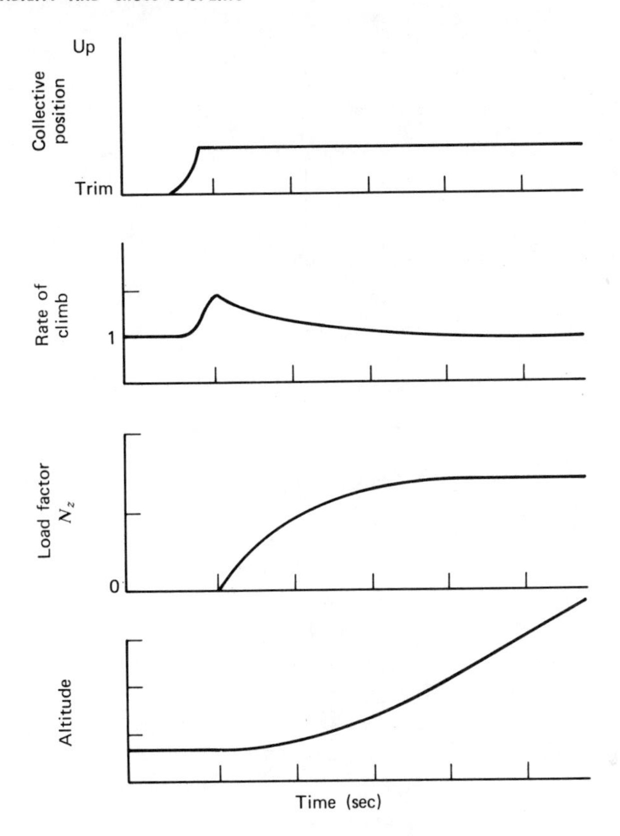

Figure 5.12 Response to collective step input from OGE hover.

in gusty conditions. The intial response to an upgust (or downgust) will be magnified however, for larger damping cases.

The other two variables besides vertical translation are fore-aft translation and pitching. They are obviously coupled, since, for example, pitching noseup tilts the rotor thrust vector aft causing backward translation. A helicopter hovering in zero wind does not have a disc angle of attack and does not exhibit an angle of attack response characteristic. The hovering helicopter is primarily disturbed in the short term by horizontal gusts working through the speed stability term previously discussed. Figure 5.13 traces the development of the short term response to a horizontal gust. There are several factors at work: blowback of the rotor disc with consequent noseup pitching, X-force development to fuselage drag, and horizontal component of rotor thrust, nosedown pitching moments opposing pitch-up rate (i.e., pitch damping).

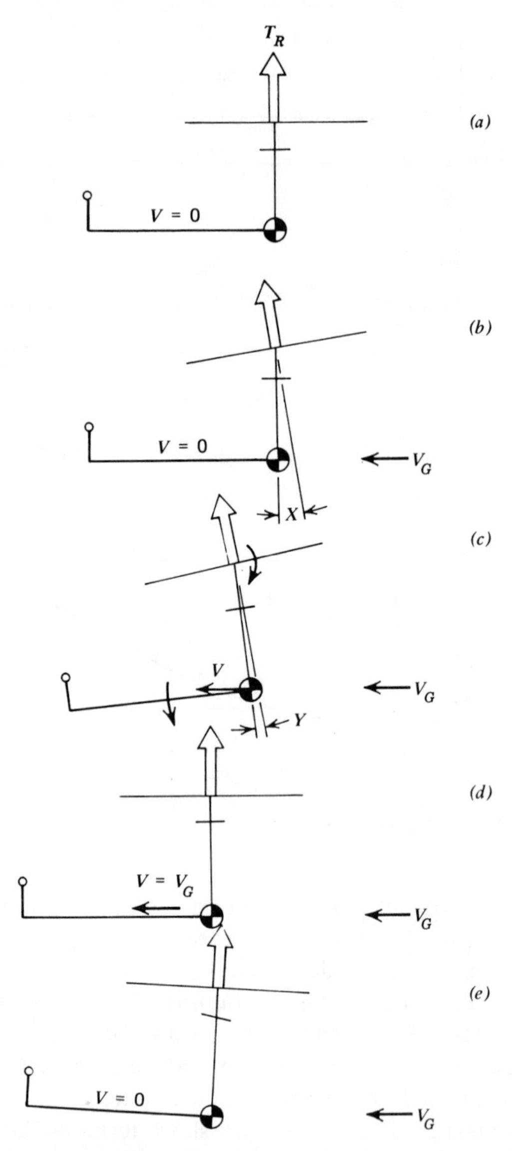

Figure 5.13 Short term response to horizontal headwind step gust. (*a*) Stable hover, no wind. (*b*) A horizontal headwind step gust causes rotor to blow back, tilting thrust vector ahead of the center of gravity and leading to a noseup moment on fuselage. Horizontal component of rotor thrust plus fuselage drag cause rearward acceleration. Swash plate commands disc to tilt forward. (*c*) Fuselage pitches up and disc pitches down, bringing the two closer to agreement and reducing fuselage pitching moment. The lag of the rotor in returning represents the pitch damping. Still no pilot input. Rearward groundspeed

The result is that the short term dynamic longitudinal response of a helicopter in a hover is normally nonoscillatory (aperiodic) and heavily damped, while the long term response is oscillatory and divergent. It is this divergent mode that is the fundamental problem in hovering dynamics and forces the pilot to be attentive to his task. For the same reason, "hands off" hovering is not possible in helicopters that do not have adequate artificial stability (stability augmentation) systems. Flying qualities specifications put numerical limits on the existing degree of instability.

Longitudinal: Forward Flight

In forward flight, rotor speed stability becomes less significant while vertical damping, angle of attack stability, and pitch damping become more significant. Because of angle of attack stability, vertical motions are now coupled to pitch motions and an uncoupled plunge mode does not exist. In other words, motion along the aircraft's vertical axis while in forward flight is equivalent to an angle of attack change (downward motion increasing angle of attack and vice versa). As discussed previously, the rotor creates a pitching moment in response to angle of attack changes in the unstable sense.

Figure 5.14 illustrates how vertical damping and angle of attack stability combine to influence longitudinal gust response. Here a sudden upgust has been encountered. The immediate effect is to increase rotor thrust and tilt the disc back. The first effect creates a nosedown moment, since, at that instant, the center of gravity is ahead of the rotor thrust vector. Conversely, the rotor blowback is creating a noseup moment. The latter usually predominates, thus initiating a fuselage noseup pitch motion. The horizontal tail had its original angle of attack increased, causing an initial nosedown contribution. As the pitching motion develops, this contribution is increased in proportion to pitching velocity (i.e., pitch damping). The timing and magnitude of these effects determine the subsequent character of the motion.

Helicopters in forward flight have dynamic characteristics that vary widely not only between helicopters but of the same helicopter at varying gross weight, center of gravity, and forward speed. Two oscillatory modes are the most common. One occurs rather quickly (it is short term) and the

---

Figure 5.13 (*Continued*).

increasing (V). (*d*) Requirement for steady state rearward translation at V_G speed (i.e., zero airspeed). Pilot must have applied forward cyclic to stop acceleration at $V = V_G$ and then returned cyclic to neutral. (*e*) Requirement for hovering in steady wind. Blowback moment on disc canceled by moment commanded by the swash plate. Horizontal component of thrust balances fuselage drag.

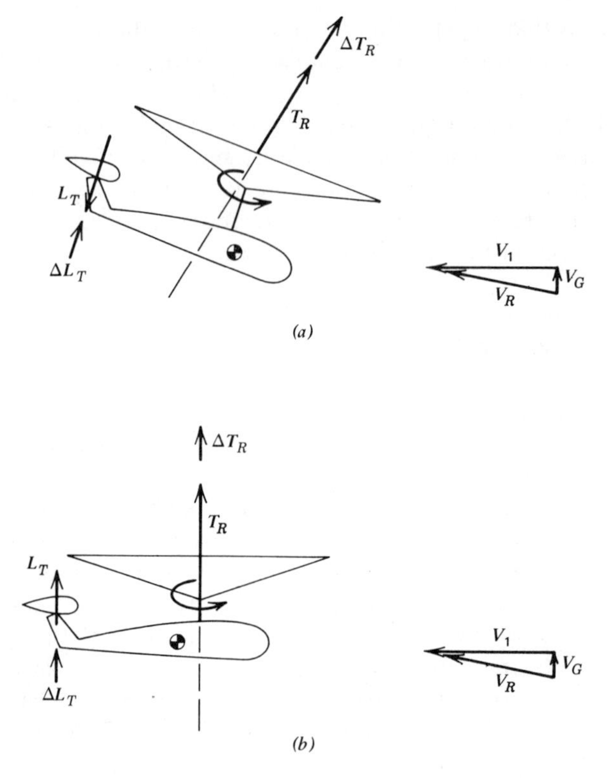

Figure 5.14 Gust response in forward flight.

other takes place over a longer term. In fixed wing dynamics there are two comparable modes called the "short period" mode and the "phugoid" mode. The short term response to a gust or to a longitudinal cyclic input should be rapid and heavily damped. The pilot wants the helicopter to maneuver promptly and without bobbling when he commands it to do so. Generally, low natural frequencies (long periods) and overdamped responses are reported to be sluggish, while high natural frequencies with low damping are reported to be lively and difficult to control. Depending on the task (reconnaissance, landing approach, weapons tracking, nap-of-the-earth, etc.), there is some optimum range of frequency/damping combinations that yields good flying qualities in the short period mode.

One can observe both longitudinal modes of motion in forward flight by suddenly deflecting the longitudinal cyclic stick to a new position and holding it there. The initial response of the helicopter is to pitch in the appropriate direction and develop G's. This short term behavior passes in 1 or 2 sec and involves primarily pitch angle, angle of attack, and G's. There will not have been time for velocity or altitude to have changed appreciably. Figure 5.15 shows a typical time history. If the control input is held fixed, it corresponds to some new equilibrium speed. The aircraft arrives at this new speed based on the long term mode of motion.

Suppose that, as in Figure 5.15, the control movement is 1 in. back. At the end of the short term motion the nose is above its original position, but the speed has not changed very much. The aricraft is decelerating, however, and the speed stability of the rotor creates a nosedown moment. As the nose comes down, the component of weight in the flight path direction increases, tending to accelerate the aircraft. Thus there is a slowly changing interplay between pitch moments and drag forces, which causes long period oscillations involving pitch attitude, speed, flight path angle, and altitude. Rotor disc angle of attack and fuselage angle of attack change little during this phase. If the long term motion is damped, eventually the aircraft settles down to a new equilibrium state—in this example, at lower velocity. If the power is unchanged, and the aircraft was on the "front side"

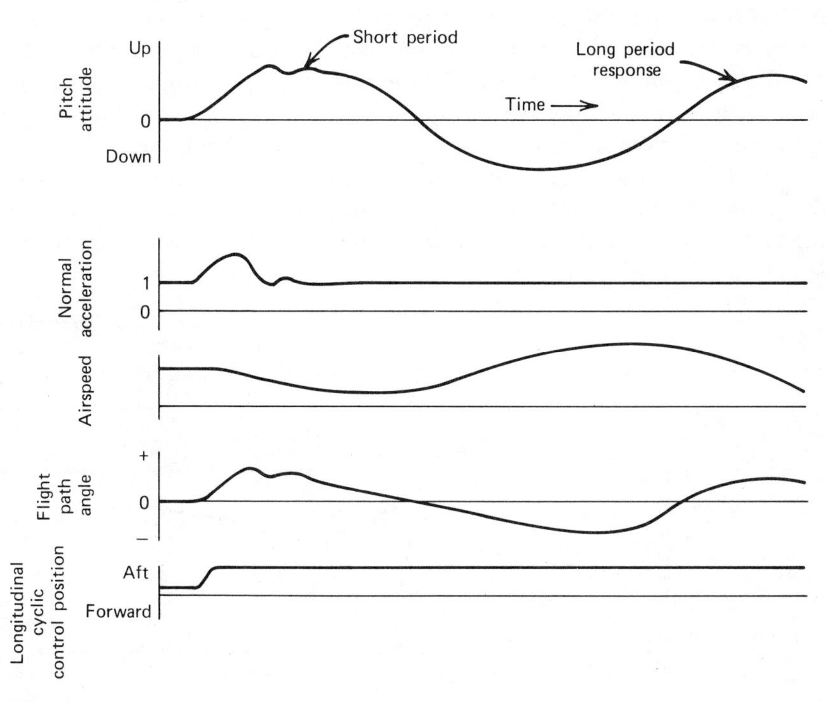

Figure 5.15 Time history to longitudinal cycle step input.

of the power curve to begin with, the excess power available at the new lower speed results in a constant rate of climb.

Lateral-Directional: Hover

Here we are interested in the motion variables of heading angle (sideslip angle is undefined in zero wind hover), bank angle, and sideward translation. In many cases the yaw response in hover is uncoupled from the other two motion variables, that is, yawing motions do not induce rolling motion or sideward translation and vice versa. This is only true for hover. This "yaw mode" is controlled with the directional control pedals alone. There are no yaw moments proportional to yaw angle (zero wind), but there are some proportional to yaw rate. The latter arise primarily from the variation of tail rotor thrust in yawing motions. When a yaw rate is established to the left, the tail rotor translates in the direction it is thrusting, thus causing a decrease in the angle of attack seen by each blade element of the tail rotor blades. This in turn causes a reduction in tail thrust, leading to an incremental right yawing moment. This is in a sense opposite to the motion and proportional to it, that is, yaw damping. Like the plunge mode in hover the absence of a spring-like term prohibits oscillations, and the response to a pedal step input is a "first order" time history of yaw rate, with no overshoot. Once the yawing moment due to pedal input is balanced by the yaw damping contribution, a new steady state yaw rate is achieved.

The other two degrees of freedom are clearly coupled, since roll motions cause sideforces and vice versa. Rolling moments due to side velocity, rolling moments due to roll rate (i.e., roll damping), and sideforces due to side

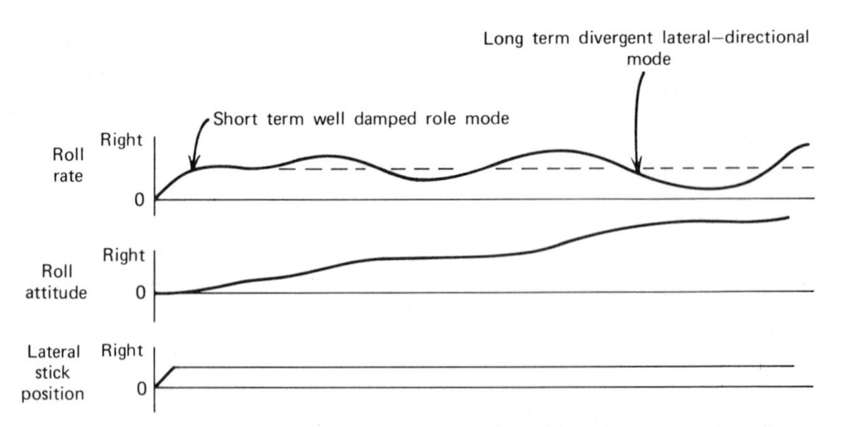

Figure 5.16 Roll response in hover to lateral stick step input.

velocity are the main contributors to what usually turns out to be a short term, well damped roll mode and low frequency unstable lateral-directional mode in hover, Again, the latter mode requires constant pilot attention, and limits are set on the acceptable degree of instability. Since both the longitudinal and lateral-directional oscillatory modes are usually low frequency, some degree of instability is allowed. If the frequency is higher, however, an unstable situation would tend to get away from the pilot quicker; hence more and more positive stability is required as the frequency of these modes increase.

The response to a lateral cyclic stick input is shown in Figure 5.16, illustrating the well damped, nonoscillatory (aperiodic) roll mode and the long term divergent lateral-directional oscillation.

Lateral-Directional: Forward Flight

In forward flight, sideslip generation, by way of yawing moments, immediately creates rolling moments (effective dihedral). Thus the independent yaw mode in hover becomes coupled in forward flight. Typically, three distinct dynamic modes of motion exist in the lateral-directional sense: (1) roll mode, (2) spiral mode, and (3) dutch roll mode. The first two are nonoscillatory, and the third is oscillatory.

Consider the roll rate response to a step lateral cyclic stick input (Figure 5.17*a*). No rudder pedal input is present. For a hypothetical helicopter in which such an input did not excite the spiral or dutch roll modes the response would look like that of Figure 5.17*b*. A steady roll rate would be achieved in some period of time. Two main effects are at work. The cyclic

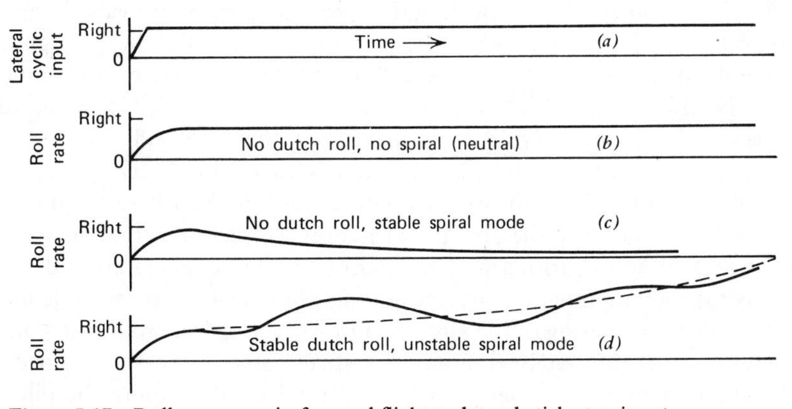

Figure 5.17 Roll responses in forward flight to lateral stick step input.

input creates a constant rolling moment, which is opposed by an opposite roll moment due to roll rate (i.e., roll damping). When the roll rate builds up to the point where the damping moment equals the control moment, no further increase in roll rate is achieved. The less the damping, the higher the steady state roll rate that will be achieved for a given cyclic input, and the longer will be the time to achieve steady state. A well damped roll mode, with no other modes interfering, would be ideal.

Unfortunately, the damping contribution from the rotor is usually quite low and is not augmented by any significant fuselage contributions, even at high forward speed. Consequently, the very long response times make it appear to the pilot like an acceleration control in roll. An initial cyclic input must be taken out when the desired roll rate response is achieved.

The spiral mode and the dutch roll mode further complicate the response. The first is best understood by considering a helicopter placed in steady flight with zero angular velocity, but with one wing low. The flight controls of this aircraft are in the proper positions for wings level flight. Should the aircraft right itself to a wings level attitude, the spiral mode is convergent. A roll into the existing bank indicates spiral divergence and no roll motion at all indicates a neutral mode. Suppose that in the example above the aircraft is released from a left wing down left sideslip condition. If the dihedral effect is very strong and positive, the aircraft rolls back toward wings level flight. At the same time the sideslip angle is being driven toward the trim value (usually close to zero) because of the directional static stability. As the aircraft yaws in the direction of the sideslip, there may well be a significant roll due to yaw rate, which causes the aircraft to roll into the turn. Likewise, during yawing motions yaw moments are developed (i.e., yaw damping), tending to counter the yawing motion.

Thus the dynamic stability of the spiral mode depends on the relative magnitude of the dihedral effect, static directional stability, yaw damping, and roll due to yaw rate. When the directional static stability is high and the stable dihedral effect is low, the roll due to yaw rate rolling moment can cause the aircraft to roll into a larger and larger bank angle. The continued increase in bank angle results in an increase in the inside sideslip, which in turn causes an increase in yaw rate and classic spiral divergence. The example of Figure 5.17*c* illustrates a convergent mode, where the dihedral effect is large relative to the directional stability. Helicopters that do manage to have stable spirals (often with the aid of stability augmentation devices) usually take a long time to converge and do not play a significant role in the short term maneuvering of the aircraft. For a stable spiral mode a step input in lateral cyclic ultimately commands a steady state bank angle, since the roll rate goes to zero. A neutrally stable spiral would require the pilot to take back out his cyclic input once his desired bank angle has been achieved.

The dutch roll mode is an oscillatory mode coupling roll and sideslip excursions. It is usually lightly damped. It is a "nuisance" mode, requiring continual pilot compensation in precise lateral maneuvers. Figure 5.17*d* shows a dutch roll mode superimposed on the roll rate response to a lateral cyclic step input. The dutch roll gets "excited" in this maneuver by yaw due to lateral cyclic input and/or yaw due to roll rate. The first is usually characterized as being "adverse" or "proverse." If, for example, the aircraft immediately yaws right with the application of a left cyclic input (which can be seen by observing the nose motion relative to the horizon or the turn needle on the turn and bank indicator), the yaw is away from the direction of intended turn and is called "adverse." Adverse yaw due to lateral cyclic requires immediate directional control into the turn to prevent sideslip and keep the ball in the center. On some helicopters with lots of adverse yaw pilots almost lead their turn maneuvers with a little pedal application into the turn.

Regardless of what excites the dutch roll (including gusts) it is characterized by a combination of sideslip and roll excursions at the same frequency but not in phase, that is, the maximum sideslip excursion does not necessarily occur at the same time maximum roll angle or roll rate does. The best way to observe this mode, without exciting the roll mode or spiral mode, is to put in a directional pedal doublet. For example, from a trimmed level flight condition, insert 1 in. of left pedal, hold for 1 sec, immediately put in 1 in. of right pedal, hold for the same time, and then return to neutral. An oscillation in roll angle, roll rate, sideslip angle, heading, yaw rate, and side acceleration (watch the ball) is then noted. Aircraft in a flight condition where dihedral effect is large in comparison to directional static stability has a large roll-to-sideslip ratio, that is, the dutch roll is mostly rolling with very little sideslip. Other aircraft exhibit low roll-to-sideslip ratios, or a "flat" dutch roll, being mostly sideslip with very little roll.

It is the characteristics of the dutch roll (frequency damping, roll-to-sideslip ratio, and roll-to-sideslip phasing) that determine the pilot's degree of difficulty in turn coordination. Flying qualities specifications place definite limits on these parameters.

Cross-Coupling

Cross-coupling is the effect on motions in an axis caused by motions in another axis. We saw examples of cross-coupling in yaw caused by lateral stick input (control cross-coupling) and roll caused by sideslip (dihedral). For purposes of discussion we have separated longitudinal stability from lateral-directional stability. In fact, they are also cross-coupled to some degree for both aerodynamic and inertial reasons. In the lateral-directional group the most important ones are gyroscopic.

The behavior of a spinning mass when subjected to external forces and moments is different from that when it is not spinning. The mathematical derivation of the equations describing the motion of a gyroscope is beyond the scope of this book. Suffice it to say that Newton's second law, $F = ma$, is strictly true only when the force and acceleration are measured in inertial space, that is, in a nonrotating axis system with fixed orientation with respect to the stars. Even an axis system fixed to the earth is rotating in space because of the earth's spin, its orbit around the sun, and the sun's orbit in the galaxy. The latter accelerations often contribute little, depending on the problem, and may be ignored. The contributions of the rotation of a helicopter rotor, however, *are* significant and cannot be ignored.

A classic physics experiment illustrating this point involves suspending a rotating mass horizontally on a vertical support at one end of the axis of rotation (Figure 5.18). The weight of the mass times its moment arm creates a moment that tends to topple the system from its support. Certainly, if the mass were not spinning, it would topple. Instead of rotating about the y-axis, however, the system precesses about the z-axis at some finite rate. It can be demonstrated that the procession rate is proportional to the applied moment and inversely proportional to the spin rate. As the spin rate decays, the precession rate increases. Finally, at sufficiently low spin rate the centrifugal forces outward from the support, together with the

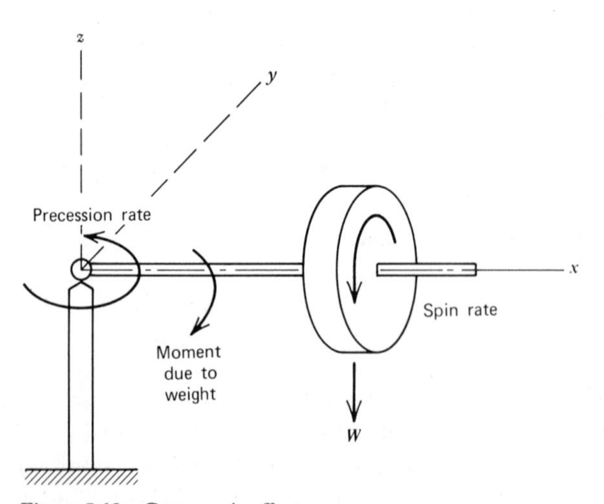

Figure 5.18 Gyroscopic effects.

toppling moment, cause the system to come unglued. The tendency of a rapidly spinning body to turn about a second axis not parallel to the axis of spin, when acted on by a moment about a third axis, is called gyroscopic action. It follows from this discussion, and can be proved mathematically or by experiment, that as a rapidly rotating body is to be forced to turn or precess about an axis perpendicular to the axis of spin, a moment must be applied about an axis that is perpendicular to the other two axes.

Applied to the main rotor of a helicopter (assuming counterclockwise rotation when viewed from above), the first gyroscopic action above has the following effects:

Applied Moment	⟶	*Gyroscopic Precession*
Nose up		Rolling left
Nose down		Rolling right
Roll right		Nose down
Roll left		Nose up

Once a rotational rate has been established, from whatever cause, the the converse principle above predicts:

Established Motion	⟶	*Gyroscopic Moment*
Nose up		Roll right
Nose down		Roll left
Rolling right		Nose up
Rolling left		Nose down

Pitching or rolling rates or moments do not appreciably cross-couple with yaw, since the plane of rotation of the rotor is essentially in the yawing plane.

These inertial cross-coupling terms make the behavior of a helicopter fundamentally different from that of a fixed-wing aircraft (although airplanes with large rotating engine components may also experience gyroscopic effects). The aircraft then behaves asymmetrically in that a roll into a right turn produces effects different from those when rolling into a left turn. To compound the problem, often aerodynamic cross-coupling effects are also at work. For example, a single positive dihedral tail surface, such as those found on some light training helicopters, generate additional lift in sideslips. In one model the normal right sideslip after a sudden loss of engine torque causes less download on the tail surface than previously (i.e., and incremental upload). This produces a significant nose-down moment, which is sometimes called "tuck." The situation is aggravated if the student has been flying with some right sideslip or if he steps on the left pedal instead of the right one following power loss. The same configuration couples pitching motion to roll, since the tail protrudes on only one side of the ship. Thus the center of lift on the surface is offset laterally from the center of gravity, and changes in lift produce changes in rolling moment—another aerodynamic cross-coupling effect.

Figure 5.19 shows an actual time history of a helicopter performing a pull-up maneuver. Note that the aft cyclic stick displacement causes the expected noseup pitch behavior and increased normal load factor, but large unwanted right roll is also induced, along with a slight left yawing tendency.

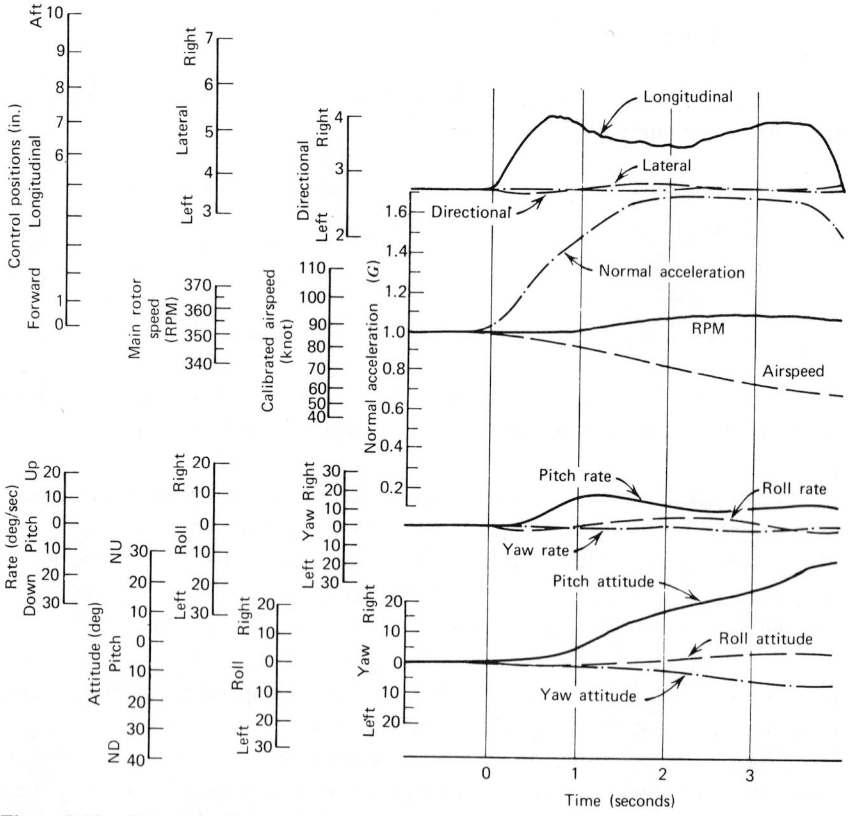

Figure 5.19 Cross coupling in maneuvers.

5.5 FLIGHT CONTROL SYSTEMS AND STABILITY AUGMENTATION

We have been discussing the inherent motions of a helicopter when disturbed from trim by gusts or by control inputs. We now examine the mechanics of rotor control, and the requirements for adequate control. Fundamentally, a rotor can be controlled by directly tilting the hub or by changing the blade pitch (collectively or cyclically). The latter can be achieved directly by the swash plate, aerodynamic servo tabs, auxiliary rotors, fluidically controlled jet flaps, and pitch links from a control gyro. All of the methods have both advantages and disadvantages, but all have the same purpose—control of the rotor thrust in both magnitude and direction. Figure 5.20 illustrates the most common type of blade pitch control—the swash plate system. Direct hub tilt is used in some very small helicopters and gyrocopters. The forces that this type of control requires become excessive as the aircraft size increases, however, so that it is much more efficient (and easier on the flight control system structure) to let the aerodynamic forces do the work.

Main Rotor Control

The rotating swash plate is mechanically attached to pitch horns in such a way that pure vertical translation upwards increases the pitch on all blades by the same amount. Cyclic stick movement directly controls the tilt of the swash plate relative to the shaft. In Figure 5.20 a forward displacement of the stick has caused a corresponding displacement of the swash plate in a nosedown direction. Because of the geometry of the attachment of the feathering axis the blade pitch is decreased at the 90° advancing position and increased at the 270° retreating position. In the fore-and-aft position no change in blade pitch has occurred. Through the flapping mechanism, the tip path plane is then tilted forward, orienting itself with the swash plate. This motion is rapid, usually taking less than half a second. Again a thorough appreciation of the aerodynamically induced flapping behavior obviates the necessity of using gyroscopic analogies in discussing this control mechanism. For a review of flapping, return to Section 4.2.

The flight control system consists of all-mechanical, hydraulic, or electrical systems that act between the pilot's cockpit controls and the rotor. It includes a maze of rods, bell cranks, pulleys, and cables as well as hydraulic boost actuators, electromechanical stability augmentation devices, and artificial "feel" systems.

In an unaugmented system the stick is mechanically geared directly to the swash plate system, and no "boost" is provided to overcome the aero-

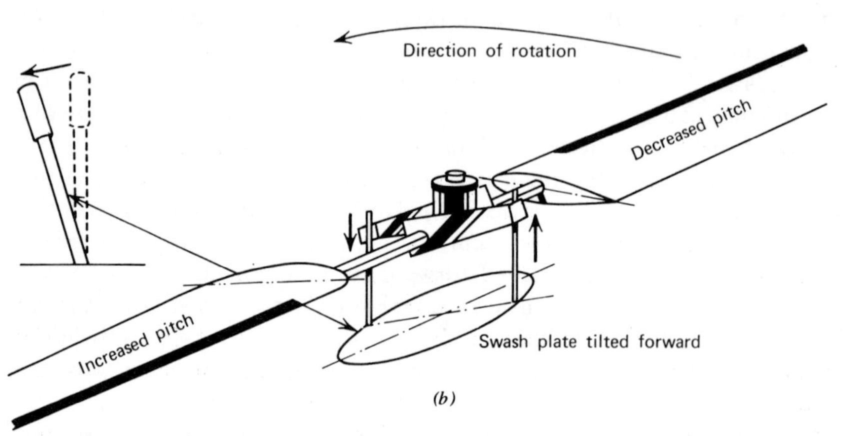

(b)

Figure 5.20 Swash plate system of control.

dynamic and inertia forces tending to resist motion. Such a system may be used when the control loads are sufficiently low and mechanical gearing can serve to bring the forces felt by the pilot within normal bounds. The unaugmented system is attractive because of its ease of maintenance and its general reliability. A number of helicopters rely on an emergency capability to fly unaugmented control systems that are normally augmented. Vibratory feedback from the rotor system may cause the flight control to shake in an unaugmented system, which can be reduced only by changing flight condition or by increasing control friction, neither of which is very satisfactory.

The large control forces in larger helicopters, especially in the high speed portion of the flight envelope near retreating blade stall, generally require augmentation. The pilot still controls the rotor, but he has additional help in a hydraulic or electric actuator, which acts as a "gain" between control stick forces and rotor pitch link forces. This link is, or tends to be, irreversible in the sense that pilot control forces are fed to the rotor but rotor forces are not transmitted back to the pilot. The control force and position trim characteristics of an augmented system can normally be tailored to provide an extremely wide range of force characteristics, whereas the unaugmented system is less flexible.

Tail Rotor Control

Tail rotor control is accomplished by collective blade pitch alone, as commanded by pedal displacement, thus the magnitude of the tail rotor thrust, hence yawing moment, is controlled. In forward flight the tail rotor has an "advancing" and "retreating" side (located at the top and bottom or vice versa, depending on rotational direction). Thus lift dissymmetry exists, which must be compensated for by a flapping hinge. Often the magnitude of tail rotor flapping becomes excessive; for this reason designers tilt the orientation of the flapping hinge so that it is not parallel to the blade chord. This is called a "delta three" hinge and is shown in Figure 5.21. With ths type of hinge, flapping motions automatically induce cyclic feathering. The orientation is such that downflapping produces increased blade pitch and upflapping, decreased blade pitch. With this automatic cyclic feathering the magnitude of flapping does not have to be so severe in order to distribute the rotor thrust more uniformly over the disc in forward flight.

Offset Flapping Hinge

Many articulated rotors have offset flapping hinges, which are located outboard from the hub (Figure 5.22). This system offers the advantages of

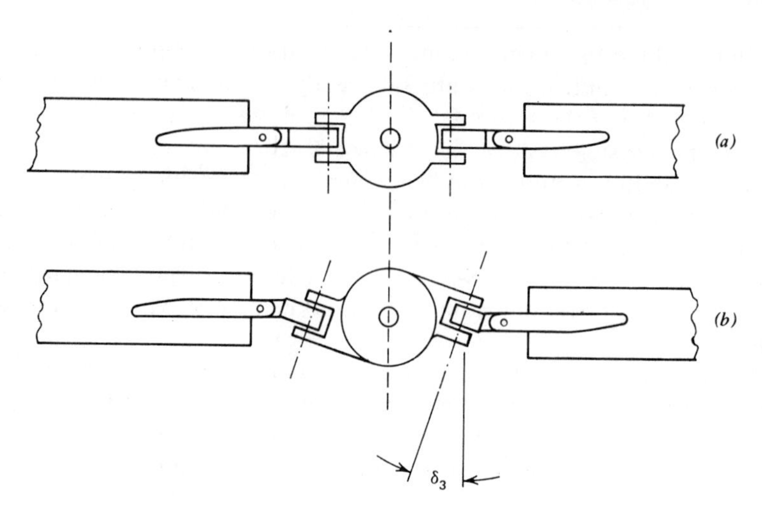

Figure 5.21 "Delta three" hinge. (*a*) Plain flapping hinge. (*b*) Delta-three hinge combines flapping and cyclic feathering.

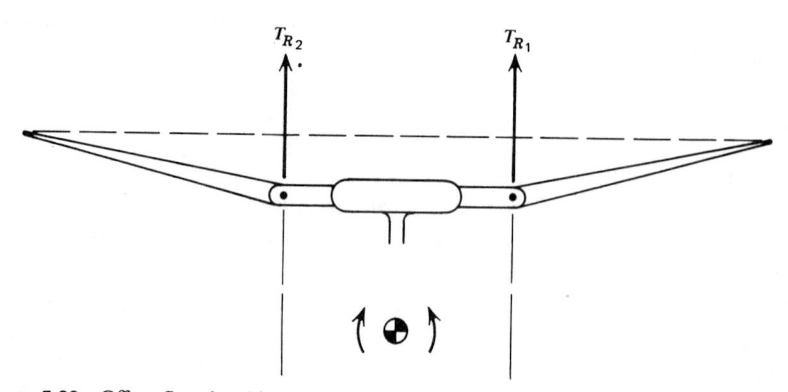

Figure 5.22 Offset flapping hinge. Flapping hinge offset from center produces moments without disc tilt.

increased control power and rotor damping. A centrally hinged system obtains a moment only from the tilting of the thrust vector, which produces a moment around the helicopter's center of gravity. With an offset flapping hinge the tilted blade centrifugal forces act on the hinges to produce a substantial additional control moment on the hub. Since centrifugal forces are usually about ten times the rotor thrust, a very high control power can be achieved with offset. Thus in the OH-6A light observation helicopter offset supplies control power twice that offered by the tilting of the thrust vector.

Rotor damping is produced by the rotor lagging behind the movement of the fuselage, with the damping moments being created in the same manner as the control moments. Again, the contribution to damping by the offset flapping hinges can be over three times the contribution of the thrust vector tilt.

One of the important advantages of offset flapping hinges is the presence of control regardless of lift condition, since the blade centrifugal force is independent of lift. In the case of the teetering rotor, the control power is directly proportional to the rotor lift. When flying over a hill, a zero *G* flight condition can be experienced with the rotor lift at zero, at which time the teetering rotor loses its pitch and roll control capability (unless special means have been incorporated to avoid it). The offset flapping hinge articulated rotor avoids this problem, provided other considerations are not limiting.

Stability Augmentation Systems

Because little pitch and roll damping can be obtained from the rotor's normal behavior, many modern helicopters incorporate a stability augmentation system (SAS) to improve their flying qualities. The SAS may be all-mechanical (e.g., Lockheed AH-56A "control gyro" and the Bell Stabilizer Bar) or it may employ electrical signals. The general theory behind both is identical: use some of the available control power to automatically create moments proportional to the desired motion variable. The general scheme is illustrated in Figure 5.23.

Suppose that the longitudinal damping in hover is judged to be inadequate in a particular helicopter. In response to a longitudinal cyclic control input the aircraft continuously diverges in pitch. By sensing pitch rate, say with an internally mounted gyro sensor, an electrical signal proportional to pitch rate can be obtained. The positive or negative sign of the signal can be made to correspond to pitching up and pitching down, respectively.

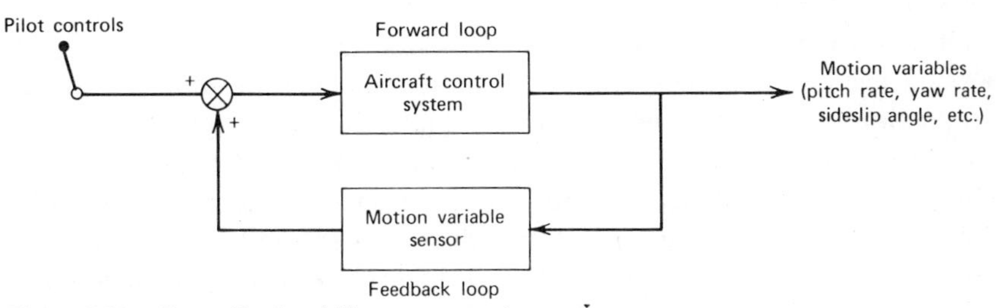

Figure 5.23 Generalized stability augmentation system.

This signal can then be sent to the longitudinal control actuator and command a cyclic pitch change in the sense to oppose the pitching motion and proportional to the pitch rate. The pilot is completely unaware of the event, since nothing gets fed back to his controls. The response of the aircraft, however, appears completely different. Where before an ever-increasing pitch rate developed, now a constant rate is obtained to a step input. Moreover, the pilot finds (assuming that the SAS gains are correct and no other SAS induced problem arises) that the pitch control is much more precise than before.

The Bell Stabilizer Bar tries to do the same (Figure 5.20). Here an additional gyro bar rotates with the rotor and is connected to the pitch control links, but first it passes through a mechanical viscous damper. The gyro bar tends to remain rigid in space, as the mast to which it is attached pitches. The angular orientation between the bar and a line perpendicular to the shaft causes cyclic pitch inputs to the main rotor. There is a moment, however, created by the viscous damper, which tend to bring the bar back perpendicular to the shaft. The size of this moment is directly proportional to the pitch rate. As a result, a longitudinal cyclic pitch input, proportional to pitch rate but somewhat lagging behind, is produced. The same mechanism introduces lateral cyclic inputs proportional to roll rate, that is, roll damping. Without a massive control bar the effect in the case of the Bell bar is minimal in most installations.

Electronic SAS systems are much more flexible and can be made to create moments as a function of almost any variable that can be sensed. For example, by feeding back signals proportional to pitch angle and bank angle an "attitude hold" system is created. Such a system, given proper authority, always returns the aircraft to the commanded attitude (which can include zero pitch and bank), even in gusty environments. The more stability is augmented in this manner, however, the less control power remains for pilot inputs. The degree of required augmentation and the total control power available drive the SAS design.

Once good "inner loop" stability has been achieved through appropriate SAS, it is a simple matter to add the navigation function through an autopilot. For example, a "heading hold" function may easily be achieved by sensing heading and comparing it to the commanded heading. A signal, proportional to the difference in these signals, drives the appropriate control. For hover this would be the directional control only. For forward flight it might be the lateral control, with coordination automatically supplied by the inner loop stability augmentation. Altitude hold and VOR radial tracking are similarly accomplished, and a logical extension includes automatic ILS localizer and glideslope capture and tracking. Fully automatic approaches, including deceleration to a hover and a vertical descent to landing have been accomplished entirely "hands off." Such systems are operational from some fixed-wing airplanes but it will be a long time before it is routinely done in helicopters—mostly because of inherent stability problems, especially at low speed. We discuss such operations from the pilot's viewpoint in Section 6.5.

5.6 FLYING QUALITIES

Flying qualities, or handling qualities, is the name given to the total set of characteristics that make an aircraft suitable or unsuitable for a particular task. It is a difficult area to define precisely, as it is a function of very many variables. Civilian certification requirements and military specifications have been written to record, as quantitatively as possible, those characteristics that ensure good flying qualities in the mission e.g., References 23, 85. Four basic categories of characteristics are listed in such specifications: (1) basic "open loop" stability, (2) response to control inputs, (3) flight control system characteristics, and (4) emergency conditions. In each category limits are set for various "levels" of flying qualities. When all systems are operating satisfactorily the highest level is required. When the probability of subsystem failure exists (e.g., pitch damping SAS failure), lower levels of performance may be allowed. In some cases different requirements are applied as a function of vehicle class (lightweight, trainer, medium weight-medium maneuverability, heavy-low maneuverability, high maneuverability) and flight phase [(1) rapid maneuvering, precision tracking, and precise flight path control, (2) gradual maneuvering and non-precision tracking, and (3) terminal flight phase]. The requirements for a particular aircraft, considering vehicle class, flight phase, and failure state, must be met at the flight conditions (speed, altitude) at which the tasks within the flight phase are normally accomplished.

This is a complex area, involving a multidimensional matrix of conditions. It has been found necessary to have this complexity, since in actual practice the "goodness" of the flying qualities required does in fact depend on all these things. An adequate treatment of the entire spectrum is beyond the scope of this book, and we here merely give a few examples to illustrate the approach.

First, how is a quantitative requirement arrived at? One would assume that flying qualities are subjective, opinions varying considerably from pilot to pilot. This is not so. The degree of pilot variability can be reduced substantially if the pilots are properly briefed as to the precise task they are being asked to evaluate. The practice of having a test pilot fly an aircraft and then give an overall rating of its flying qualities has long since ceased to be useful. Instead, the pilot is told that the flight phase, for example, is weapons delivery air to ground. He is further told to inspect the characteristics associated with precise longitudinal tracking in this mission. How well is he able to move to, and stop precisely on, his selected target? How well is he able to hold his target while the aircraft gains speed in the dive and while moderate turbulence exists? A distinction is made between tracking performance (which could be measured without the pilot's opinion) and the degree of difficulty associated with accomplishing that performance. The test pilot's skill is not what is being assessed—it is the vehicle's suitability for an exact task when flown by an "average" pilot.

An invaluable aid in the quantitative determination of a helicopter's flying qualities is the Harper-Cooper rating scale shown in Figure 5.24. This scale, like others, has undergone considerable change and refinement over the years to arrive at this state of maturity and usefulness. It is a 10-point scale, 10 being the poorest, and 1 the best rating. The evaluation pilot, after having performed the task a sufficient number of times, asks himself a series of questions, the answers to which lead him to a final numerical rating. The first question is the easiest—is the aircraft controllable during this task? A "no" answer demands the poorest rating of 10. The next series of questions, as can be seen from Figure 5.24, relate to the level of pilot workload (compensation) required to achieve adequate performance. If adequate performance cannot be achieved without an intolerable pilot workload, the rating must fall within the 7 to 9 range depending on severity. If it takes moderate to extensive pliot compensation, such that the deficiencies warrant improvement, the 4 to 6 category is appropriate. The top three ratings are reserved for minimal (or less) compensation cases. Evaluation pilots, properly instructed and familiar with the use of this scale, demonstrate remarkable consistency in their rating, usually with standard deviation of 1 rating unit only.

The quantitative requirements of flying qualities specifications were determined on the basis of massive data and pilot ratings of this kind. For normal operation (no unusual failure state) the requirement equals a rating of at least 3.5. Degradation to the equivalent of a 6.5 level is allowed under stated conditions of system failure. It is quite permissible to demonstrate compliance to the requirement with SAS on, but it must be further shown that the expected failure rate of the SAS channels is more remote than a given probability—otherwise the failure state becomes "normal" and compliance must be demonstrated with SAS off.

Here are just a few examples of flying qualities requirements extracted from reference 85.

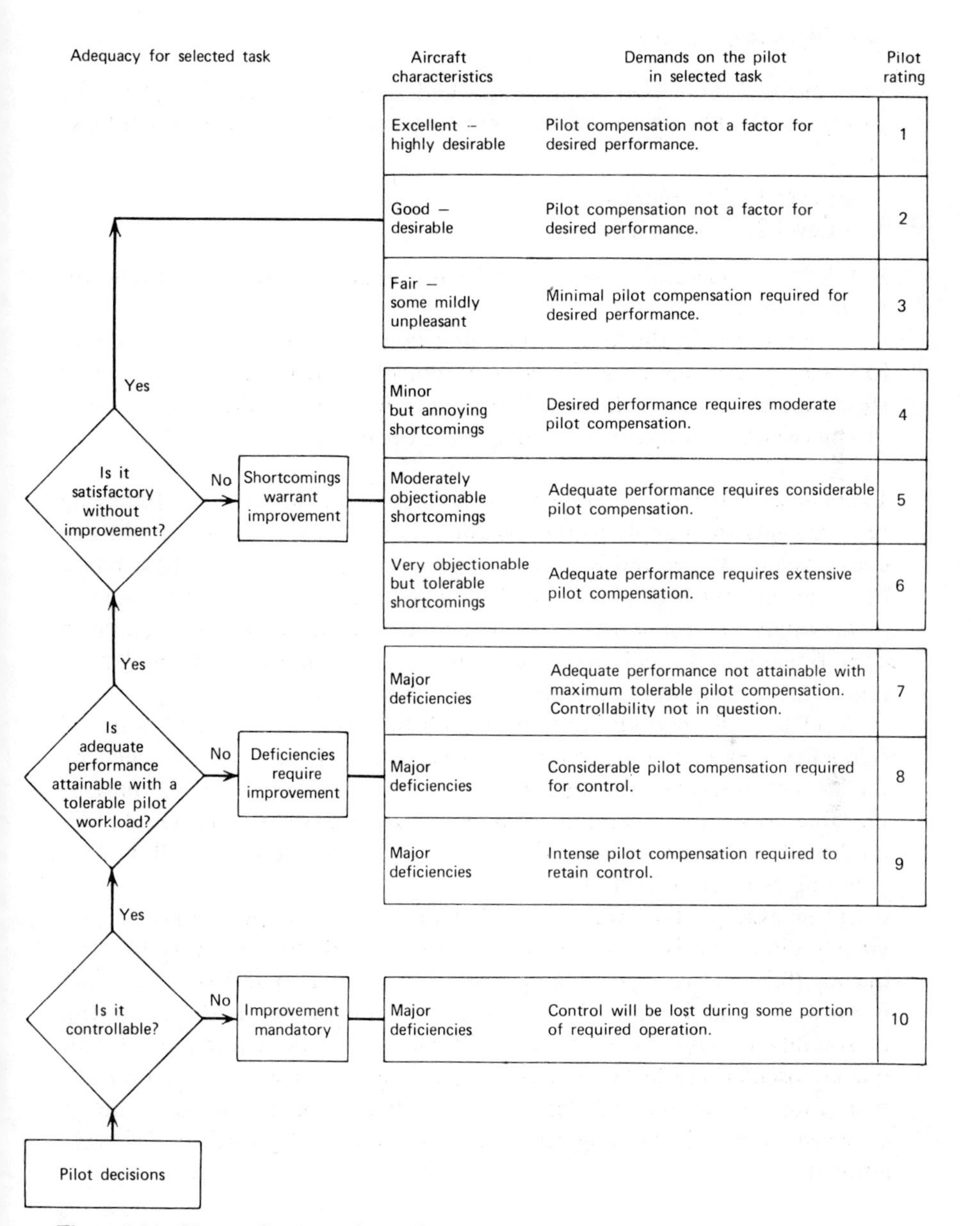

Figure 5.24 Harper-Cooper rating scale.

Basic "Open-Loop" Stability

Example 1. "Directional damping: While hovering at zero airspeed, the yaw mode shall be stable and the time constant shall not exceed the following:

Level 1: 1.0 seconds
Level 2: 2.0 seconds

For Level 3 operation there shall be no tendency toward aperiodic divergence in yaw."

In this example the term "time constant" means the time required, following a step input of directional control, to reach 63% of the final steady state yaw rate achieved. The various levels refer to different failure or emergency states, level 1 being normal operation.

Example 2. Dynamic pitch response requirement in hover: "The following requirements shall apply to the dynamic responses of the aircraft with the cockpit controls free and with them fixed following an external disturbance or an abrupt pitch or roll control input in either direction. The requirements apply for responses of any magnitude that might be experienced in operational use. If oscillations are nonlinear with amplitude, the oscillatory requirements shall apply to each cycle of the oscillation.

Level 1. All aperiodic responses shall be stable. Oscillatory modes of frequency greater than .5 radians per second shall be stable. Oscillatory modes with frequency less than or equal to 0.5 radians per second may be unstable provided the damping ratio is less unstable than −.10. Oscillatory modes of frequency greater than 1.1 radians per second shall have a damping ratio of at least .3 . . . ."

In this example the oscillatory behavior of the helicopter in hover, previously discussed, is regulated with respect to stability. For very low frequency (0.5 rad/sec = 0.0796 cps, or a period of 12.6 sec) some stability is allowed. None is allowed between 0.5 and 1.1 rad/sec and a good deal of stability is required above 1.1. (Damping ratio is a measure of how quickly oscillations decay. A damping ratio of 0.3 corresponds to no more than four overshoots, of decreasing amplitude, before steady state is achieved. Negative damping ratios refer to the rate of growth of the oscillations).

Response to Control Inputs

Example 1. "With the wind from the most critical directions relative to the aircraft, control remaining shall be such (in hover) that simultaneous abrupt application of pitch, roll and yaw controls in the most critical combination produces at least the attitude changes specified below within one second from the initiation of control force application."

Level	Pitch	Roll	Yaw
1	±3.0°	±4.0°	±6.0°
2	±2.0	±2.5	±3.0
3	±2.0	±2.0	±2.0

Note the severity of the requirement, in terms of critical wind direction and simultaneous control inputs. As we have seen, the control power required to hover at maximum gross weight from a critical direction sometimes leaves *no* control for maneuvering (Figure 5.10)—clearly a violation of the requirement above.

Example 2. Roll control effectiveness in forward flight. "The time to change bank angle by 30 degrees (t_{30}) to the right or left from a trimmed zero-roll-rate condition shall not exceed the value specified below. The time shall be measured from the initiation of roll control force application. Yaw control may be used to reduce sideslip that retards roll rate (not to produce sideslip that augments roll rate), provided that yaw control inputs are simple, easily coordinated with roll control inputs, and are consistent with piloting techniques for the aircraft in its mission."

	t_{30} (sec)		
Aircraft Class	Level 1	Level 2	Level 3
Small, light, such as light utility, observation, and primary trainer aircraft	1.3	1.8	2.6
Medium weight, low to medium maneuverability, such as utility and search and rescue aircraft	1.8	2.5	3.6
Large, heavy, low to medium maneuverability, such as HLH, cargo, and heavy search and rescue aircraft	2.5	3.2	4.0
High maneuverability aircraft, such as attack helicopters	1.0	1.3	2.0

Flight Control System Characteristics

Example 1. Cockpit control force gradients. "At speeds up to 35 knots, the pitch, roll and yaw control force gradients shall be within the range specified below throughout the range of control deflections."

	Level 1		Level 2	
Control	Minimum	Maximum	Minimum	Maximum
Pitch	0.5 lb/in	3.0	0.5	5.0
Roll	0.5	2.5	0.5	5.0
Yaw	5.0	10.0	5.0	20.0

Example 2. Trim system. "At all steady flight conditions within the Operational Flight Envelope, the trimming devices shall be capable of reducing the pitch, roll, and yaw control forces to zero for levels 1 and 2. At all steady flight conditions within the Service Flight Envelope, the untrimmable cockpit control forces shall not exceed 10 pounds pitch, 5 pounds roll, and 20 pounds yaw. For Level 3, the untrimmed cockpit forces shall not exceed 10 pounds pitch, 5 pounds roll, and 20 pounds yaw."

Emergency Conditions

Example 1. SAS failures. "Special provisions shall be incorporated to preclude any critical single failure of the flight control system including trim devices or stability augmentation system which may result in flying qualities which are dangerous or intolerable. Failure-induced transient motion and trim changes resulting either immediately after failure or upon subsequent transfer to alternate control modes shall be small and gradual enough that dangerous flying qualities will not result. In addition, the crew member concerned shall be provided with immediate and easily interpreted indications whenever failures occur in the flight control system."

Example 2. Autorotation entry. "The aricraft shall be capable of entry into autorotation (power off) at all speeds from hover to V_{con}. Following power failure a delay of 1 second prior to pilot corrective action is mandatory, and a delay of 2 seconds is desired. During the delay, no dangerous flight conditions of excessive changes in aircraft attitude or altitude shall occur. Changes in aircraft attitudes shall be considered excessive if they exceed 20 degrees in 2 seconds following complete loss of power with controls fixed."

These are only a few examples of the kinds of requirements that should be imposed when procuring new helicopters. They help to ensure that the helicopter's characteristics and the pilot's abilities in performing the many tasks associated with the vehicle's mission will match.

PROBLEMS

5.1 Explain why increasing weight (e.g., when a sling load is lifted) requires increased left pedal to maintain heading. For the same weight, does pedal requirement change with an increase in density altitude? How? Explain.

5.2 Some helicopters have independent fore-aft force control by way of and additional rotor (propeller) facing aft. Determine, using the conditions for equilibrium, how this capability allows the helicopter to hover over sloped terrain, with the fuselage parallel to the slope.

5.3 (*a*) A helicopter suddenly loses engine power while in trimmed straight and level flight at high speed. Identify all sources of unbalanced moments in pitch roll and yaw at the time of failure. Include all aerodynamic and inertial contributions and estimate their sense (roll right, roll left, etc.).

(*b*) Assuming the pilot does not react immediately, what additional contributions will exist as the helicopter responds to the initial unbalanced moments?

Figure 5.25 Courtesy Kaman Aerospace Corporation.

SPECIAL PILOTING PROBLEMS

6

6.1 INTRODUCTION

As the reader knows by now, this book is not a how-to-fly-a-helicopter manual. The technical discussion, however, has been kept at a level that can be understood by helicopter pilots with limited academic experience, as well as by undergraduate engineering students. We depart from this approach in this chapter to discuss some special piloting problems that have commanded the pilot's attention and skills ever since helicopters first appeared. Wherever possible we relate the problem to the physics of the situation, trying to marry the academic and practical approaches.

6.2 AUTOROTATION

We are concerned here with what happens to a helicopter following loss of engine power, for whatever cause, and the pilot's options for safe descent to touchdown. Three phases of the autorotation maneuver are identified and discussed separately: entry, steady state descent, flare and touchdown.

Entry

The immediate and obvious effects of power loss are rotor RPM decay and out-of-trim rotational accelerations. The most abrupt rotor RPM decay rates occur when collective pitch and consequent torque are the highest. Heavy weight, high density altitude, and V_{max} speeds are the critical conditions. The rate at which a rotational system decays is directly proportional to the applied torque and inversely proportional to the moment of inertia (Newton's second law applied to rotation). Recall that the latter property is determined by the weight of the system and how that weight is distributed radially:

$$I = \Sigma mr^2$$

A given mass 20 ft from the center of rotation is four times more effective in producing rotational inertia than is the same mass 10 ft away. Rotor inertia is one parameter that the designer can control somewhat, and we hear of "high inertia rotors" and "low inertia rotors." From the standpoint of minimizing rotor RPM decay following power failure, the high inertia rotor is preferred. However, in terms of increasing RPM during the cyclic flare prior to touchdown, the opposite is true—a high inertia rotor here resists significant rates of RPM increase. Moreover, the high inertia rotor tends to lag collective input commands during the steady state portion of the descent (although the final RPM change achieved may be high). This characteristic can cause a tendency for the pilot to "chase the rotor speed," requiring extensive pilot effort in precise RPM control.

Figure 6.1 illustrates the magnitude of rotor RPM decay experienced on one helicopter. Note that in the most severe case it takes only seconds for the decay to reach published minima, that is, the pilot must react quickly in initiating a decrease in collective and/or cyclic flare to prevent excessive RPM decay. When the failure occurs at high speed in this helicopter a firm cyclic flare must be initiated and held to maintain flight rotor speed and decelerate to normal autorotation airspeed. The cyclic flare must be maintained as the collective is decreased so that the rotor remains loaded during the maneuver. Without the positive load on the rotor while lowering collective, very small cyclic movements result in very high rotor flapping angles on this helicopter. (*Note.* This technique is required for the helicopter in this example; it is not necessarily a technique of universal applicability. Consult the appropriate literature for your aircraft.)

The motions of the helicopter following loss of power vary greatly from helicopter to helicopter and from one flight condition to the next. The universal tendency for a left yawing moment (for "conventional" helicopters) comes from the out-of-trim condition that now exists directionally.

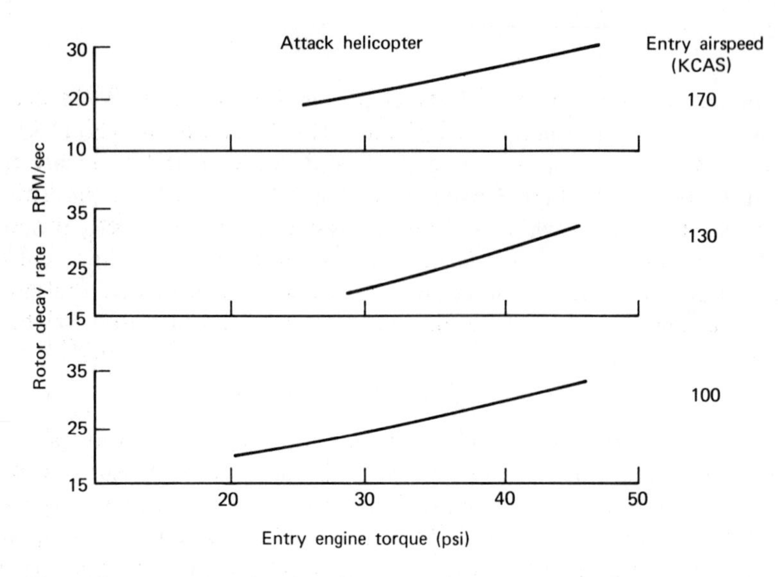

Figure 6.1 Rotor rotational speed decay following engine failure.

The tail rotor thrust is not diminished at the moment of power loss, since its RPM and collective pitch setting have not yet changed. There is an inevitable left yaw, causing right sideslip (at forward speed). The magnitude of the yawing moment is exactly equal to the main rotor torque prior to failure. Thus it is again most severe in the high weight, high density altitude, high speed condition. Once the sideslip begins, the cross-coupling with roll, previously discussed, occurs. In some helicopters there are conditions where a complete and sudden engine failure finds the aircraft upside down within 3 sec if no pilot action is taken.

Figure 6.2 is a time history of a simulated engine failure, taken in flight by rapidly reducing throttle setting from a high speed condition.

The pilot was instructed not to take control until he thought he had to in the interest of safety. Notice that while he resisted collective movement for a little over 1 sec, right pedal and right cyclic were coming in almost immediately (along with the SAS inputs) to counteract a strong left yaw and left roll. Even with this correction a yaw rate of 5°/sec and a roll rate of 10°/sec developed within 1 sec, and within 2 sec the aircraft had rolled 17° left (starting from a 7.5° left banked turn). Note also that both the yaw and lateral SAS channels became completely saturated. The motions were becoming execssive so quickly that other than immediate recovery would have resulted in an uncontrolled condition. While not all aircraft exhibit these

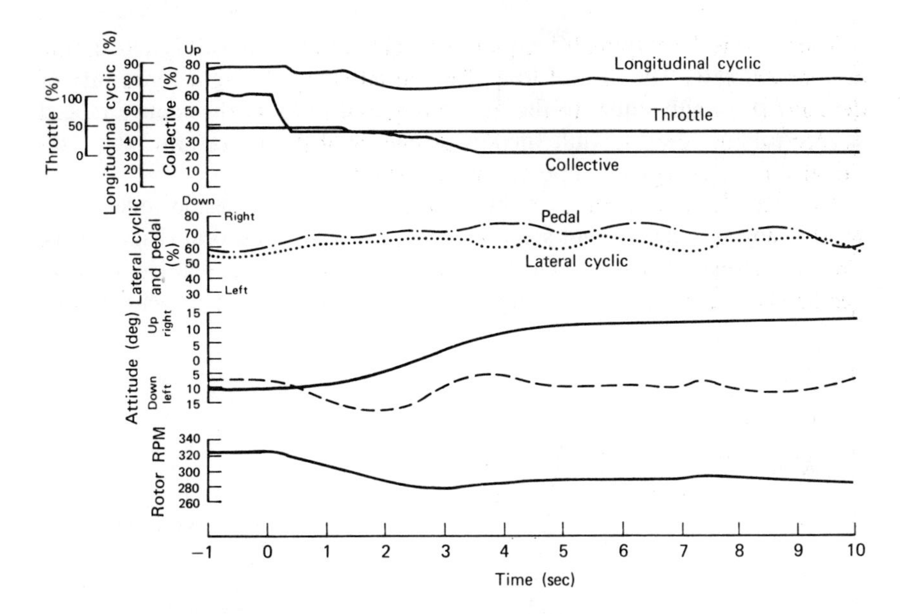

Figure 6.2 Time history of simulated engine failure. (U.S. Army data.)

characteristics (even this one is better behaved at lower speed) almost all helicopters have a critical flight condition where, for all practical purposes, immediate recovery action is necessary. Adequate warning to the pilot of the failed condition (aural, visual, and/or kinesthetic) is clearly required.

The time it takes to establish a fully developed steady state autorotation depends very much on flight condition and pilot technique. On all helicopters at least 5 to 8 sec are required, using optimum technique, to establish the autorotative flow state from the powered flow state. Clearly, there are some combinations of speed and altitude from which a steady state condition cannot be achieved prior to contacting the ground. The optimum technique for these conditions is obviously quite different from others as is discussed later when considering the height-velocity diagram (dead man's curve).

Steady State Autorotation

By definition, a steady state autorotation exists when there is zero torque maintained on the rotor, resulting in constant RPM, despite zero power being delivered from the engine.

The rotor is developing lift, equal to weight, and the aircraft is descending at constant rate. The rate of loss of potential energy (weight times rate of descent) is roughly equal to the power required to fly at the same airspeed at zero rate of descent, while the kinetic energy of the aircraft and the rotational kinetic energy of the rotor are constant.

How can zero net torque on the rotor be achieved? Consider once more what a single blade element sees in the autorotative condition (Figure 6.3). The lift and drag are perpendicular and parallel to the relative velocity vector. The latter is determined from a vector summation of velocity due

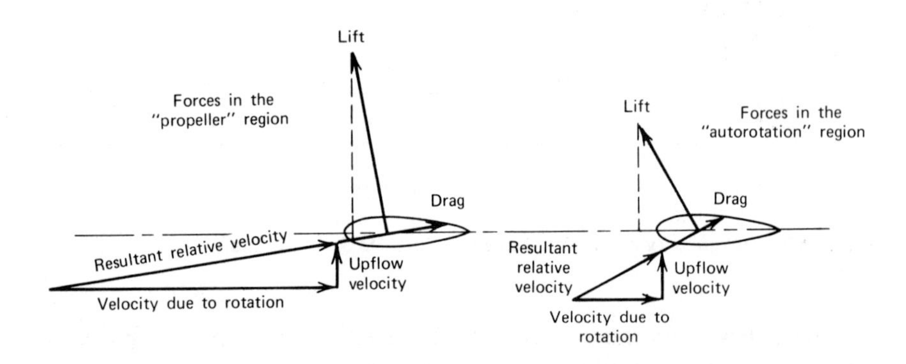

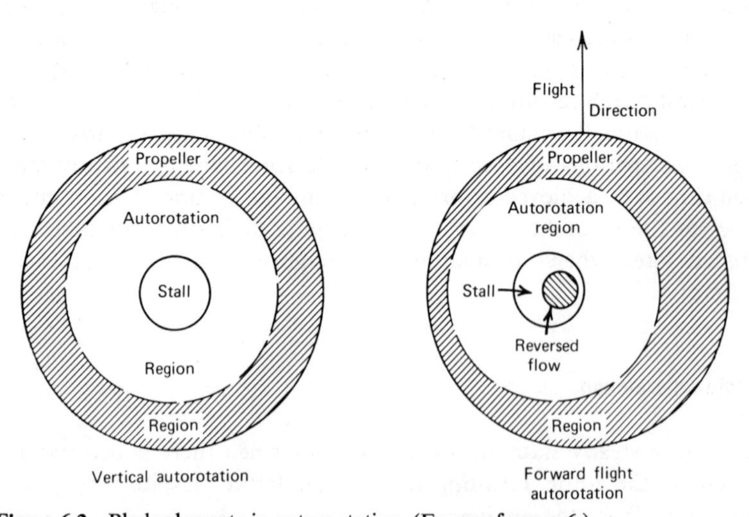

Figure 6.3 Blade elements in autoraotation. (From reference 6.)

to rotation, velocity due to translation (in this case a forward descent), and velocity due to flapping. For simplicity, the latter has been omitted in Figure 6.3. The magnitude of the lift and drag on the element depends on the magnitude of the resultant velocity vector and the angle of attack. The angle of attack is determined by the direction of the relative wind and the blade pitch angle. The question of torque depends on the distance of the element from the center of rotation and the component of aerodynamic force in the plane of rotation. Notice that it is quite possible, and in fact quite necessary for autorotation, for the lift force to have a component in the forward direction in the plane of rotation.

To have the *element itself* contribute zero moment, the forward component of lift must equal the retarding component of drag in the plane of rotation:

$$L \sin(\alpha - \theta_A) = D \cos(\alpha - \theta_A)$$

or

$$\frac{\sin(\alpha - \theta_A)}{\cos(\alpha - \theta_A)} = \frac{D}{L}$$

or

$$\tan(\alpha - \theta_A) = \frac{1}{(L/D)}$$

The angle $(\alpha - \theta_A)$ is solely determined by the magnitude and direction of V_r and V. The L/D ratio is determined solely by α. Thus θ_A, the pitch angle required for autorotation *of the element itself*, is determined from the equation above. Therefore, for a given blade element, RPM and flight velocity vector there is one and only one pitch angle that the element can have and be in autorotation itself.

Unfortunately, we do not have independent control over the pitch of each blade element. For a given structural spanwise twist, setting the collective determines the blade angle distribution. Thus some sections have pitch angles greater than their θ_A, and others have smaller ones. Consequently, some areas of the blade tend to accelerate the rotor to higher RPM, and others tend to retard it. For a given airspeed and collective setting there is one RPM-rate of descent combination in which these two opposing influences cancel out. At this stage the rotor is in *overall* autorotation.

Figure 6.3 shows that, for a given pitch setting, the lift vector has a larger component forward if angle of attack is large. This occurs on the inboard portions of the blade, since the velocity due to rotation is low there. Figure 6.3 illustrates a typical inboard and outboard condition and also shows the disc areas that are accelerating (incorrectly called the "autorotation region") and those that are decelerating ("propeller region").

Torquewise, the two areas must contribute equal and opposite effects for total rotor autorotation to exist. There may be a small region close to the hub where the vector sum of a low velocity of rotation and a high rate of descent produce an angle of attack larger than the stalling value.

Most helicopters can achieve steady state autorotation at any forward speed within the normal flight envelope. The accompanying rate of descent and flight path angle vary widely, however. At constant RPM and airspeed, the only energy change is that of potential energy. Since the engine is not supplying the power required for level flight (at that airspeed and RPM), potential energy must be sacrificed—at the rate corresponding to the power required. That is,

$$\text{rate of change of PE} = P_{\text{req}}$$

$$\frac{W \cdot h}{\Delta t} = P_{\text{req}}$$

or

$$V_v = \frac{h}{\Delta t} = \frac{P_{\text{req}}}{W} \qquad \left(\frac{\text{ft-lb}}{\text{sec}} \cdot \frac{1}{\text{lb}} = \text{fps}\right)$$

For fixed wing aircraft this is an excellent approximation to the actual case, since the aerodynamics are identical in level flight or descent at the same airspeed (i.e., same angle of attack). For helicopters it is not valid, since the aerodynamic flow field around the rotor is fundamentally different in autorotation from what it is in the normal thrusting flow state. We know that both weight and density altitude affect P_{req} in level flight at a given airspeed. Consequently we observe changes in the rate of descent (with power off) in fixed wing aircraft that closely follow the equation derived above. There is a far less dramatic effect with helicopters in this respect. The flight manual of one common helicopter says: "Auturotational descent performance is a function of airspeed and is essentially unaffected by density altitude and gross weight." To be sure, extremes of weight or density altitude must affect descent performance but within normal limits the change is minimal.

To visualize this, look again at a single blade element in autorotation (Figure 6.4). If either weight is changed or density altitude is changed, the angle of attack must increase to support the weight. Suppose that this is accomplished by increasing blade pitch. For the autorotation state to be accomplished, the component of additional lift in the plane of rotation must be balanced by the component of additional drag in the same plane:

$$\text{condition A:} \quad L_A \sin(\alpha_A - \theta_A) = D_A \cos(\alpha_A - \theta_A)$$

$$\text{condition B:} \quad L_B \sin(\alpha_B - \theta_B) = D_B \cos(\alpha_B - \theta_B)$$

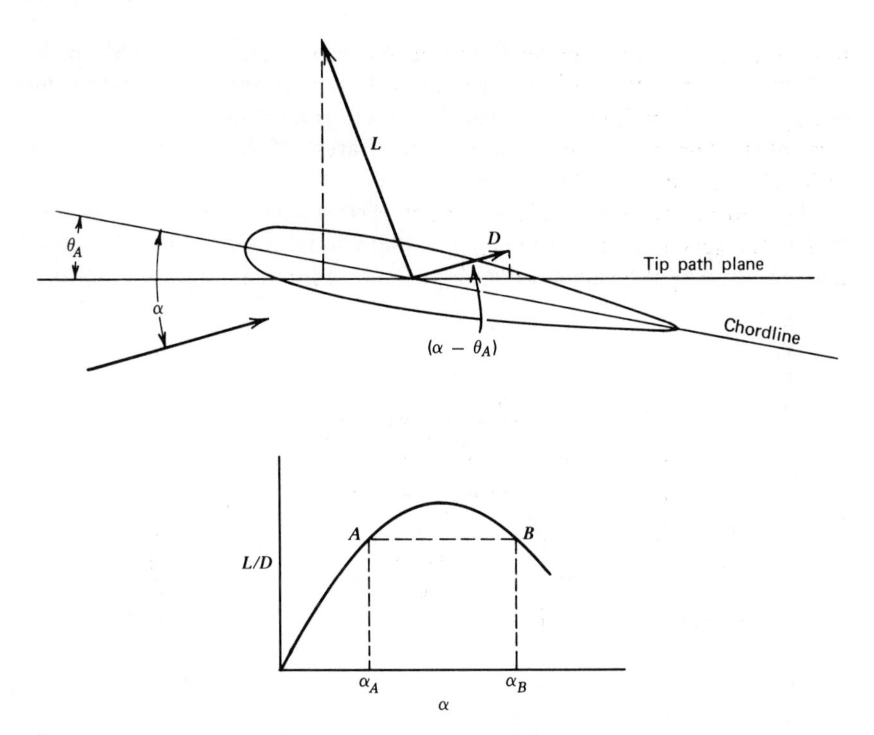

Figure 6.4 Single blade element in autorotation. For autorotation: $L \sin(\alpha - \theta_A) = D \cos(\alpha - \theta_A)$, $L/D = \tan(\alpha - \theta_A)$.

But

$$\alpha_B = \alpha_A + (\theta_B - \theta_A)$$

$$\therefore\ L_B \sin(\alpha_A - \theta_A) = D_B \cos(\alpha_A - \theta_A)$$

That is,

$$\frac{L_B}{D_B} = \frac{L_A}{D_A}$$

In other words, to maintain autorotation at the same rate of descent, the increase in blade pitch (required for greater weight or density altitude) must result in an angle of attack change that produces no change in the lift-to-drag ratio. Recall that L/D depends on angle of attack, as shown in Figure 6.4. Thus for a single blade element this can occur only when the angle of attack changes over the peak in the L/D curve.

For an entire rotor the restriction is not so severe. As we know, there is a wide distribution of angle of attack over the disc. Thus some elements have angles of attack smaller than that corresponding to the peak in the L/D curve, and others have larger ones. It is necessary only that *on the average* L/D be maintained. Thus while there is a change in the respective sizes of the "propeller" and "autorotation" areas of the disc, there may be little, if any, change in the rate of descent.

The two variables that affect descent performance greatly are airspeed and rotor speed. Note in Figure 6.5 the dramatic sensitivity of rate of descent to airspeed changes. The speed for minimum rate of descent is

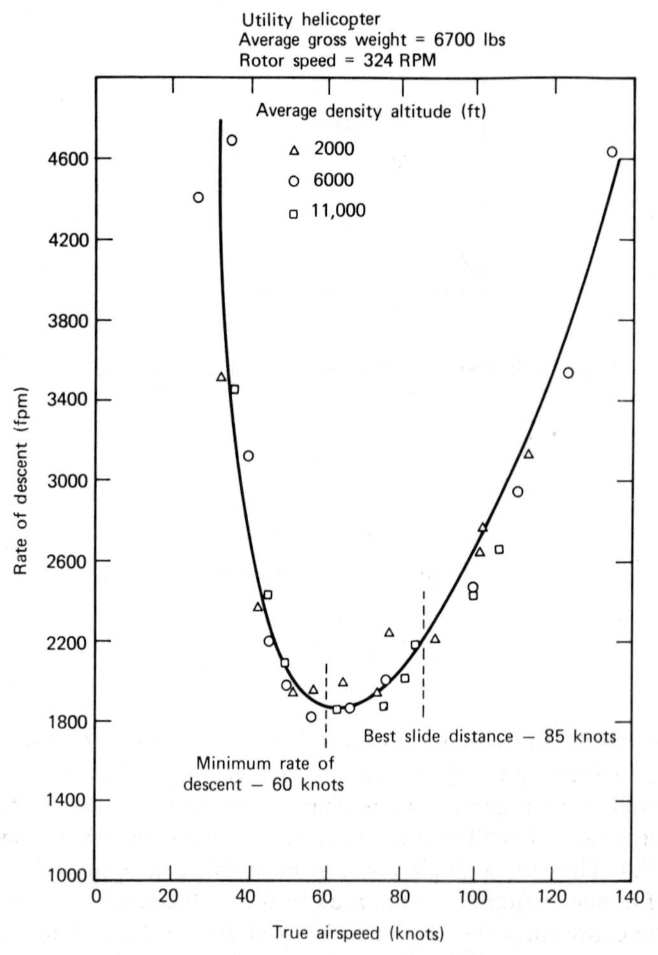

Figure 6.5 Autorotation rate of descent versus airspeed. (Data from reference 25.)

an important parameter to the pilot. It corresponds with the speed for minimum power, discussed in Chapter 4. There we saw that this speed corresponds to an advance ratio of about 0.14 for most helicopters:

$$\frac{V_{(\text{min ROD})}}{V_{\text{tip}}} \doteq 0.14$$

Here both $V_{(\text{min ROD})}$ and V_{tip} must be in the same units. Converting $V_{(\text{min ROD})}$ to knots, and using the relation between V_{tip}, rotational speed, and rotor radius, the equation becomes:

$$V_{(\text{min ROD})} \doteq \frac{0.14 \cdot R \cdot \text{RPM}}{9.55 \cdot 1.69}$$

$$\boxed{V_{(\text{min ROD})} \doteq 0.00867 \cdot R \cdot \text{RPM}} \qquad \text{knots}$$

This simple, though approximate, formula covers a wide range of helicopters with surprising accuracy. For the helicopter of Figure 6.5 it predicts 61.7 knots, which is very close to the experimental data.

More remarkable, perhaps, is the fact that the rate of descent (at the airspeed for minimum rate of descent) divided by the tip speed is essentially the same for single rotor helicopters:

$$\frac{V_{v(\text{min})}\ (\text{fpm})}{60 V_{\text{tip}}\ (\text{fps})} \doteq 0.04$$

or

$$\boxed{V_{v(\text{min})} \doteq 0.251 \cdot R \cdot \text{RPM}} \qquad \text{fpm}$$

The latter result indicates that a reduced rate of descent can be achieved by attaining as low a rotor speed as possible without exceeding published limits. This is indeed true, as illustrated in Figure 6.6. Note however, that below a certain RPM, rate of descent increases again, and the higher the weight, the higher the RPM at which this reversal occurs.

An interesting fact comes to light when we combine the last two equations to find the descent angle while autorotating at the speed for minimum descent rate:

$$\begin{aligned} \sin \gamma &= \frac{V_v}{V} \doteq \frac{0.251 \cdot R \cdot \text{RPM}}{0.00867 \cdot R \cdot \text{RPM}} \cdot \frac{1}{60} \cdot \frac{1}{1.69} \\ &= 0.286 \\ \gamma &\approx 16.6^\circ \end{aligned}$$

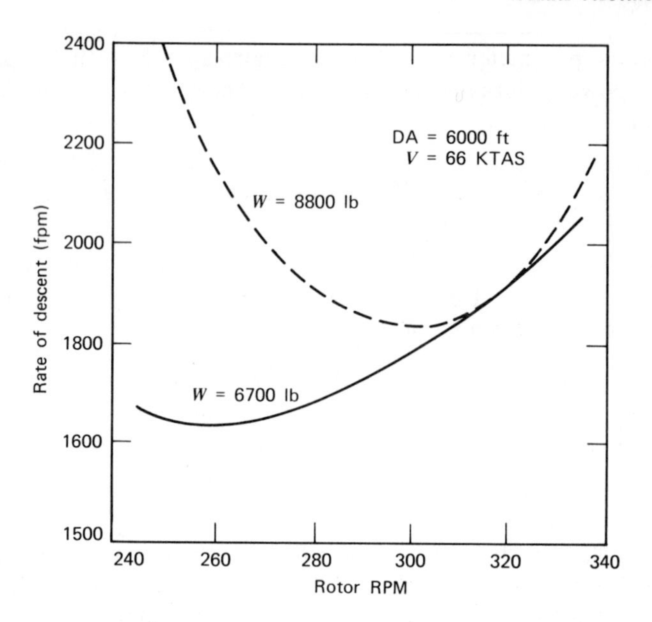

Figure 6.6 Autorotation rate of descent versus rotor RPM in a utility helicopter.

Therefore, when a single rotor helicopter autorotates at the speed for minimum descent rate it is descending along a flight path of approximately 17° in calm air.

These conclusions come as a surprise to most helicopter pilots and engineers on initial inspection. One would have expected a wide variation with the helicopter, its weight, and the density altitude. Furthermore, dual rotor helicopters, according to experimental evidence, also act independent of gross weight and density altitude. The rate of descent is about 25% higher than the single rotor formula would indicate, probably because of greater fuselage blocking and tandem rotor interference. However, the above mentioned observations are applicable only to the steady state portion of the autorotation maneuver. Weight and density altitude may greatly affect the flare characteristics at the termination of the maneuver.

The speed for minimum descent rate is not the same as that for maximum glide distance. In the latter case we minimize the descent angle:

$$\sin \gamma = \frac{V_v}{V}$$

Therefore, we minimize the ratio of V_v to V, not just V_v itself. This corresponds graphically, on a plot or V_v versus V (e.g., Figure 6.5), to the point on a straight line drawn from the origin just tangent to the V_v versus V curve. This point represents the most V_v for the least V, hence is the minimum flight path angle.

The differences between glide distance achievable by flying at the best glide speed (higher than the speed for minimum rate of descent) can be significant. In the example of Figure 6.5 the best glide speed is 85 KTAS, giving a rate of descent of 2200 fpm:

$$\text{(a)} \quad \sin \gamma_{\min} = \frac{2200}{60 \cdot 85 \cdot 1.69} = 0.255$$

$$\gamma_{\min} = 14.8°$$

At the speed for minimum descent rate (60 knots) at 1870 fpm rate is achieved:

$$\text{(b)} \quad \sin \gamma = \frac{1870}{60 \cdot 60 \cdot 1.69} = 0.307$$

$$\gamma = 17.9°$$

This is very close to the approximate 17° previously discussed. From a height of 5000 ft AGL the horizontal glide distances would be:

$$\text{(a)} \quad R = \frac{5000}{\tan 14.80} = \frac{5000}{0.264} = 18{,}939 \text{ ft}$$

$$\text{(b)} \quad R = \frac{5000}{\tan 17.90} = \frac{5000}{0.323} = 15{,}480 \text{ ft}$$

This difference of 3459 ft is significant, and could well mean the difference between landing on flat ground or in the trees. Pilots, unwilling to accept the higher rate of descent that goes along with the increased speed, often land short. "Stretching the glide" by pulling the nose up and decelerating does not work in the steady state portion of the descent.

It should also be appreciated that the rate of descent can be extremely sensitive to airspeed. Note in Figure 6.5 that flying 10 knots below the minimum descent rate speed increases the rate of descent from 1870 to 2090 fpm (11.8% increase); flying 20 knots below the minimum leads to 2680 fpm (43% increase). Recall that landing loads and *G*-forces are proportional to the square of the rate of descent. In this case flying 20 knots slow would increase the landing loads (assuming that there is no flare) by a factor of 2 or more.

The criticality of speed should be noted in the context of airspeed system errors (discussed in Chapter 2). It is not uncommon to have errors as large as 10 knots in many systems during autorotation (see Figure 2.9). Another source of error in airspeed measurement is sideslip, but more important is the additional increment of rate of descent that occurs in sideslip autorotations. Figure 6.7*a* illustrates this effect for one helicopter, showing the degraded performance. The pilot's problem is compounded by the difficulty in assessing sideslip. As speed is reduced, the ball (which actually measures side force) becomes less sensitive as a sideslip indicator. Figure

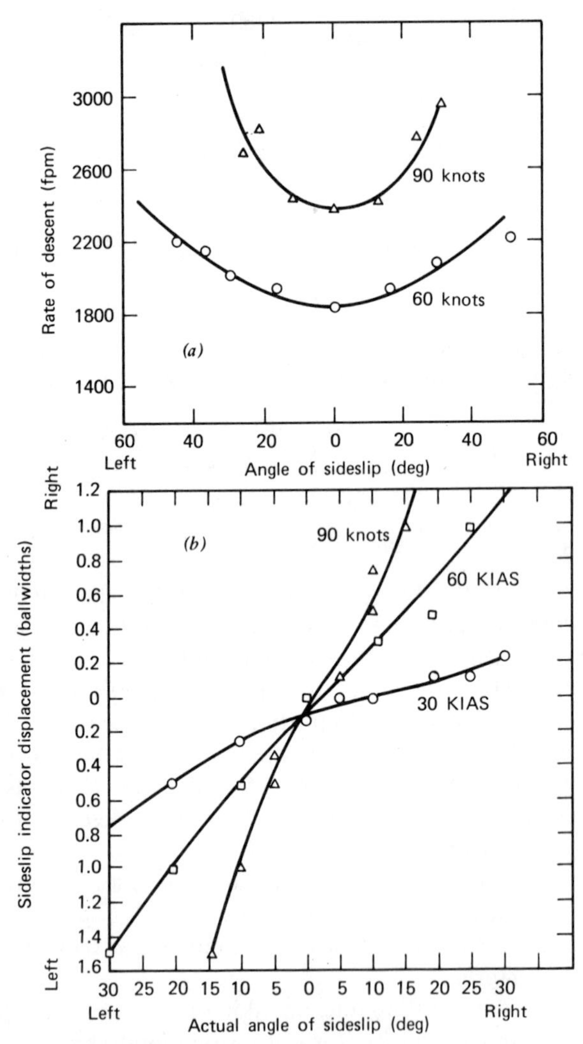

Figure 6.7 Autorotation rate of descent versus sideslip angle in a typical helicopter. (U.S. Army data.)

6.7*b* is an extremely important one in this respect. Notice that half a ball-width is equivalent to about 10° of sideslip at 90 KIAS (on this particular helicopter), 15° at 60 KIAS, and more than 45° at 30 KIAS! Thus the pilot who prides himself in keeping the ball within one half of the width may not be saying very much at low speed. The implications for autorotational descent rate are clear.

It is interesting to compare the descent characteristics of helicopters and of fixed wing aircraft. In the example above the minimum flight path angle was found to be 14.8°. This corresponds to a L/D ratio of $1/\tan 14.8° = 3.8$. At least one helicopter has demonstrated a 9.5° minimum descent angle, corresponding to an L/D of 6. While high performance gliders may achieve L/D ratios of 40 or higher, some jet fighters achieve only 4 or 5 at best. More important, the rates of descent are usually higher for fixed wing aircraft at comparable L/D. Thus the power-off performance of helicopters is better or worse than that of their fixed wing counterparts only in terms of which characteristic is most desired—minimum rate of descent or maximum glide distance.

Flare and Touchdown

Successful autorotation terminates with a carefully timed exchange of potential, kinetic, and rotational kinetic energies, so as to achieve as closely as possible a zero speed condition at the moment of touchdown. "Success" here is like "beauty in the eye of the beholder." There is, for example, the definition that "any autorotation you can walk away from is successful." However, here we wish to examine the requirements for controlled, level attitude touchdowns at minimal rates of descent and forward speed.

In the steady state approach to the flare kinetic energy of the aircraft and of the rotor is constant. Potential energy is being bled off at a rate proportional to the power required to generate a rotor thrust equal to weight. To arrest the rate of sink requires an upward vertical force greater than weight and a backward horizontal force greater than the horizontal component of rotor thrust. The last two results can be accomplished simultaneously with a cyclic flare. When the disc is tilted further aft, a number of things happen:

1. The upward vertical component of rotor thrust increases immediately as the thrust vector is tilted back toward the vertical.
2. The forward horizontal component of rotor thrust is diminished.
3. The aircraft fuselage pitches up to a higher angle of attack, increasing drag on the fuselage along the relative flight path direction, thus aiding effects (1) and (2).

4. The magnitude of the rotor thrust increases, since all blade elements see higher angles of attack than before because of the increased velocity component perpendicular to the tip path plane (regions close to stall may now actually stall with resultant loss of lift); this further contributes to the desirable result of (1) and (2).

5. The stall and "autorotative" areas of the disc increase while the propeller region decreases because of the general increase in blade element angle of attack; the natural result is an increased RPM and eventually an even greater rotor thrust.

As velocity is dissipated the effects of (4) and (5) diminish, that is, the amount of thrust and RPM increase is limited, since the kinetic energy pot is finite. The skill involved in the maneuver comes in determining the correct altitude to begin the flare and the rate of flare, so as to arrive at the preselected ground point and preselected height as close to zero speed as possible. At this point rotor RPM should be at the high side of the allowable range. Since we now want to generate a thrust almost equal to weight, without appreciable rates of descent, collective pitch must be increased at the expense of RPM. Since there is a minimum RPM allowable for control reasons, only a finite amount of excess energy is available for thrust generation during the final vertical descent. The aircraft essentially free-falls the remaining distance if this limit is reached prematurely. Note that in the flare maneuver the flow state has been reversed from the autorotative state to the normal thrusting state.

The essence of the maneuver is timing. Some low inertia rotors increase their speed very rapidly in the flare prohibiting large fuselage pitch attitudes for fear of overspeed. This restricts the decelerating drag force that can be developed and influences the correct techique. Other high inertia rotors must be flared to high attitudes and/or for longer periods to increase RPM significantly. Fuselage characteristics, especially drag characteristics during the flare, are also important. There are two operational helicopters flying with the same rotor system but with vastly different fuselage shapes. The techniques for successful flare and touchdown, from the same entry conditions, are quite different.

As in dead stick landing with a fixed wing aircraft, there is no go-around from an actual emergency autorotation, that is, there is no second chance to correct mistakes. Most helicopters are very sensitive to nonoptimum touchdown conditions, especially to nonlevel attitudes and sideward drift. Despite concentrated instruction in this area of flight, a recent U.S. Army study revealed that in a $2\frac{1}{2}$ year period one half of all emergency autorotations had "unsuccessful" conclusions, that is, a "saves ratio" of 1 to 1. The type of aircraft and especially the mission profile are undoubtedly important here (some missions are generally conducted at a lower average altitude than others, giving less time to select a suitable landing spot and set up the correct conditions).

Height-Velocity Diagram (Dead Man's Curve)

The purpose of an H-V diagram is to identify for the pilot the portions of the flight envelope from which a safe landing can be made after a sudden engine failure. Figure 6.8 illustrates the shape characteristics of an H-V diagram, which can usually be found in the operator's manual. Too often the manual conveys the following message along with the diagram:

> This diagram is the result of flight tests and indicates the combinations of airspeed and height above the ground which will allow the average pilot to successfully complete a landing after an engine failure.

The connotation here is that if a satisfactory landing is not executed from "safe" areas, the pilot's performance is below average or substandard. Even more important, there is an inference that a really good pilot can probably accomplish a successful autorotation from well within the "avoid" area of the curve. Neither is necessarily true. The problem arises from the method of determining the curve itself.

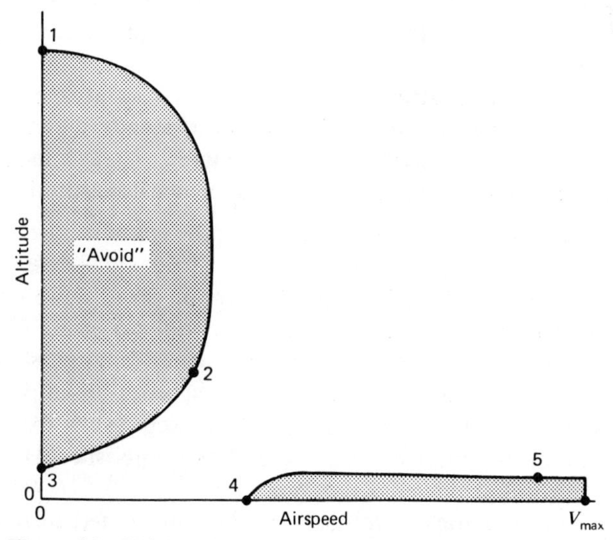

Figure 6.8 Height-velocity diagram (dead man's curve).

The manufacturer's test pilots usually define the curve. They do so by approaching the expected boundary in careful steps. For example, the minimum height for high hover (point 1 in Figure 6.8) is usually found by initiating autorotation at zero airspeed and at heights well above the expected curve value. The test pilot experiments with technique and then slowly lowers the entry height in steps until he feels he has found the point below which the "average" pilot would not be successful. Among faults in this approach are the following:

1. It is in the manufacturer's best interests to have as small an "avoid" area as possible (from a business competition point of view), which may influence the test pilot's opinion in this rather subjective and fuzzy area.

2. The test pilot must assume a certain skill level as being that of the average pilot who will fly a helicopter not yet on the market. No "average" pilots are used in test flying.

3. Some specifications allow only a 1 sec pilot reaction time in demonstrating the H-V curve. Many average pilots, especially in machines lacking adequate visual, aural, and/or kinesthetic cues, will take much longer to diagnose the problem and to react.

4. The curve is demonstrated by simulating an actual failure (by retarding throttle) rather than shutting down the engine. Measurements have shown that there is a significant amount of engine output torque with normal engine rigging at the flight-idle position. This can produce a false sense of security in an individual faced with an actual emergency.

5. The curve is often determined, and demonstrated, from a straight and level steady state condition. Failures from climbs, descents, and turns are often not required.

6. Tests and demonstrations are usually conducted at one gross weight condition (often design mission weight) and at standard sea level conditions. Recent experiments have shown that curves so determined are on the unsafe side compared to higher weight and/or density altitude conditions.

To add to the problem, flight manuals usually contain little information on proper technique. The technique required to demonstrate a successful autorotation from the "knee" of the curve (point 2 in Figure 6.8) is vastly different from that at high speed, low altitude (point 5 of the figure). Most training programs emphasize autorotation practice from a "slot" position about 500 ft above terrain and at a moderate speed well within the "safe" area. In one experiment a group of instructors were asked to demonstrate touchdown autorotations from the "knee" of a published H-V diagram. All failed, reqiuring a powered recovery.

All these considerations have undoubtedly contributed to the high rate of autorotation accidents. Suffice it to say that increased engine and component reliability and twin engine configurations have decreased the rate of incidents in which emergency autorotations are necessary. Most helicopters however have portions of their normal mission profiles within even the published "avoid" areas. This is a known risk, which must be assumed by those responsible for defining procedures and ultimately by the pilot.

6.3 HIGH GROSS WEIGHT AND DENSITY ALTITUDE OPERATION

We saw in Chapters 3 and 4 that the power required for helicopter flight depends on the lift that is needed to support weight. Furthermore, as density diminishes at higher altitudes, more blade pitch is required to sustain the same weight. Moreover, the power *available* from the air-breathing powerplant is decreased as the air is rarified. The net effect, then, is increased power required, as weight and altitude increase, accompanied by a decrease in what is available.

All performance parameters suffer in such conditions. Reduced hover ceilings (IGE and OGE), rates of climb, maximum speeds, as well as a general degradation in flying qualities, are experienced. Induced power required increases with both weight and altitude. The profile and parasite powers decrease with altitude and are unaffected by weight change. Thus the critical flight condition, with respect to weight and altitude increases, is the hover where induced power dominates.

The increase in torque requirements with both weight and altitude increases requires more tail rotor thrust for directional balance. While this also requires more power from the engine, some helicopters will be limited by marginal yaw control rather than by power.

The exact influence of these parameters on performance varies from one configuration to another, and the performance section of the pilot's flight manual should be consulted for these effects. The problems given at the end of this chapter illustrate the seriousness of these limitations.

6.4 EXTERNAL LOADS

Suspending cargo loads by means of cables below the helicopter has fundamental consequences for both the stability and control characteristics experienced by the helicopter/load combination. Depending on the geometric configuration of the sling assembly (one, two, or three attach points, cable lengths, etc.), the basic stability of the helicopter alone, and the aerodynamic and inertial properties of the load, various interesting and often dangerous modes of motion may exist.

The presence of the load introduces as many as six new degrees of freedom, since, within limits, the load may pitch, roll, and yaw about its own axis system *independently* of the corresponding helicopter variables, as well as translate along all three of its axes. Thus the possibilities for undesirable load oscillations are many, requiring considerable attention by designers. Nonetheless, sling load operations are still carried out with extreme caution and require careful pilot attention and slow maneuvering. Cruise speeds of most cargo helicopters are restricted by load oscillations, which may be so severe as to result in emergency load jettison or helicopter/load collision. The load oscillations are often caused by the load's directional instability, which produces periodic yawing, which in turn excites lateral swinging along with drag variations that ultimately results in a longitudinal pendulum motion.

Before examining the origins of such oscillations, and possible methods for their control, let us first consider the trim effects alone. A simple single-point system is shown in Figure 6.9 for a zero wind hover case. The load

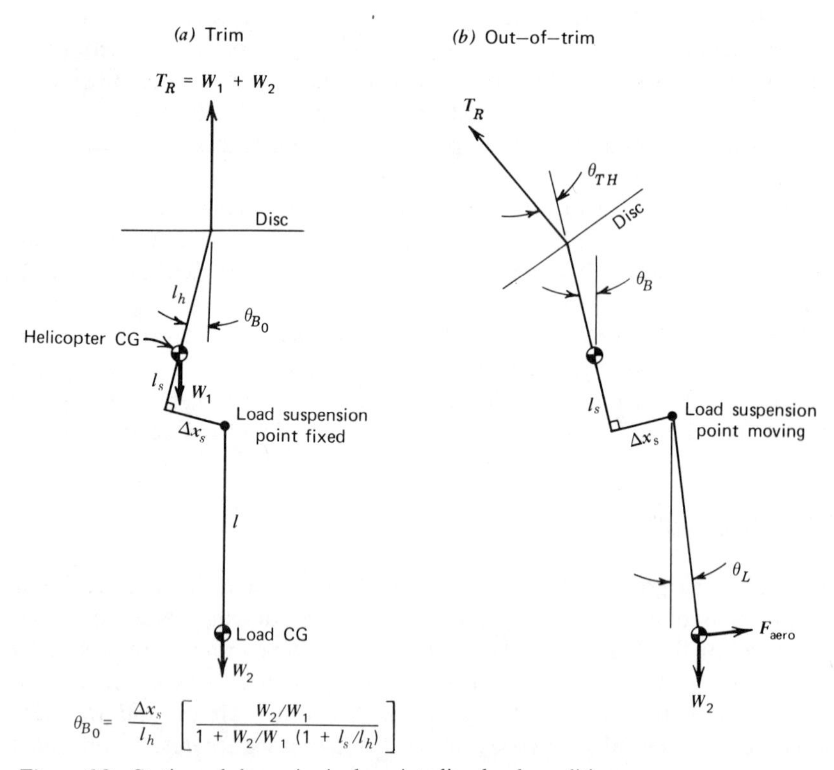

Figure 6.9 Static and dynamic single-point sling load conditions.

suspension point here is below and forward of the helicopter's center of gravity, and the load itself is hanging straight down. Notice that the conditions of equilibrium require that the rotor thrust vector be vertical and equal in magnitude to the sum of the helicopter weight W_1 and the load weight W_2. Furthermore, the helicopter's center of gravity must be behind the thrust axis and the load center of gravity must be ahead. The helicopter thus must assume a more nosedown trim attitude than it had before it picked up the load. A simple moment balance shows that the amount of forward tilt is a function of three variables: (1) the weight ratio, W_2/W_1; (2) the ratio of the forward offset of the load to the distance between hub and the helicopter's center of gravity, $\Delta x_s/l_b$; and (3) the ratio of the vertical offset of the load to the same distance, l_s/l_n. A similar relationship occurs when the load is offset laterally, which will give the trim bank angle in hover.

Naturally, if the load gets too far offset from the helicopter's center of gravity, the limits of control power may soon be reached. In a single-point suspension system, for example, there are definite restrictions on load carrying capability for trim control reasons. Some systems attempt to locate the load suspension point as close to the helicopter's center of gravity as is practical, to minimize this effect.

Let us now consider slight variations from the trim condition of Figure 6.9. If the thrust vector angle θ_{TH} and/or the cable angle θ_l are disturbed from trim, for whatever reason (control input, gust, etc.), a pendulum-like motion of the load about the suspension point can exist independently of the helicopter's movements. Recall also, from basic physics, that the "natural" frequency of oscillation of a pendulum depends on the pendulum length, l, and the weight, W_2. If, in attempting to damp this oscillation with longitudinal cyclic, the pilot gets out of phase with the motion (because of all the lags in the system), resonance can occur, which amplifies the motion. The motion of the load affects the helicopter and vice versa. Unpleasant effects have resulted, especially with short cable lengths where load oscillations are "too fast" for the pilot to follow.

A second problem is the aerodynamics of the load itself. Frequently these loads are very unaerodynamic, having many bluff body features. In hovering oscillations, or in steady motion in forward flight, unsteady vortices are shed from many locations, causing unsteady airloads. The oscillation itself may shed vortices, at the same frequency, which add energy to the system. Most bluff bodies suspended in wind tunnels sit there oscillating at constant amplitude ("limit cycle") because of this interplay of unsteady aerodynamic forces, inertial forces, and suspension system restraints.

Active control of such oscillations has been attempted. Figure 6.10 shows a three-point load suspension system in which each cable is attached to a

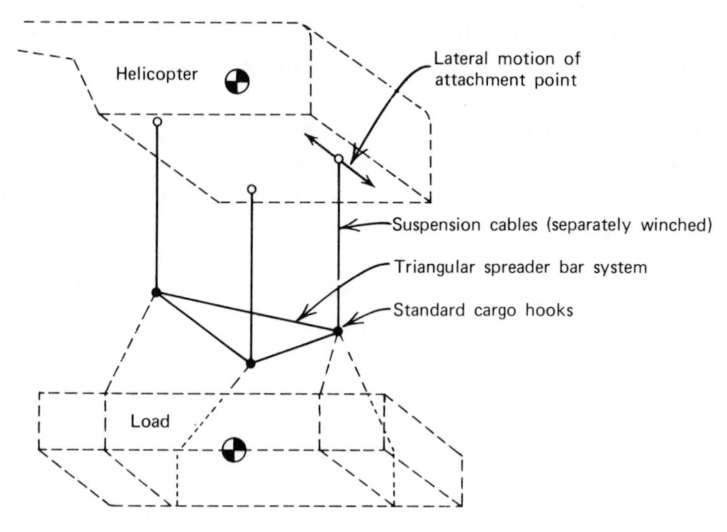

Figure 6.10 Geometry of a three-point suspension system with active oscillation control.

separate fast response winch system; the front attach point can also be moved from side to side. Moving all vertical winches in unison raises or lowers the load; differentially moving the front and rear winches causes the load to pitch, while differentially moving the left and right winches causes the load to roll. The yaw attitude of the load is changed directly by moving the front helicopter-cable attachment point laterally. The movements are made automatically by electromechanical actuators driven by electrical signals proportional to a sensed motion variable. For example, if the load is pitched in response to a sensed pitch rate, damping in pitch is provided, thus diminishing the amplitude of the oscillation. In this sense the system is like a SAS for sling loads.

On some systems the pilot cannot see the hookup point from the cockpit. A signalman, in addition to the hookup man, must direct the pilot to the proper position for either hookup or release. The use of rearview mirrors and radio devices has had limited utility. Some Sikorsky helicopters have a second control station, facing aft toward the load, from which a second pilot can fly the aircraft for precision hover tasks and load placement. The versatility of some sling load operations has permitted foresting of logs from otherwise inaccessible locations (e.g., steep slopes), the raising of electrical towers (which weigh more than the allowable payload of the lifting helicopter) by tilting them up from a horizontal position, and towing objects through bodies of water. Sling loading people in rescue operations has been a legendary role for the helicopter. Sling load operations in "nap-of-the-earth" missions presents continuing challenges.

6.5 INSTRUMENT FLIGHT

Proper control of a helicopter solely through the aircraft's instruments requires much more pilot proficiency and skill than it does under visual flight rules (VFR) conditions. The difficulty is far greater in helicopters than in fixed wing aircraft. The basic problem is lack of inherent stability. Though many other factors contribute to the problem—crew requirements, displays, cockpit environment, aircraft subsystem performance and reliability—the requirements of acceptable stability and control predominate.

The rotor itself is statically unstable with respect to angle of attack, as we saw in Chapter 5, and fixed external surfaces must be provided to counteract this instability. The effectiveness of these control surfaces is degraded by the turbulent wake emanating from the rotor hub and usually bluff fuselage afterbodies, as well as by strong destabilizing rotor induced sidewash and downwash. The resulting static and dynamic instabilities of the airframe, together with the strong aerodynamic and inertial cross-coupling previously discussed, make the pilot workload unbearably high, especially when the many visual cues available in VFR conditions are removed and the pilot must interpret displayed information of degraded content and quality.

It has been argued that since a given helicopter can satisfactorily perform its entire mission visually, we need only transpose the visual information to appropriate displays within the aircraft to be able to perform the same task under zero visibility conditions. This concept lacks nothing in logic, but putting it into practice has proved to be very difficult, expensive, and, in the limit, impossible. The problem is threefold: (1) identification of the exact signals and their quality, which a pilot extracts from the visual scene and acts upon, (2) same-quality detection and measurement of these signals by means other than the human eye and other senses, and (3) the presentation of these signals in such a form that the pilot can recognize and act upon them at least as accurately as before.

Consider a simple example of a helicopter performing a straight-in descent to a landing zone at constant airspeed. For whatever reasons, the pilot is satisfied that his current attitude, velocity, rate of descent, and so on, will take him to a preselected position in space, from which a deceleration and vertical touchdown can be made. An unexpected crosswind change comes into play. We can predict analytically the resulting time history of heading, drift rate, and lateral offset that would result if the pilot took no

Figure 6.11 Helicopter instrument panel. (Courtesy Sikorsky Aircraft Company.)

action. We observe, however, that at some point the pilot did take action. What determined this point? What determined the sense and magnitude of his control inputs? Did he sense a side acceleration, a side velocity, a side displacement, or all three? What are the threshold values of these variables that must be exceeded before he will respond? Did he sense the yaw acceleration into wind, or was it the yaw rate or heading change that he observed? These are tough questions that even experiment cannot easily answer. Moreover, the answers appear to be a function of the task itself.

Suppose that we find quantitatively the proper blend of sensed motion variables that the pilot uses. How can we measure these quantities in flight so as to blend them together in the same proportions and display them to the pilot? We could sense side acceleration with a linear accelerometer mounted sideways somewhere near the pilot's station. A suitable transducer converts this measurement to an electrical signal. How about sideward velocity? Remember that there are two kinds of velocity—velocity relative to the air and that relative to the ground. Since the pilot cannot "see" the air, he would act, we suspect, on groundspeed information. But it was a change in *airspeed* (which in this example is the sideward component) that caused the sideforce, which in turn caused the side acceleration. Sideward airspeed measurements are not easy (see Section 2.3) and sideward groundspeed is at least as difficult (requiring the integration of the side acceleration signal, that is, one channel of an inertial navigation system). Lateral displacement can only be measured by reference to guidance provided by fixed ground installations (such as an ILS localizer) or by a second integration of the acceleration signal. Errors tend to accumulate when integrating signals. For example, a small error in rate measurement means an ever-increasing error in displacement determination.

Modern guidance systems on fixed wing aircraft have demonstrated, albeit at great cost, extreme levels of accuracy in motion detection. Suppose that we can afford all the sophistication that money can buy and can equip our helicopter with the required hardware without performance degradation. How can we then bridge the information gap and transmit the information to the pilot? What about displays?

Figure 6.11 illustrates a fairly standard helicopter instrument panel. The flight parameters displayed are: pitch attitude and bank angle, forward airspeed, altitude, heading and relative bearing of navigation facility, localizer and glideslope angular error, rate of climb/descent, turn rate and side acceleration, clock, and marker beacon indicators. Depending on the basic stability of the particular helicopter, this information, displayed on off-the-shelf instruments, may be sufficient to complete ILS approaches at constant speed to category 1 minimums (see Table 6.1). Some aircraft with equivalent displays cannot safely accomplish this on a routine basis when their SAS is inoperative.

Table 6.1 ICAO Low-Visibility-Landing ILS Categories

Category	Runway Visual Range (RVR)[a] (ft)	Decision Height[b] (ft)
I	2400	200
II-A	1600	150
II-B	1200	100
III-A	700	—
III-B	150	—
III-C	0	—

[a] Minimum visibility, determined by photocell and light source measuring of transmissivity up glidescope.

[b] Height above runway at which pilot must have runway in sight in order to legally proceed.

One of the basic deficiencies of the raw ILS information is that only actual *errors* in position are presented, that is, for the pilot to be aware that things are not right, a physical off-localizer or off-glideslope error must first develop. In the visual world the pilot can sense, to some degree of accuracy, that things will not be right *in the future*; that is, he can *lead* the situation by sensing accelerations and/or rates that will eventually result in a position error if he does not correct the situation. No such lead information is available in a standard instrument layout, hence the difficulty in keeping ahead of the situation increases dramatically. Controlled experiments have shown that the pilot worklead increases sharply with loss of such lead information.

One widely accepted solution is the use of a flight director system. Typically this appears to the pilot as vertical and horizontal command bars superimposed on the attitude indicator. The needles are driven with electrical analogs of *both* position error and position rate error. The needles are centered only when both position and rate errors are zero. For example, if the helicopter is on the localizer but has a velocity vector not aligned with the localizer, an error soon develops. The vertical needle is out to one side telling the pilot to bank in that direction to anticipate the situation. The pilot flies toward the needles and cross-checks the raw position information on the normal ILS instrument. He may find that he is not on glideslope or on localizer at a particular time even though the flight director needles are centered. This simply means that he is acting correctly, and if he continues to do so the aircraft will close on the desired track in the programmed manner, without overshoot.

Other instrumentation such as a horizontal situation indicator (HSI), collective command indicator, and radar altimeter have met with varying degrees of success. The critical requirements of Cat 3, in normal turbulence environments, and the deceleration to hover and subsequent vertical touchdown have only been accomplished in research projects using heavy stability augmentation and autopilot coupling. Stability is the key. Even the flight director is akin to stability augmentation since, if the pilot follows the commands, he is putting in inputs proportional to whatever drives the needles—that is, the pilot takes the place of the SAS servoactuator and completes the loop from sensed quantity to control input.

Government has placed strict controls on IFR certification of helicopters and helicopter IFR operations. Though always subject to change, the regulations currently in force essentially dictate a complete all-axis SAS system for even normal instrument procedures and, in some cases, the use of a two-man crew. Good SAS systems, even assuming that a suitable one can be designed for a given helicopter, are necessarily expensive. Additionally, there are some fundamental limitations to SAS performance on helicopters, which have two main sources: (1) limited control power—the pilot and the SAS can only command forces and moments up to the physical limits imposed by full control deflection, and (2) low frequency rotor structural modes may be excited by the SAS feedbacks, causing catastrophic aeroelastic instabilities.

The latter effect is very real and is a fundamental consequence of the rotary wing concept. It is an axiom of SAS design that "fixing" a problem in one area only causes it to reappear somewhere else. The trick is to get the problem to reappear at a flight condition outside the normal envelope so that it is not encountered again.

The design of helicopters for complete IFR flight must begin with stability, either aerodynamically inherent or artificially augmented. It remains one of the greatest design challenges in the helicopter world. Only when it can operate freely in the absence of adequate external visibility will the helicopter's full potential and performance versatility be realized.

The problem of icing must also be faced when considering helicopters flying in the clouds above the freezing altitude. Both fixed and rotary wing aircraft suffer aerodynamic penalties when the shape of their airfoil sections (wings or rotors) is altered by ice accumulation. In general a loss of lift and an increase in drag occur. Many fixed-wing aircraft employ heating elements in critical areas as well as mechanical deicing boots on leading edges. Engine inlets are also critical in that they reduce airflow to the engine when iced, and may shed chunks of ice into the compressor.

Helicoptors are particularly vulnerable to icing problems because the rotor blades, or tail rotor blades, may shed ice asymmetrically. The resulting aerodynamic and mass unbalance may cause severe vibration problems, which can quickly lead to structural failure. Aside from vibration, the increased drag of the blade elements increases the required torque. The lift loss necessitates increased blade pitch to maintain lift equal to weight, thus increasing drag and torque even more. Soon the aircraft becomes power limited and must lose energy—either speed, altitude, rotor speed, or a combination of these.

The loss of aerodynamic efficiency is especially prevalent in autorotation. The complete loss of power requires much higher rates of descent to maintain autorotational RPM with iced blades. Very few helicopters can stand more than a hint of iced blades before their autorotational performance is seriously degraded. Existing helicopters must avoid icing conditions until such time as operational blade anti-ce systems are incorporated. Reference 49 discusses this problem in more detail.

6.6 WINDS, WIND SHEARS, AND TURBULENCE

Much of our discussion has implied calm air conditions. Aerodynamically, the helicopter flies relative to the airmass in which it finds itself and has no concern with how the airmass is moving relative to the earth. Thus hovering over a point on the ground in the presence of a steady 30 knot headwind is aerodynamically equivalent to flying forward in calm air at the same speed. The rotor does not know the difference. When considering flight relative to the ground, however, as in navigation problems and in descents along an ILS glideslope, wind and wind changes are important. We now examine three kinds of airmass motion and their effect on flight from the pilot's viewpoint: steady horizontal winds, horizontal wind shears, and turbulence.

Steady Horizontal Winds

In navigating from point *A* to point *B* over the surface of the earth at constant airspeed it is the magnitude of the steady wind and its direction relative to the line *A*-*B* that determine the aircraft's heading and groundspeed. The problem is one of trigonometry; we must solve the vector triangle involving windspeed and direction, airspeed and heading, groundspeed and track. Figure 6.12 illustrates the problem. Most pilots solve it by a graphical technique, using, for example, their E6B computer. The triangle is geometrically laid out with the known quantities (e.g., windspeed and direction form one vector, the desired track determines the orientation of the second side, and the desired airspeed forms the magnitude of the third).

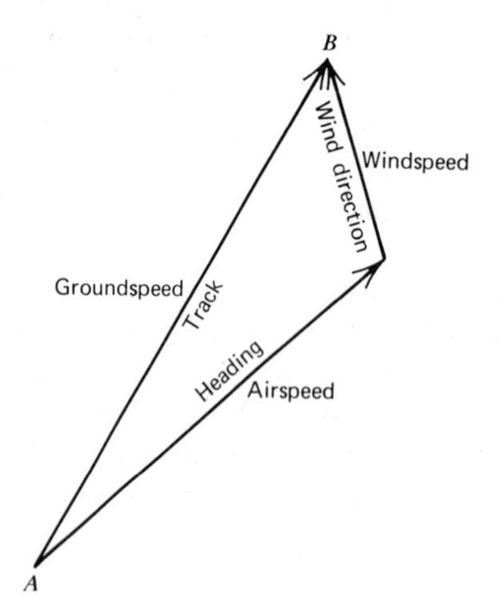

Figure 6.12 Navigation vesctor relationship.

The ends of the windspeed vector determine two points of the triangle; the intersection of an arc, whose radius represents the airspeed magnitude, with the straight line defining the desired track is the third point. Thus aircraft heading, required to maintain track and groundspeed along that track, are determined.

Note that in this case there is no sideslip on the aircraft— it is pointed directly into the *relative* wind. When landing in a crosswind, a similar situation exists in a crabbing approach; that is, the aircraft is pointed into the relative wind, but is tracking down the runway. For the aircraft be lined up with the runway, a sideslip angle must exist (for which a bank angle, into wind, must be established to prevent drift). The relationships involved in this technique are shown in Figure 6.13.

The effects of steady winds on *vertical* navigation are not so easily appreciated. Consider the vector relationships in a steady state descent in the presence of a steady headwind (Figure 6.14). Here the aircraft is physically moving down a line defined by its inertial velocity vector ($\mathbf{V}_E$), oriented from the horizontal by the inertial flight path angle γ. Relative to the airmass, however, the aircraft has an airspeed vector ($\mathbf{U}$) oriented at an aerodynamic flight path angle $\boldsymbol{\Gamma}$. The wind vector, $\mathbf{u}_w$, completes the triangle.

aircraft relative to earth

= aircraft relative to airmass + airmass relative to earth

$$\mathbf{V}_E = \mathbf{U} + \mathbf{u}_w$$

Suppose that an aircraft flies at a preselected airspeed and power setting, which results in a certain inertial flight path angle in calm air. At the same airspeed and power setting, as Figure 6.14 shows, a steady headwind present steepens the steady state inertial flight path angle and a tailwind makes it more shallow. It is also clear that a given headwind influences inertial flight path only in relation to the size of the airspeed vector. In other words, a 30 knot headwind has less effect at 150 KIAS than at 60 KIAS, which seems intuitively obvious. The vector triangle of Figure 6.14 is solved in Figure 6.15 for a variety of wind conditions and approach speeds and shows the quantitative effect on inertial flight path.

The exact expression relating inertial and aerodynamic flight path angle is

$$\boxed{\tan \gamma = \frac{\sin \Gamma}{\cos \Gamma + (u_w/U)}}$$

(Here u_w is positive for a tailwind and negative for a headwind.)

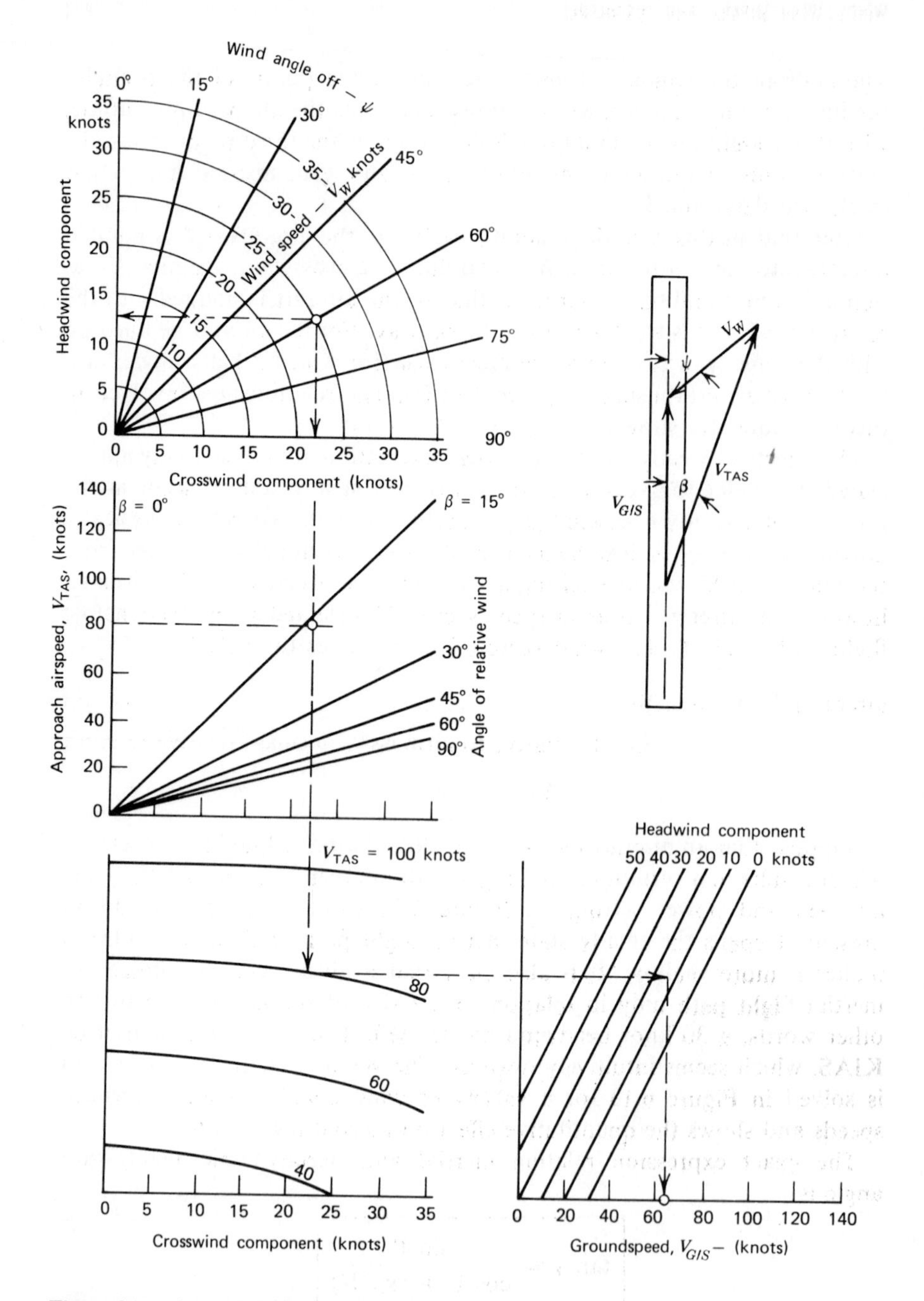

Figure 6.13 Crosswind landing geometry.

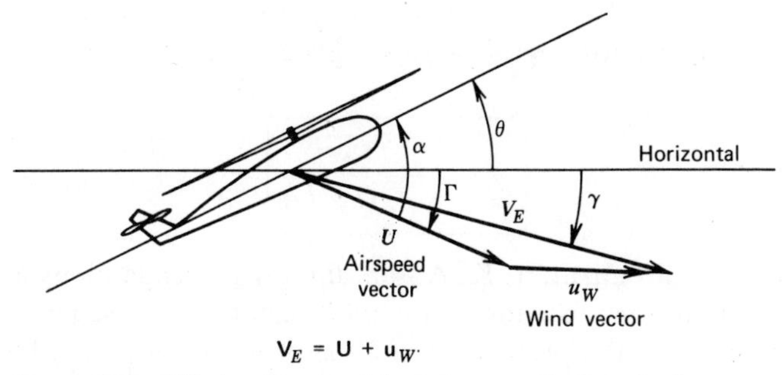

Figure 6.14 Effects of horizontal winds on vertical navigation.

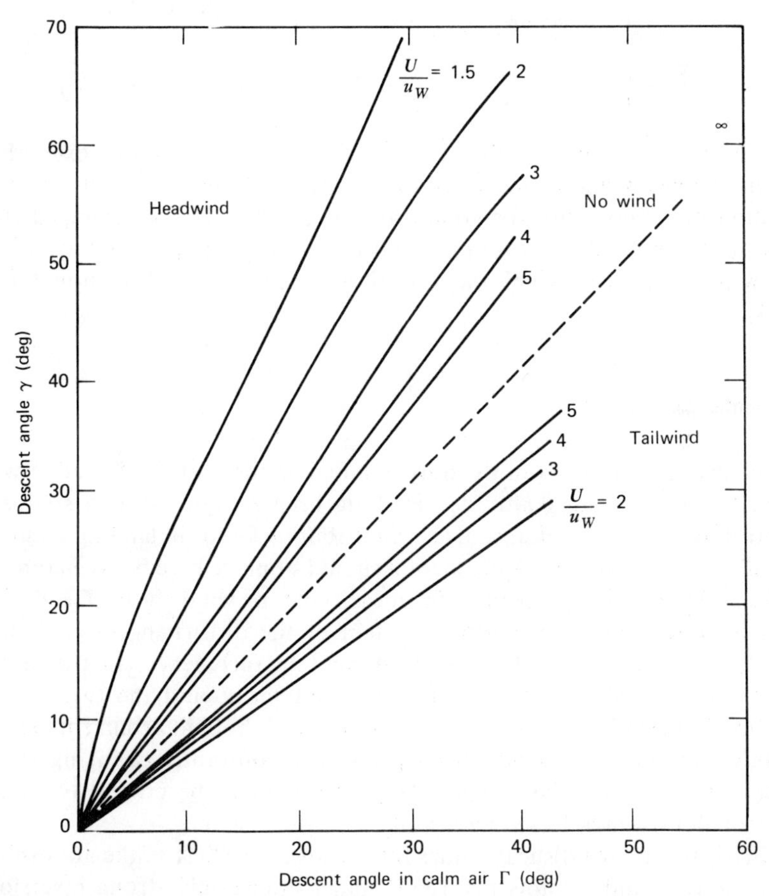

Figure 6.15 Effect of headwinds and tailwinds on descent angle (shear close to ground). Airspeed = U; windspeed = u_w.

For small flight path angles (<15°) a good approximation to this relationship is

$$\gamma = \frac{\Gamma}{1 + (u_w/U)}$$

Example. In calm air at 80 KTAS an aircraft descends along a 3° flight path at a certain power setting. If the pilot maintains the same power setting and airspeed in the presence of a 20 knot headwind, what flight path results? What if it were a tailwind?

$$\gamma_1 = \frac{3}{1 - (20/80)} = \frac{3}{0.75} = 4° \qquad \text{(steeper by 1°)}$$

$$\gamma_2 = \frac{3}{1 + (20/80)} = \frac{3}{1.25} = 2.4° \qquad \text{(shallower by 0.6°)}$$

The same reasoning applies to climbs and descents. In our example, a 3° climb angle would be increased to 4° by the headwind. Note also that the relationships above are for equilibrium flight. If the wind changed from zero to 20 knots, the *end result* would be a 4° flight path— but we do not know the manner in which the aircraft attained that result or how long it took.

Horizontal Wind Shears

Wind shear, a variation in the horizontal component of the "steady" wind velocity with changing altitude, has long been recognized as a source of control problems for pilots and as a contributing factor in landing accidents for all classes of aircraft. A distinction should be made here between random gusts and a velocity gradient in the mean wind, or wind shear. The distinction is largely one of frequency content of the disturbance—wind shear effects occur less often than do most random turbulence. In the atmosphere, turbulence usually accompanies wind shear, and the two may be confused. Turbulence may cause the aircraft to bobble around its steady state condition while wind shears produce a constantly changing steady state condition. The latter effect (Figure 6.16) can be critical to precise control along a preselected glidepath.

Characteristic wind shear values for the lowest 1000 ft of the atmosphere lie between 3 and 5 knots per 100 ft under moderately strong inversions, with extreme values reaching 10 knots per 100 ft. One author claims that shears up to 30 knots per 100 ft have been experienced in flight.

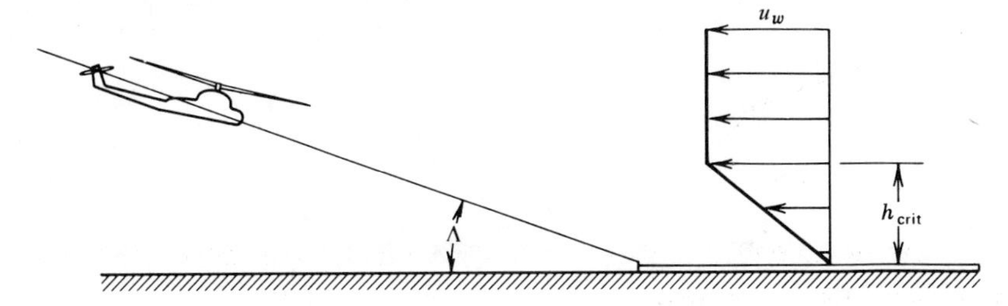

Figure 6.16 Horizontal wind shears.

A direct and immediate result of a change in wind velocity are changes in both the aerodynamic forces and moments on the aircraft, which may cause it to deviate from the desired path. Consider the case of the decreasing headwind shear, which is often encountered. Returning to Figure 6.14, we see that the first effect of shrinking the wind vector is twofold:

1. A decrease in airspeed magnitude.
2. An increase in rotor angle of attack.

In the special case of level flight only airspeed is initially affected. In general, the effect of (1) is to decrease lift and drag. The effect of (2) is the opposite. Additionally, an increase in angle of attack causes a nosedown pitching moment for a statically stable aircraft, and a noseup moment for aircraft with an unstable angle of attack characteristic (such as most helicopters at low speed).

No general result can be stated, since it depends on the aerodynamic characteristics of the aircraft, the initial flight conditions, and the magnitude of the shear. Note that if the pilot does nothing, the decreased headwind *ultimately* results in a shallower flight path. However, a descent below the intended glide path may well occur before that, especially in the case of a low initial flight path angle where the effects of (1) above predominate (i.e., the lift loss). This causes the aircraft to descend below the glidepath *initially*. Figure 6.17 illustrates what often happens. Note that the helicopter's tendency to land short or long depends on the altitude at which the shear occurred, the magnitude of the shear, the aerodynamics of the aircraft, and the pilot's actions.

What should the pilot do? This basic concern is to keep the aircraft positioned on the glidepath and his *airspeed* fixed at the desired value. This is important on a visual approach and essential on an ILS approach, when glideslope information is utilized. How can a pilot control these two variables? The technique varies considerably among fixed wing pilots depend-

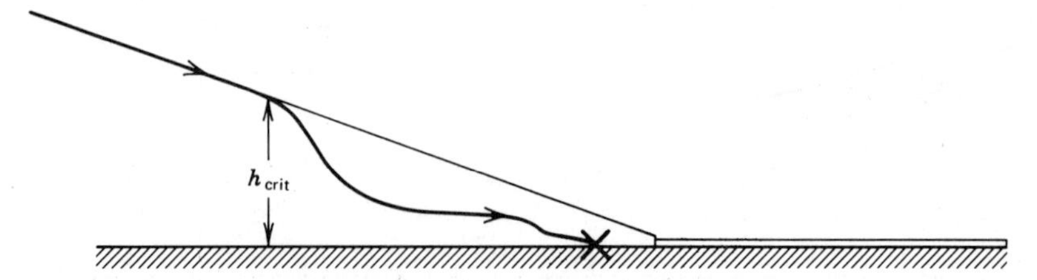

Figure 6.17 Effects of decreasing headwind shear on approach.

ing on aircraft type and pilot training. Some pilots hold that the throttle controls flight path and pitch attitude controls airspeed. Others maintain the opposite, and still others consider the correct technique to be a mixture of both, depending on the magnitude of the error that has occurred in each of the variables. Helicopter pilots, too, use a variety of techniques. At very low speed altitude (hence position on the glideslope) is most directly controlled with collective and airspeed with longitudinal cyclic stick. At high speed cyclic stick alone is very effective in controlling height. At intermediate speed, such as that used in a normal approach, the correct technique is still open to question, depending on the magnitude of the error.

For example, small deviations from the glidepath are normally corrected with stick only, since the resulting speed change is also small. For large height errors collective is used to control height, and any resulting changes in attitude and/or speed are compensated for with cyclic stick. Note also that the airspeed on the approach is important with respect to the power required. If the aircraft is operating on the "front side" of the power required curve (above the speed for minimum power), a sudden decrease in airspeed produces excess power available and the aircraft tends to rise in a decreasing headwind shear. Conversely, operating on the backside leads to an initial descent, in the same shear condition.

Turbulence

The motion of an aircraft in turbulence is akin to that of a ship on a rough sea or an automobile on a rough road. It is subjected to buffeting by random external forces, so that the attitude angles and trajectory vary randomly with time. The time scale and intensity of these responses are governed by the frequency content and intensity of the turbulence, as well as by the aircrafts aerodynamic and inertial characteristics at a particular flight condition. They produce degraded man/machine performance, cause fatigue in both pilot and structure, endanger the aircraft's structural integrity, make the ride uncomfortable, perhaps even unacceptable, for passengers and cargo, and impair the precise control of flight path needed for accurate approaches and safe landing.

Meteorologists and flight dynamicists have measured atmospheric turbulence under many conditions and have reduced it to a mathematical description of velocity vector components. The total "velocity field" of the atmosphere varies in both space and time. It has simultaneous changes in all directions, and has no preferred direction except at locations close to the ground (where the magnitude of the vertical component diminishes with respect to the two horizontal vectors) and in the wake of buildings, mountains, or other aircraft.

These changes cause corresponding changes in forces and moments felt by the aircraft. The same turbulence spectra produce different forces and moments on different aircraft and at different speeds on the same aircraft. Usually, the change is greatest at high dynamic pressure, that is, high speed and low altitude. Since the outboard portions of a helicopter rotor are always at high dynamic pressure, the variation with airspeed is less distinct.

The forces and moments produce (1) structural forces and moments and (2) vehicle motions. Again, the nature and extent of these effects vary with the aircraft, even if the external forces and moments are identical. A 2000 ft-lb pitching moment has a much smaller effect on the pitch rate of a Boeing CH-47 than on a Hughes 500, since the former has a much larger rotational inertia about its pitching axis.

The pilot, and/or SAS system, plays the most important role in determining the aircraft's "closed loop" response to turbulence. Both wait until a motion is observable before attempting to prevent it. No matter how quickly the pilot detects the motion and applies a control input, the vehicle itself cannot respond instantaneously. Hence there is always a lag between the open loop effects of turbulence and the closed-loop response in trying to minimize it. Even if the pilot (or SAS) had perfect knowledge of what was coming (a virtual impossibility), he *still* would not be able to insert control motions that produce forces and moments equal and opposite to those produced by turbulence.

The difficulty is that the pilot does not have *independent* control of the six possible degrees of freedom. For example, suppose that a pilot is forewarned, while hovering in calm air, of a sudden side gust, generating an 80 lb sideforce. What would he do about it? If he applies side cyclic input, the aircraft may be made to bank into wind just enough to prevent sideward drift. However, the aircraft must roll to balance the sideforces, since there is independent means for doing so. Thus there is no such thing as absolute turbulence *suppression* in helicopters (or any conventional aircraft)—only turbulence response *modification*.

Thus regardless of his skill the pilot's ability to decrease airframe structural stresses is limited. Severe turbulence must be avoided; when turbulence is encountered, a flight condition that tends to minimize the effects should be attained. In this respect care must be exercised in interpreting pilot reports of turbulence intensity. A condition reported as "moderate" by the captain of a Boeing 747 may be "disastrous" to a Bell 47. Turbulence severity is in the eye of the beholder, and the aircraft is an effective filter between cause and effect.

6.7 RETREATING BLADE STALL

The aerodynamic causes of stall near the tips of retreating blades at high forward speed were discussed in Section 4.3. This type of stall was shown to be a natural consequence of the blade flapping mechanism, and a fundamental limitation to high speed for conventional helicopters. The factors that cause the phenomena to begin to occur at lower speeds are those that require high blade pitch, that is, low RPM, high gross weight, high density altitude, and positive *G* maneuvers. Figure 6.18 shows how these factors affect the airspeed for blade stall on one helicopter.

From the pilot's viewpoint, retreating blade stall is usually evidenced first by roughness and erratic forces as the retreating blade stall area begins to grow to critical proportions and high 1P vibration. As separation continues to move inward on the retreating blade, roughness increases. A partial loss in control effectiveness follows, accompanied by a definite pitch-up tendency (the sudden lift loss around the 270° position causes increased downflapping displacements 90° later). Since, because of dynamic stall, the area of the disc experiencing stall may be displaced further back than the 270° position, a right rolling tendency may also be present. Once the pitch rate has developed, there is an additional right rolling moment, which is due to gyroscopic precession (Section 5.4). Aerodynamic cross-coupling may easily mask these effects, however, and helicopters have exhibited both right and left rolling moments (though not severe) as well as zero observable rolling moment.

Any technique that decreases the blade angle of attack is a good one. The pitch-up motion is fortunate: the helicopter thereby decelerates to prestall values. The natural tendency to resist the pitch-up with forward cyclic can be disastrous, because this increases blade pitch at the 270° position. As deceleration takes place, a reduction in collective setting, an increase in rotor RPM and a decrease in *G*'s will all aid in the recovery.

Compound helicopters, by way of lift sharing between rotor and wings, can operate at somewhat reduced collective setting, thus postponing retreating blade stall until higher airspeeds. Note, however, that in the absence

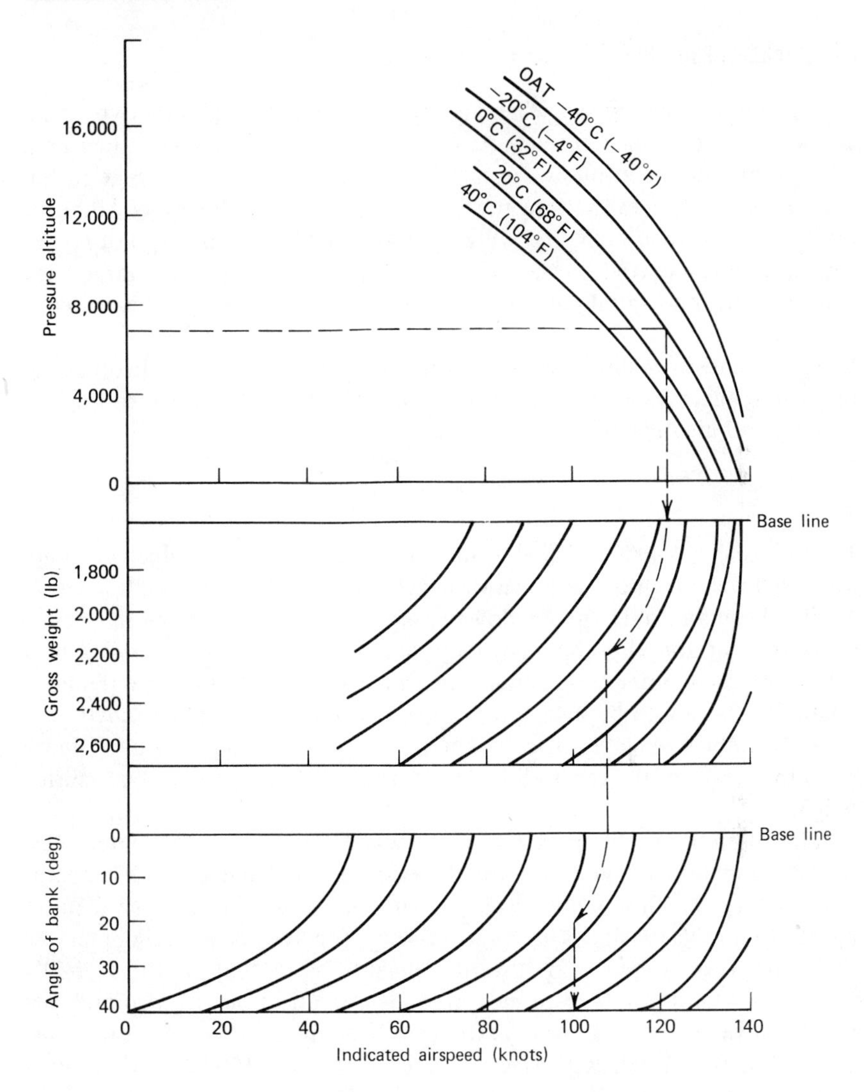

Figure 6.18 Maximum airspeed for blade stall. (U.S. Army data.)

of an auxiliary thrusting device the rotor must still provide the forward thrust component and the means of aircraft control. A number of schemes for completely stowing away the rotor for high speed and redeploying it during transition back to low speed are being investigated. The mechanical and dynamic problems in doing so are obvious, and no operational vehicle yet employs this method.

6.8 WAKE TURBULENCE

The turbulence that occurs when an aircraft passes through otherwise calm air has received much recent attention, since it has been identified as a contributing factor in many aircraft accidents. We include in wake turbulence all disturbances that are caused by bluff body fuselages, jet exhausts, lifting surface downwash, and wing tip vortices. The helicopter pilot is concerned about operating in the wake of other aircraft, especially large fixed wing aircraft, and should also be concerned about the wake of his own aircraft.

In Section 3.2 we discussed the downwash from a hovering helicopter out of ground effect and found the downwash velocity to be related to the disc loading and air density:

$$v_f = \sqrt{\frac{2\text{DL}}{\rho}}$$

For example, a 46,000 lb CH-47C has a disc leading of 8.13, which at standard sea level produces a downwash velocity of 82.7 fps (48.9K), OGE. While the magnitude of the downwash component decreases in ground effect the horizontal component increases, as anyone who has stood near a hovering helicopter can testify. Experiments, set up to measure the horizontal winds caused by helicopters, have discovered that it is a function of many variables such as disc loading, density, hovering height, distance from the center of the rotor, direction from the rotor center, and measuring height.

It has been found that peak horizontal winds occur at approximately 30% of the rotor radius beyond the tip, decaying beyond that point. This is the place where the flow field "necks down" the most, causing the Venturi effect. Figure 6.19 shows averaged results for two large helicopters of different gross weight and hovering height. Note that in the CH-54A example 80 knot winds were measured. The implications to men and materials on the ground, as well as to other helicopters hovering nearby, are clear. Note that for the CH-47A a 35 knot wind exists 120 ft away. Another helicopter hovering here, at the measuring height, might well experience loss of control depending on his heading relative to the wind direction.

The real threat is from large fixed wing aircraft wing tip vortices. Jet aircraft can also generate considerable jet blast with at high power settings on the ground, but accidents attributable to tip vortices are more numerous. The basic structure of the wake turbulence caused by tip vortices is shown in Figure 6.20. Two large circular flows rotating counterclockwise from the right tip and clockwise from the left (as seen from behind the aircraft) lead to serious vertical velocity fluctuations across the wake. The tangential

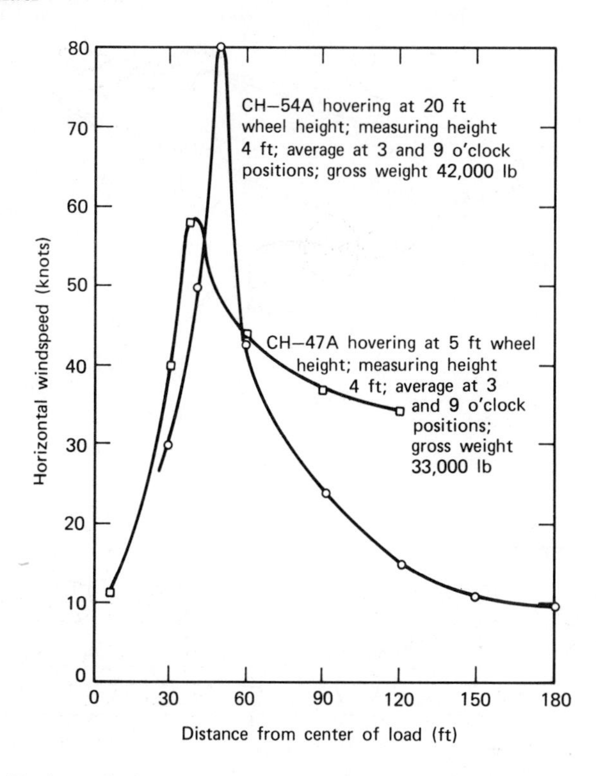

Figure 6.19 Horizontal windspeeds for two hovering helicopters.

circular velocity increases from zero far away from the center of the vortex to a maximum at some point at the edge of the "core" of the vortex. In perfect fluid theory the tangential velocity is inversely proportional to the distance measured from the center. This model predicts infinite velocity right at the center, which is of course not possible in any real fluid. The magnitude of the tangential velocity and the diameter of the main vortex have been found to depend primarily on span loading, that is, the lift's spanwise distribution. Aircraft with high span loadings tend to exhibit the most severe vortices.

An aircraft following a large fixed wing aircraft would be concerned with two key questions: where do the vortices go and how long do they last? Out of ground effect, tip vortices descend below the aircraft along with the general downwash field that must accompany the production of lift. It has been found that they stop descending about 900 ft below the generating aircraft. In the presence of the ground, however, as in the landing sequence, the situation is quite different. Figure 6.20 illustrates that with the vortices

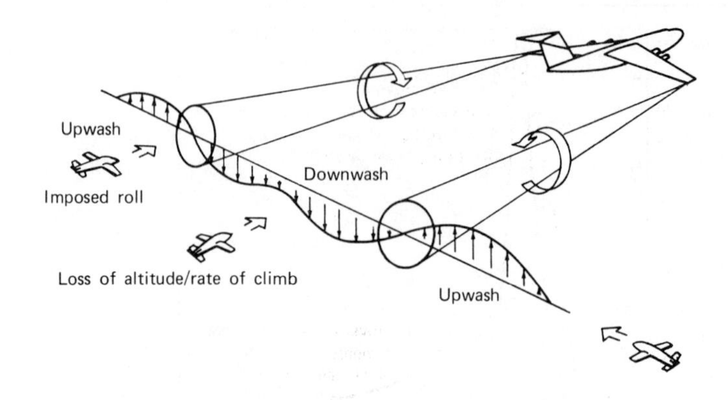

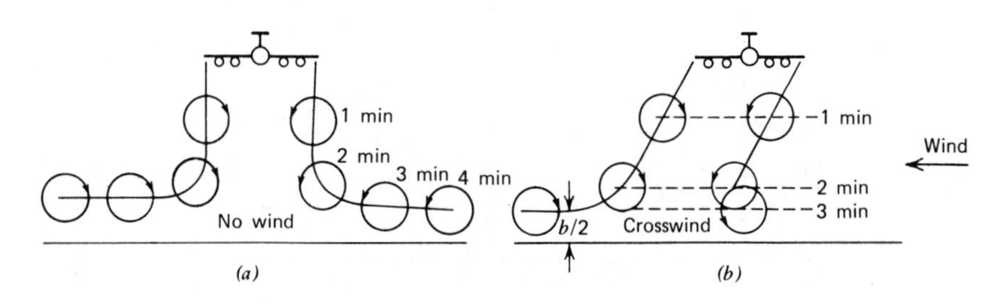

Figure 6.20 Basic structure of tip vortex system. (From reference 87.)

in ground effect a separation occurs, causing the vortices to change their vertical direction to a horizontal one at about 4 to 5 knots. A similar effect can be seen by blowing a smoke ring toward a wall. As it approaches the wall, its velocity decreases and the ring diameter increases.

This lateral movement may cause one vortex to drift on to a parallel runway at about the time when the pilot intends to land. More important, a crosswind component of 4 to 5 knots tends to keep one of the vortices on the same runway. Consider an aircraft landing behind the one shown in Figure 6.2*b*. If the pilot is so unfortunate as to fly precisely into the center of the right vortex, an extreme left rolling moment will be experienced. Often, the magnitude of the induced rolling moment exceeds the aircraft's roll control power, and control is lost. Worse yet, consider the same aircraft landing slightly to the left of the vortex core. The right wing experiences the downdraft, causing the aircraft to bank right, hence to move toward the core center. At about this time the pilot has applied full left roll control, trying to arrest the right bank. Now *both* the roll control and the vortex are in the roll left sense. For this reason, not a few aircraft have hit the ground in an inverted position.

A full discussion of vortices is beyond the scope of this book. Much work has been done and much insight gained. There have been attempts to dissipate vortex strength by wing tip modifications, water injection, and so on. So far no practical solution has been found other than operational procedures, which put limits on the minimum spacing between aircraft in time and space. A landing aircraft should attempt to stay above the aircraft in front of it, and land beyond its touchdown point. Similarly, it should attempt to take off at a point prior to the place where the leading aircraft took off, and to climb above its flight path.

The time required for vortex dissipation is also a function of many variables, not the least of which is the meteorology of the atmosphere itself, especially the general turbulence level. The higher the level of turbulence, the sooner a wing tip vortex breaks up.

Some wake parameters for selected aircraft are listed in Table 6.2. The critical situations are at low speed, heavy weight, clean configuration (in the landing configuration secondary vortices emanate from flap tips, decreasing somewhat the severity of the wing tip vortices). A helicopter in forward flight has a similar vortex structure far behind. Figure 6.21 gives dramatic proof of the tendency for the shed vortex sheet to roll up into two discrete vortices. To date, helicopter weight and span loading parameters have

Table 6.2 Approximate Parameters and Wake Values for Selected Aircraft

Aircraft	Maximum Gross Weight (lb)	Span (ft)	Span Loading (lb/ft)	Airspeed (knots)	Vortex Separation (ft)	Vortex Sink Rate (fpm)	Vortex Core Radius (ft)	Maximum Tangential Velocity (knots)
Convair C-131	46,000	92	500	140	72	162	7	16.8
Boeing 727	169,000	108	1560	161	86	372	9	38.2
Boeing 707	328,000	145	2260	178	115	366	12	37.2
Boeing 747	710,000	196	3620	178	155	432	16	43.8
C-5	750,000	222	3380	172	175	345	18	36.4
Concorde SST	385,000	84	4580	200	67	1120	7	120.0
Boeing SST	750,000	143	5250	200	112	760	11	79.3

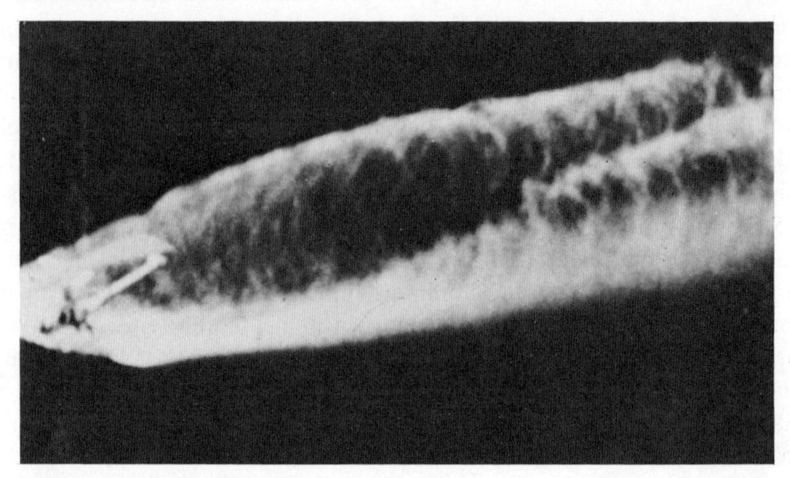

Figure 6.21 Helicopter trailing vortex formation.

not reached the levels of large fixed wing transports; hence the problem is not so severe, but caution nevertheless is in order.

PROBLEMS

6.1 For the helicopter in Figure 6.5 determine the glide distance in a steady state autorotation from 500 ft AGL for the following speeds: (*a*) 35 KTAS, (*b*) speed for minimum rate of descent, (*c*) speed for maximum glide, and (*d*) 115 KTAS.

6.2 For the instrument shown in Figure 5.7 calculate the component of side velocity when flying at 60 KIAS, and the ball one full width out to the left (assume IAS = TAS).

6.3 A helicopter is making a crabbing approach at 80 KIAS to runway 29. The wind is 360° at 25 knots. For standard sea level conditions determine: (*a*) the headwind component, (*b*) the crosswind component, (*c*) the aircraft's groundspeed, and (*d*) the sideslip angle that would occur if the pilot suddenly yawed the aircraft to align with the runway.

6.4 The helicopter in Problem 6.3 is maintaining a 3° glideslope. If the wind should suddenly cease and the pilot made no power or attitude corrections, what flight path angle would the helicopter *eventually* attain? (Ignore the transient dynamics.)

6.5 The helicopter in Figure 6.18 is in level flight at 100 KIAS. The pressure altitude is 8000 ft, and the temperature is standard. For a gross weight of 2200 lb, determine the maximum G's the helicopter can pull in a level turn without experiencing retreating blade stall.

6.6 Using the performance charts of the Appendix, for a 2400 lb aircraft on a standard day determine: (*a*) the speed for the maximum rate of climb at sea level, (*b*) the maximum rate of climb at sea level, (*c*) the time to climb to 14,000 ft from sea level, (*d*) the average climb rate while doing so, (*e*) the maximum climb rate upon reaching 14,000 ft, and (*f*) the average climb angle during the climb.

Figure 6.22 Courtesy Hughes Helicopter Company.

HELICOPTER STRUCTURES

7

7.1 INTRODUCTION

All structural systems have many basic requirements in common. They must be able to withstand all normal loads imposed by the weight of the structure itself (dead loads) and loads due to normal use (live loads). Not only must they not fail under these loads, but they must not deform beyond clearly stated limits. Furthermore, they are required to perform as specified for a given lifetime.

The obvious way to make a structure strong, rigid, and durable is to build it large and heavy. Bridges and buildings are designed to accommodate loads at least twenty times larger than they are expected to encounter in normal use. The aircraft designer, on the other hand, cannot afford to oversize his structure. Every pound of empty weight above that needed to meet the load requirements costs him dearly in terms of vehicle performance. also, in flight vehicles a small increase in basic structural weights increases the aircraft's gross weight by factors of up to 20. To carry extra structural weight, and still meet the requirement of hover ceilings, rates of climb, endurance, and so on, requires increases in powerplant weight, transmission weight, fuel weight, and landing gear weight.

While being as light as possible, the aircraft structure must also be accessible for repair, inspection, and maintenance. Often the accommodation for easy access must be foresaken simply to obtain reduced structural weight.

The structure must, however, support safely the loads typical of the mission. Thus the specific details of the intended mission determine the nature and magnitude of the critical loads, hence size the structure. It is therefore imperative that structural designers be provided with a detailed, quantitative description of precisely what it is the vehicle will be required to do and, equally important, the nature of the environment in which the vehicle will find itself. Any subsequent use of the aircraft in a mission or environment for which it was not originally intended, must be thoroughly studied to make sure that loads do not exceed previously determined design levels.

7.2 STATIC STRENGTH AND STIFFNESS

Static Loads

The static strength requirement is the consideration given to the effect of simple static loads (constant or slowly applied loads) with none of the ramifications of the repeated or cyclic variation of loads. An important reference point in the static strength requirement is the limit load factor N_L, which is defined as the maximum load factor to which the vehicle can be subjected in the static sense without objectionable permanent deformation. It is specified by determining the maximum of all static loads expected to be encountered during normal operation. This maximum load, for the case of forces along the vertical axis of the helicopter, is then divided by the design gross weight (usually the maximum gross weight of the aircraft when it first enters service) to determine N_L; that is,

$$N_L = \frac{\text{maximum normal static load}}{\text{design gross weight}}$$

The limit load factors are about 2 to 3 G for observation and utility aircraft and as high as 5 G for modern attack helicopters. In conventional helicopters the only source of high static loads is the rotor. As we saw in Chapters 2 and 3, there is a definite limit to the amount of thrust a given rotor can produce under given conditions. Often the limit load factor represents a load slightly in excess of the maximum capability of the rotor. Thus it is physically impossible to "over-G" the aircraft in flight by use of collective and/or cyclic control. The desirable safety feature that this provides is obvious. For example, a utility helicopter rotor may have a maximum rotor thrust capability of 15,000 lb in the most favorable conditions. At a gross weight of 8500 lb:

$$N_z = \frac{15{,}000}{8500} = 1.77\ G$$

at 6000 lb:

$$N_z = \frac{15{,}000}{6000} = 2.5\ G$$

The limit load factor is given as 2.0 G at the maximum gross weight of 8500 lb. Thus the rotor limits themselves prevent the overloading of the structure. Note that limit load factors are usually stated for the maximum gross weight condition. In the example above the helicopter can pull 2.5 G at 6000 lb. This does not mean that it has exceeded the published limit load factor of 2.0, since at the reduced weight the appropriate limit load factor now is

$$(N_L)_{6000\ \text{lb}} = (N_L)_{8500\ \text{lb}} \cdot \frac{8500}{6000} = 2.0 \cdot 1.42 = 2.84\ G$$

In some high speed conventional helicopters and in most compound helicopters it is possible to over-G the aircraft in the high speed portion of the envelope. The wings of a compound helicopter increase the total aerodynamic z-force capability in proportion to the square of the forward velocity. Thus at high speed at 1 G the wing and rotor share the load. If a maneuver is performed whereby the maximum lifting capability of the wing is generated simultaneously with maximum rotor lift, large load factors result that might be in excess of the limit load factor. In such a case, objectionable permanent deformation of at least one member of the primary load-carrying structure will occur.

Figure 7.1 shows the relationship between G capability, speed, and structural limits for two hypothetical helicopters, one conventional and one compound. The same structural limits are assumed for both. Note that by virtue of the added wing the compound helicopter has the capability to exceed limit load and come close to V_{ne} (never-exceed speed).

For the rare instances of flight when a load greater than the limit is required to prevent a disaster or when extreme turbulence causes excessive loads an "ultimate factor of safety" is provided. Experience has shown that an ultimate factor of safety of 1.5 is sufficient for piloted aircraft. Thus the aircraft must be capable of withstanding (without fracture) a load that is 1.5 times the design limit load. Loads beyond the limit load, but less than the ultimate load, permanently deform the structure. Loads above the ultimate load result in catastrophic failure.

Helicopters rarely need to sustain negative vertical loads for normal maneuvering. Some account must be taken, however, of inadvertant negative G operation that may occur in momentary out-of-control situations. Negative limit and ultimate load factors are thus specified (Figure 7.1), but they are not large.

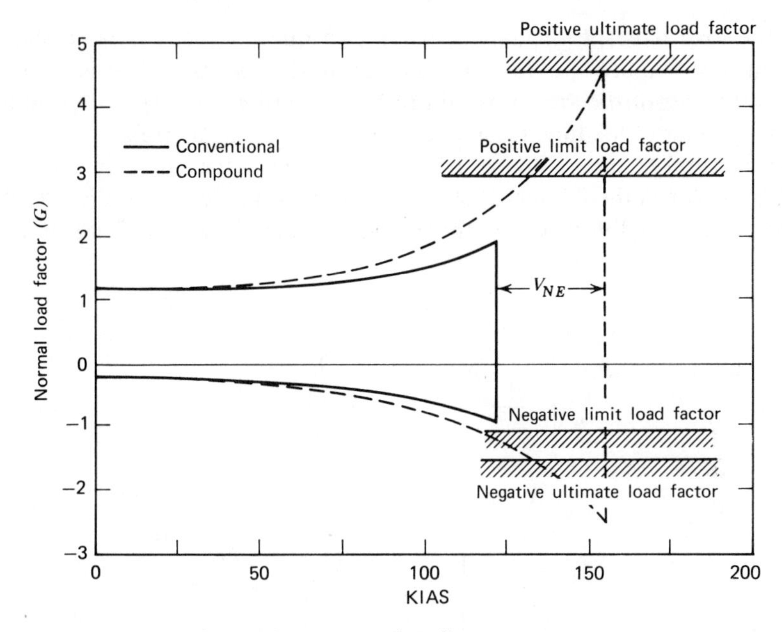

Figure 7.1 *V-N* diagram for two sample helicopters.

For highly maneuverable helicopters, additional, more stringent limits may be imposed in certain areas. For example, it is not uncommon to specify limit load factors for rolling pullouts at one half or two thirds the value of the symmetrical limit. This limit accounts for the special loads (usually in the sideward direction) that may be imposed on certain parts of the aircraft (e.g., vertical tail) during such maneuvers.

Stress and Strain

The above loading considerations just discussed pertain to the aircraft as a whole. The integrity of the structure depends on the load distribution among all structural members and each member's ability to sustain its share. Important to the discussion of this ability, or lack of it, are the concepts of stress and strain.

Stress is defined as the ratio of the applied load to the cross-sectional area supporting that load:

$$\text{stress (psi)} = \frac{\text{load (lb)}}{\text{area (in.}^2\text{)}}$$

If the load is perpendicular to the area in question, it is called either a tension or a compression load, depending on the direction. If it is applied across the face of the area, it is said to be a shearing load. Thus depending on the manner of loading, tension, compression, or shear stresses may exist in a structural member. Figure 7.2 illustrates these. It is important to distinguish between these kinds of stress, since the ultimate strength capability of the material is different in all three modes. A metal may fail, for example,

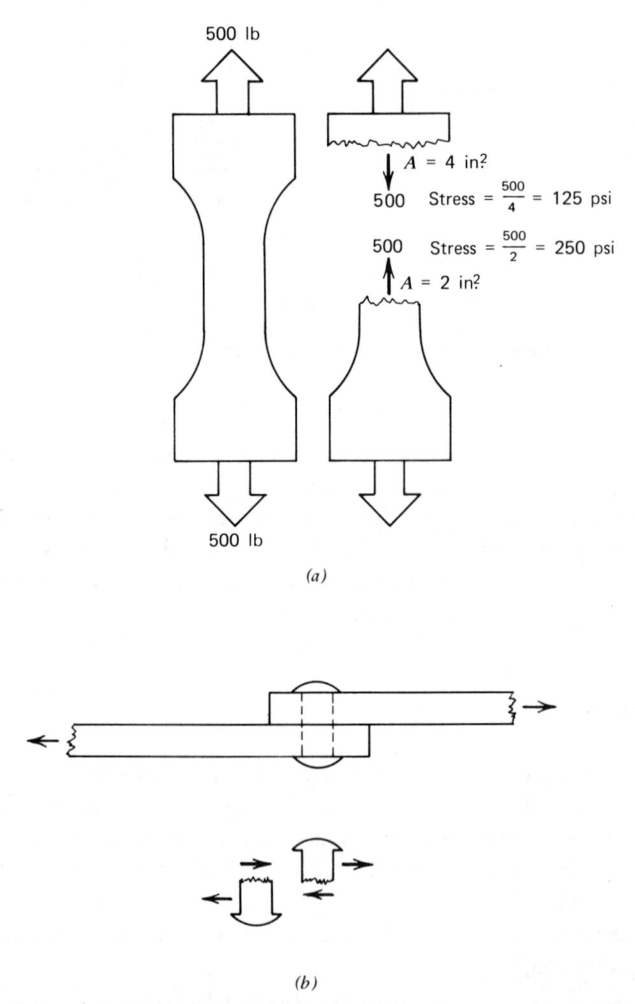

Figure 7.2 Internal stress due to external loads. (*a*) Tension stress (load perpendicular to area). (*b*) Shear stress (load parallel to area).

under a stress of 25,000 psi in tension, 75,000 psi in compression, and only 18,000 psi in shear.

It is the designer's job to do the following:

1. Determine the magnitude and direction of external loads.
2. Determine the magnitude and direction of internal loads on each member.
3. Choose a shape and size for each member, as well as the material, that will produce a smaller maximum stress than is required to deform the material under the expected tension, compression, and shear stresses.

To accomplish the latter the designer must have knowledge of the deformation characteristics of the metals he will use. For static loading in tension, for example, he will consult the stress-strain diagram of the material. Strain is defined as the amount of elongation the part experiences under load, divided by the original length:

$$\text{strain} = \frac{\text{additional elongation (in.)}}{\text{original length (in.)}}$$

Every material has a unique stress-strain relationship. Figure 7.3 shows one. Stresses below the "yield" point have a linear relationship with strain. Doubling the stress doubles the strain. When the stress is removed in this area, the part returns to its original undeformed state. This is "elastic" behavior. (The "stiffness" of the material is measured by the slope of the stress-strain diagram in the elastic region. A steep slope means that high stress is needed to achieve small strain; hence the material exhibits high stiffness.) Stresses above this value result in a permanent set (Figure 7.3) when stress is removed. The stress-strain relationship is very nonlinear in this so-called plastic region. The highest value of stress the metal can sustain is a measure of its ultimate strength, and is a fixed value for a given metal. The designer must be sure that no single member is stressed beyond its yield strength when the limit load factor is being applied to the aircraft.

Many helicopters must support external stores or sling loads. Besides the limits on the weight of such stores, which add to the gross weight and thus limit performance, care must be taken that this extra load and the method of suspension do not result in excessive stresses in any particular structural member.

Many members are subjected to large bending and/or torsional moments because of the magnitude and direction of the loads placed on them. These loads can be resolved into the basic states of stress (tension, compression, and shear) and then treated in the manner outlined above. For example, Figure 7.4 shows a member subjected to bending moments, but no net

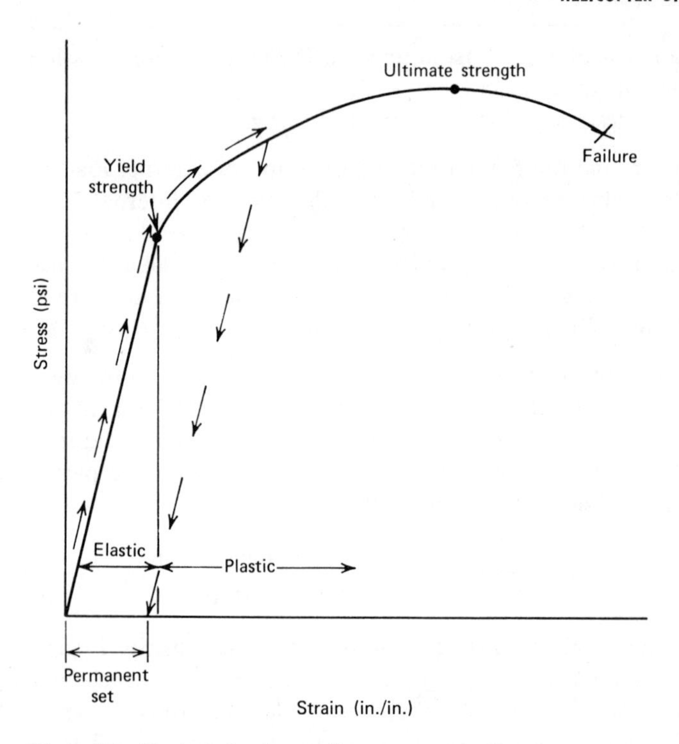

Figure 7.3 Typical aluminum alloy stress-strain diagram.

force. Such a loading results in tension stresses on one side of the member and compression on the other.

Dynamic Loads

Besides static loads, a helicopter is always being subjected to rapidly applied loads or impact loads. Such "dynamic" loads are not distributed throughout the structure in the same way as are same-size static loads. Moreover, the behavior of materials is different under dynamic loading. If the stress and strain of a ductile material are measured in the laboratory under conditions of increased rate of application of the load, characteristics similar to those shown in Figure 7.5 are obtained. It can be seen that as the loading rate is increased, so is the stress required to fail the material, but the elongation is reduced. For very sudden impact loads the material "shatters" like a brittle material, while under static conditions it may behave in a ductile manner.

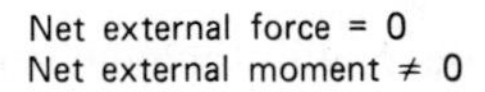

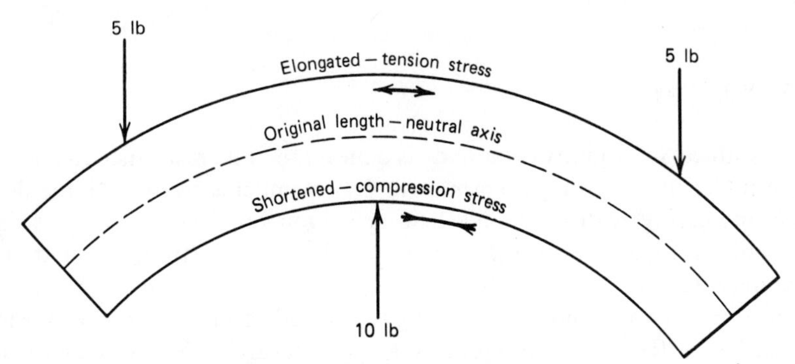

Figure 7.4 Tension and compression due to bending.

In sudden maneuvers, including landings and crashes, dynamic loads may be applied that cause brittle-type failures. More important, however, are the dynamic loads associated with repeated cyclic oscillations of rotating machinery. These dynamic loads may be high especially at high rotational rates. Though hopefully they will not exceed the ultimate limit stress for that loading rate, nevertheless there may be cumulative degradation of the

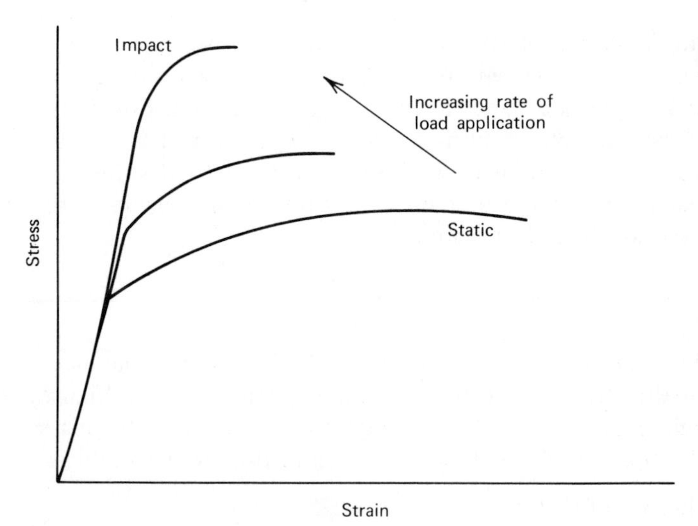

Figure 7.5 Effect of dynamic loads.

mechanical properties of the metal through the mechanism of fatigue, which is discussed later.

7.3 VIBRATION

The stiffness (or rigidity) of a body is a measure of its resistance to deformation under load. A simple spring will deflect under a given load, the deflection increasing with load. The load-deflection relationship remains linear so long as no stresses in the spring exceed the proportional limit stress of the material.

If a mass on the end of the spring is allowed to move freely, following a disturbance from rest, it vibrates at its "natural" frequency, executing periodic upward and downward motions. A graph of the mass's position, velocity, and acceleration would show them as sine waves versus time (Figure 7.6). Note that at maximum deflection the deceleration is maximum (but the velocity is zero). The spring exerts a force on the mass, proportional to the distance of the mass from its "static" or neutral position. As the mass passes through the static position, force (hence acceleration) is zero, but velocity is maximum.

The number of cycles executed in a given time is the frequency of the oscillation, and the time for one complete cycle is the period:

$$\text{frequency (cps)} = \frac{1}{\text{period (sec)}}$$

Thus an oscillation of 10 cps has a period of 0.1 sec.

The natural frequency of this simple system depends on only two things: the mass of the body and the stiffness of the spring. For a given mass, a "stiffer" spring (one requiring more force to deflect it a given amount) results in a higher frequency. With a spring of fixed stiffness, the higher the mass the lower the frequency. For this single-degree-of freedom (up-down) system the relationship is

$$P = 2\pi\sqrt{\frac{m}{K_s}} \quad \text{sec}$$

Here K_s is the spring stiffness constant (lb/ft) and m is the mass (slugs).

An analogous system is the rotational system shown in Figure 7.7. Here the single degree of freedom is rotation of the beam. In this system the natural frequency of oscillation is determined by four variables:

1. The size of the mass.
2. The position of the mass from the center of rotation.

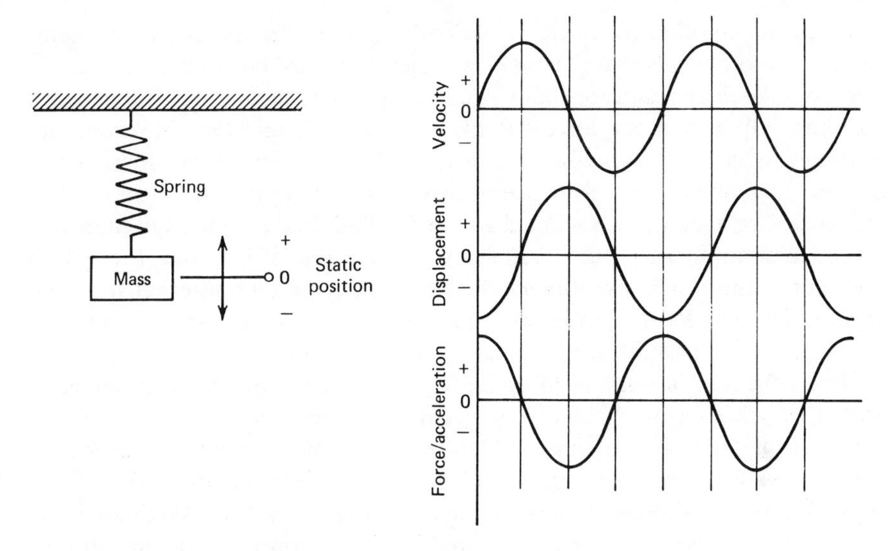

Figure 7.6 Natural oscillation of spring/mass system.

3. The stiffness of the springs.
4. The position of the springs from the center of rotation

The natural frequency is increased (smaller period) if one or more of the following are done: the mass is reduced; the mass is moved toward the center of rotation; stiffer springs are used; the springs are moved away from the center of rotation.

In a more complex system, such as a helicopter, the natural frequency depends on two basic characteristics: the distribution of mass throughout the body and the distribution of stiffness throughout the body. Moreover, generally there are more than one degrees of freedom. That is, a structure may be free to translate as a rigid body in three dimensions and rotate as a rigid body in three dimensions. Additionally, a given member may trans-

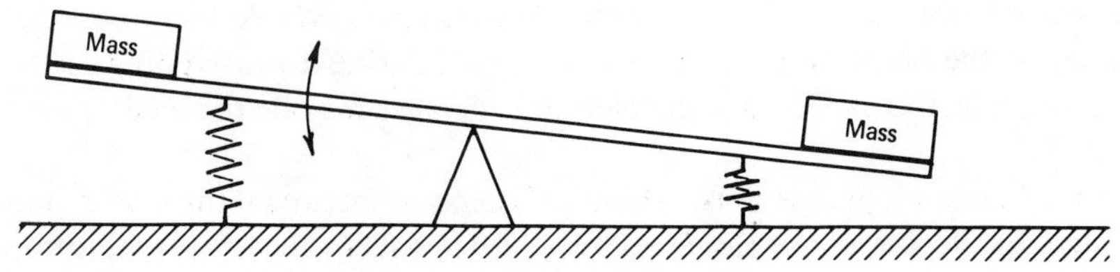

Figure 7.7 Rotational single degree of freedom system.

late relative to other members of the body in many senses, and may rotate relative to other members. Thus a complex structure has many degrees of freedom in which vibrations may occur. In general, the natural frequencies of these vibrations are all different. They are all affected, however, by changes in the mass distribution, in the stiffness distribution, or in both.

The phenomenon of resonance makes it imperative that all these modes of motion be accurately predicted and controlled. If a dynamic system has a cyclic load applied to it at a frequency equal to one of its natural frequencies, large amplitude vibrations (with accompanying high internal stresses) result. The resultant stresses may fail a component in a static overload sense, or fail it in a fatigue sense after relatively few cycles.

In a helicopter a number of cyclic forces are acting on the structure as a result of rotating machinery. Low frequency cyclic loads come from the main rotor (3 to 40 cps) and tail rotor (25 to 110 cps), while higher frequency loads come from engine and drive train components (500 to 1000 cps). Figure 7.8 shows a typical frequency distribution for a single maneuver. If one of these "forcing functions" is in tune with one of the natural frequencies of the structure, resonance occurs. Also, undesirable vibrations may result when the natural frequency is an integer multiple of a basic forcing frequency (harmonics).

In some cases mechanical dampers are installed. These devices exert retarding forces proportional to the velocity of the part to which they are attached. A piston in a cylinder of fluid is an example. It takes little force to move the piston slowly and more force to move it faster. The faster the piston is moved, the more damping force is supplied. Dampers help to reduce the amplitude of vibration at all frequencies, but may be "tuned" to provide considerable damping in a narrow band of frequencies.

If the mass and spring stiffness of an original system is not maintained, the resonant range can change and may allow dangerous response from previously tolerable frequencies. In addition, if required damping is not sustained by adequate maintenance of mechanical dampers, a dangerous response can occur in regions previously thought to be safe.

The structural motions of a typical helicopter are characterized by the coupling of many distinct types of motion. For example, the structural bending of rotor blades during flapping motions may couple with torsional twisting. If the blade twists leading edge down during downflapping on the retreating side, the expected angle of attack increase may be reduced or even reversed.

A fundamental problem is vibration isolation between the rotor and fuselage. Excitation of the fuselage caused by low frequency rotor vibration adversely affects aircraft control, subsystem operation, crew comfort, and

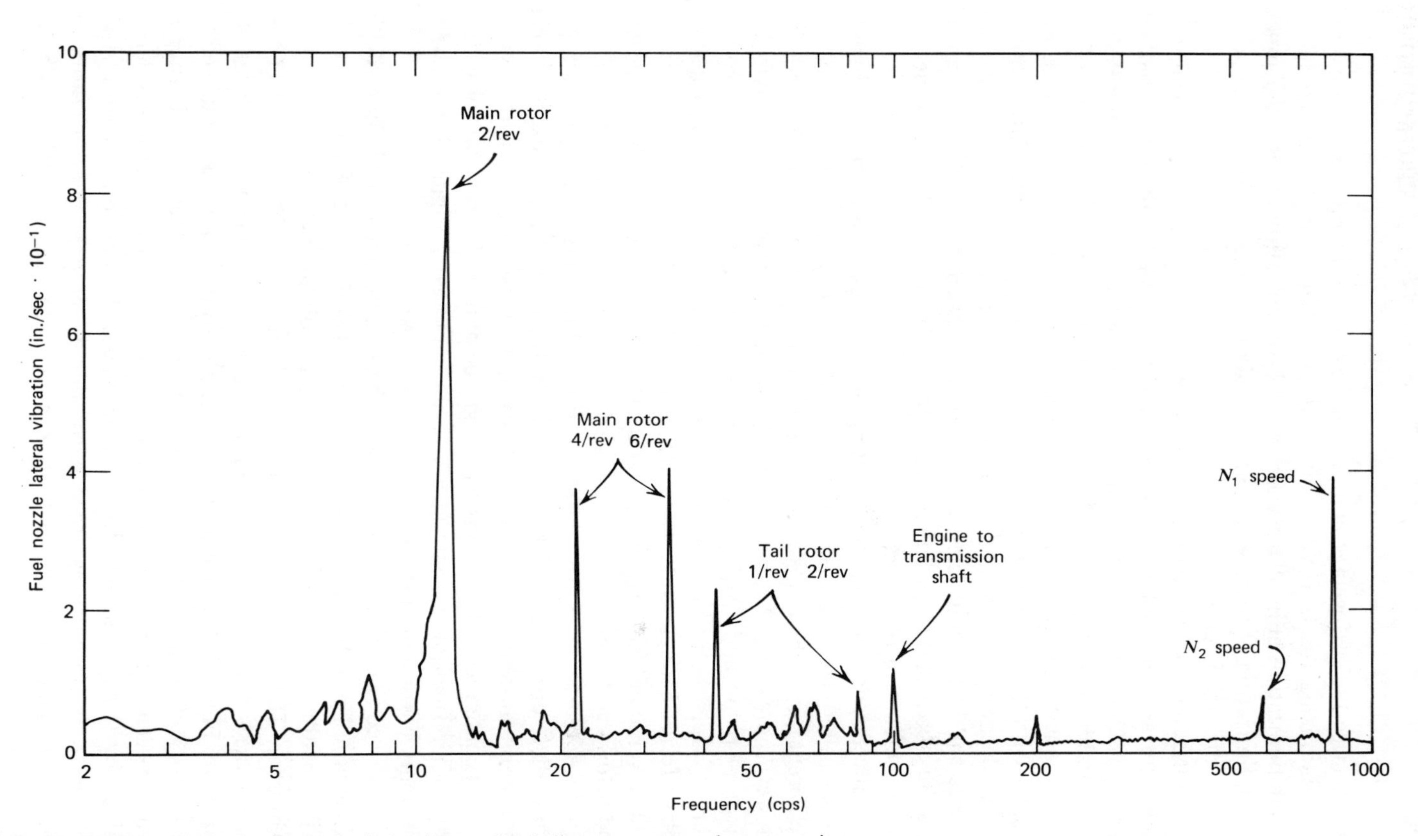

Figure 7.8 Vibration spectra of a light observation helicopter measured at one point.

the service life of fuselage components. Four considerations are involved in minimizing fuselage vibrations and improving component reliability: (1) minimization of oscillatory airloads, (2) optimization of rotor dynamics, (3) optimization of fuselage dynamics, and (4) attenuation of the excitation forces through isolation.

Efforts to reduce the oscillatory forces have had limited success. Tailoring the rotor and/or fuselage to avoid resonance is usually attempted, but will not by itself ensure low vibration. Therefore, some form of isolation system is desirable. This is particularly true for a two bladed rotor because of the low frequency and high magnitude of the rotor hub forces produced. For rotors with three or more blades, isolation is not awlays mandatory, but is often desirable to reduce sensitivity to out-of-balance and out-of-track forces and high frequencies. For rotors with articulated blades mechanical stability considerations either preclude the use of isolators or otherwise limit the control of vibrations.

Conventional methods for isolating black boxes such as electrical packages—using elastomeric springs or metal springs and friction dampers—represent one of the best known fields of vibration isolation. These methods, however, are difficult to apply directly to the helicopter, since the two free bodies—pylon and fuselage—are suspended in the *G*-field by the rotor's thrust, while the rotor-counter-torque, engine torque, and steady rotor in-plane forces act across the isolating system.

Conventional isolation requires that the natural frequency of the system be below the frequency to be isolated. For common rotor generated frequencies (e.g., $1P = 320$ RPM) relatively low stiffness ("soft" springs) must therefore be used. The large steady forces and moments, and long duration transients, then result in large static deflections across the pylon-fuselage interface—deflections that might be difficult for the control system and other functional components to accommodate. Figure 7.9 shows a conventional system and its typical characteristics.

Improved isolation methods have been developed, including Bell's Kinematic Focal Isolation System, Kaman's DAVI, Lord Manufacturing's CB Isolator, and Sikorsky's Main Rotor Bifilar Pendulum Vibration Absorber. The latter is a pendulum-type absorber tuned to counteract and cancel the vibratory forces at their source before they can be fed into the airframe. Figure 7.10 illustrates the principle, showing a mass connected to the rotor hub by an arm of radius r. The pendulum is located a distance R from the center of rotation of the hub. Because the springlike force is determined by the centrifugal forces on the mass, the pendulum natural frequency ω_n is proportional to the rotational speed Ω and the ratio of radii R/r. Thus to absorb vibration at a given frequency the device is

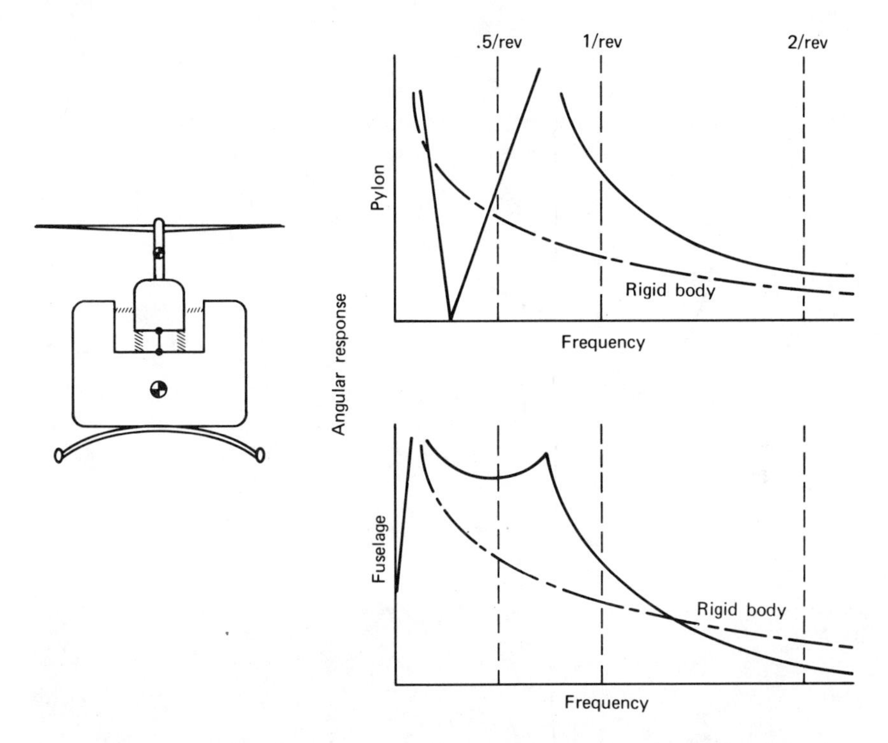

Figure 7.9 Conventional helicopter isolation system with vertical restraint. (From reference 28.)

"tuned" by changing the pendulum radius r appropriately. The mass then moves so as to provide a cyclic centrifugal force that cancels the in-plane exciting force at that frequency. Both systems have resulted in accelerations at the cockpit station (vertical and sideways) less than 0.1 G at all frequencies and throughout the speed envelope of the helicopter. Before 1972 military specifications called for vibrations less than $\pm 0.15\ G$ and many helicopters still flying vibrate more than $\pm 0.2\ G$ in some flight regimes. Some 1973 requirements call for $\pm 0.05\ G$.

When a complex structure is subjected to oscillatory loads, it vibrates in characteristic "mode shapes." The vibration of standing waves on a long string is a simple example. It is observed that there are certain points, called nodes, where no motion is taking place and others where large scale motions are occurring. A helicopter fuselage has a certain mode shape, given the frequency of the applied force. The $\pm 0.15\ G$ military requirement applies to the cockpit area. Therefore designers attempt to control the mass

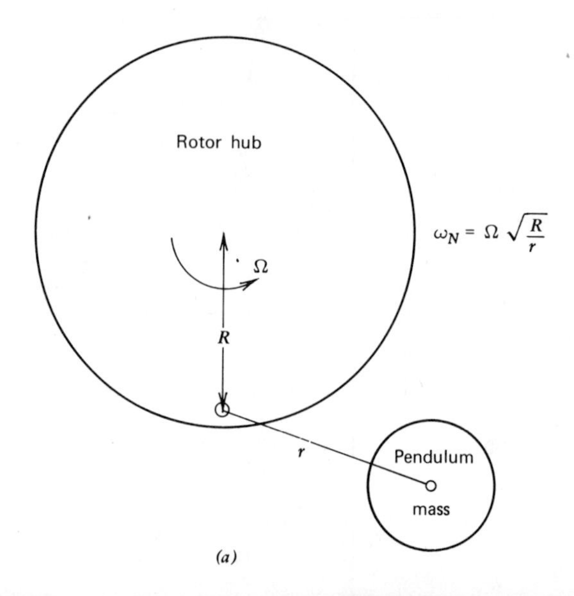

Figure 7.10 Pendulum vibration absorber.

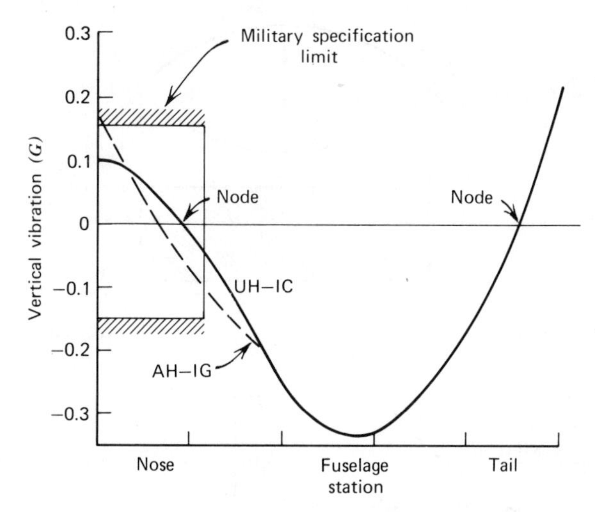

Figure 7.11 Inflight mode shapes. (From reference 89.)

and stiffness distribution of the fuselage so that one of the nodes is in the cockpit (Figure 7.11). Thus the pilot may be relatively comfortable but the aft fuselage section may be severely shaken. A way around this would be to suspend the entire payload from inflight nodal points. Ideally this would provide perfect isolation, regardless of the loading condition of the helicopter. The concept has been tried by Bell with considerable success. Figure 7.12 shows the concept and some of the results.

7.4 SERVICE LIFE

When considering the total expected lifetime of a helicopter or its components, the entire gamut of expected loads must be considered, rather than just the excessive ones. To achieve satisfactory performance during service operation, a structure must withstand the *cumulative* effect of all varieties of load experienced in normal use. Classically, three basic phenomena govern service life and determine periods of maintenance, inspection, overhaul, and replacement: corrosion, creep, and fatigue.

Corrosion

Corrosion consists of either a direct chemical attack on the metal or the formation of an electrochemical reaction that erodes the metal. In either

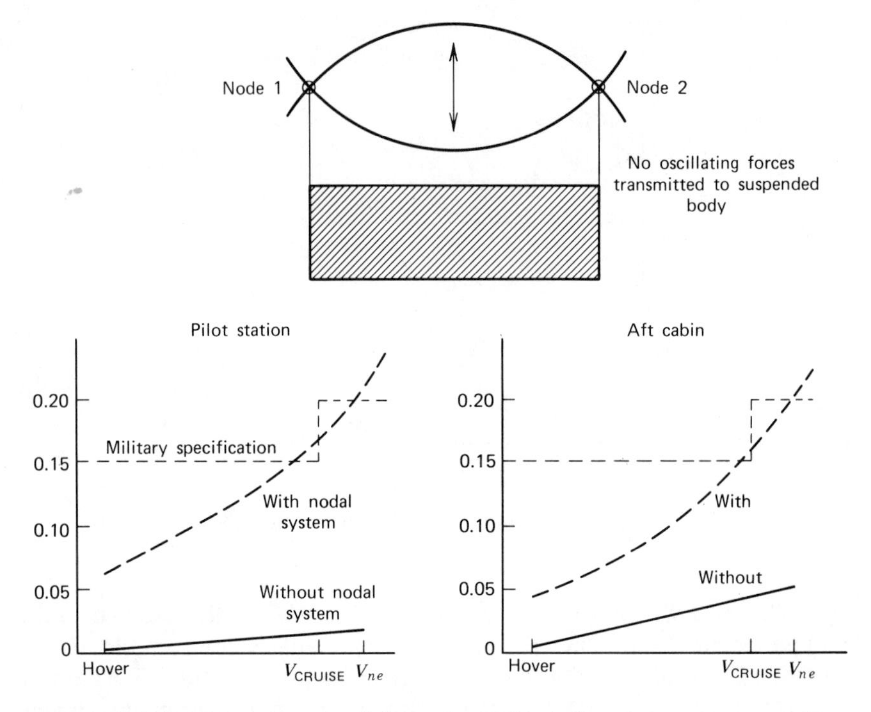

Figure 7.12 Nodal isolation of Bell light observation helicopter at two-per-rev. (From reference 89.)

case, corrosion of a primary load carrying structure creates strength degradation out of proportion to the area that may appear to be affected. In the pitting corrosion of typical aircraft aluminum alloy, for example, the small pits form points of local stesss concentration or "stress raisers." That is, the load is not distributed uniformly over the cross section, but tends to concentrate in the portion of the material near the pit, raising the value of stress experienced there. Not only can this bring about local cracking by overstress, but the component's fatigue resistance is drastically reduced.

When two dissimilar metals are in close contact, as they often are in skin/rivet/spar joints, for example, there is a natural tendency to form a miniature electrochemical cell when some electrolyte such as water, is present. Metals vary in their tendency to corrode, depending on their relative position in the "galvanic series." Titanium is one of the least corrosive metals and is near the bottom of the series. Magnesium, on the other hand, is extremely active in corrosion and is near the top of the list. If magnesium and titanium were close together in a structure, and were exposed to an environment conducive to electron flow, the magnesium would become the "anode" of the cell and titanium the "cathode." In the process the anodic magnesium would be deteriorated while the titanium would be unaffected.

It is important to recognize the requirement of an electrolyte to allow the reaction system of the galvanic cell. If dissimilar metals are in contact without water, the reaction is inhibited. This means that corrosion problems of this type are eliminated in a perfectly dry environment.

The typical environment of a helicopter of course introduces water vapor, water, saltwater, bacteria, combustion products, and all sorts of miscellaneous chemical agents. Apparently, the best maintenance that can be performed is to preserve the finishes, wash away contaminating agents and salt, and eliminate trapped water from the structural components.

Corrosion of rotating parts can be especially critical. The high centrifugal force field in a compressor, for example, make it possible for a relatively small mass imbalance due to corrosion to cause unwanted vibration and premature failure.

Usually corrosion processes combine or interact with mechanical processes to create such phenomena as corrosion fatigue, fretting corrosion, and stress corrosion cracking.

Creep

Creep is the continued plastic deformation of a part subjected to stress. Our earlier discussion of stress diagrams assumed typical room temperature tests and normal test times. If the steady stress is allowed to remain for a long time, particularly at high temperature, continued straining occurs as shown in Figure 7.13. Creep critical parts are found wherever high static stress and high temperature coexist, as on turbine blades. Here excessive deformation can cause mechanical interference with the turbine case, with unfortunate results.

It is important to realize that creep is cumulative and irreversible. Periodic precise examination of turbine components is necessary to ensure that service use has not caused excessive deformation. Also, time in service is a weak measure of accumulated creep damage, and great significance should be given to sustained high temperature operation, hotstarts, overspeed, and other overtemperature conditions.

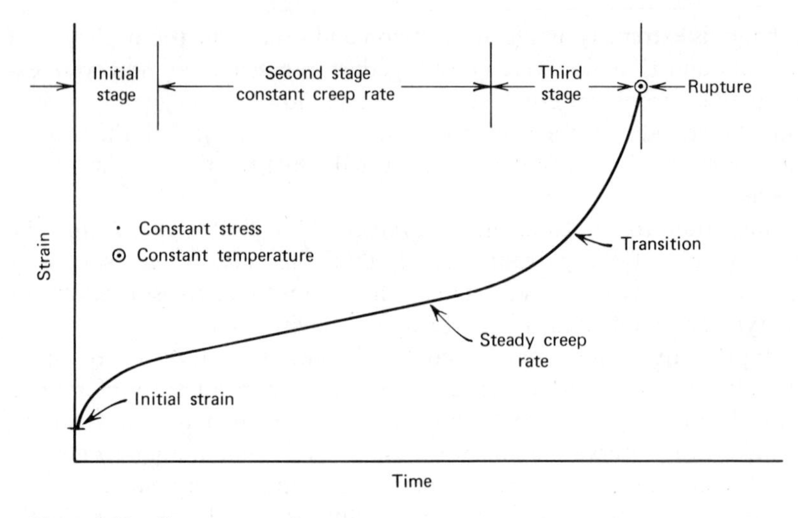

Figure 7.13 Creep progression.

Fatigue

The most important factor in the service life considerations of a helicopter is fatigue. Fatigue is failure due to repeated cyclic loading. Like creep, it is cumulative and irreversible. When it comes to repeated loads, a metal, like an elephant, never forgets. At any given level of cyclic stress a definite number of cycles can occur before failure occurs. Every flight eats into this total, and none of it can be replaced.

During an initial period of cyclic loading a minute crack appears at some critical location in the sample. With continued application of the varying stress, the crack will enlarge and propagate into the cross section. When the crack has progressed sufficiently, the remaining cross section is incapable of withstanding the imposed stress and a sudden, final rupture occurs. In this fashion, a metal can fail at stresses much lower than the static ultimate stress.

Of course, the time necessary to produce failure is related to the magnitude of the cyclic stress. This relationship is typified by Figure 7.14. As might be expected, a very high stress level requires relatively few cycles to produce fatigue failure. Moderate stress levels require a fairly large number of cycles to produce failure, and a very low stress may require nearly an infinite number of cycles. The *frequency* of the cyclic stress application (cycles per second) is not important to the fatigue phenomena except at exceptionally high frequency. The *number of cycles* is all-important.

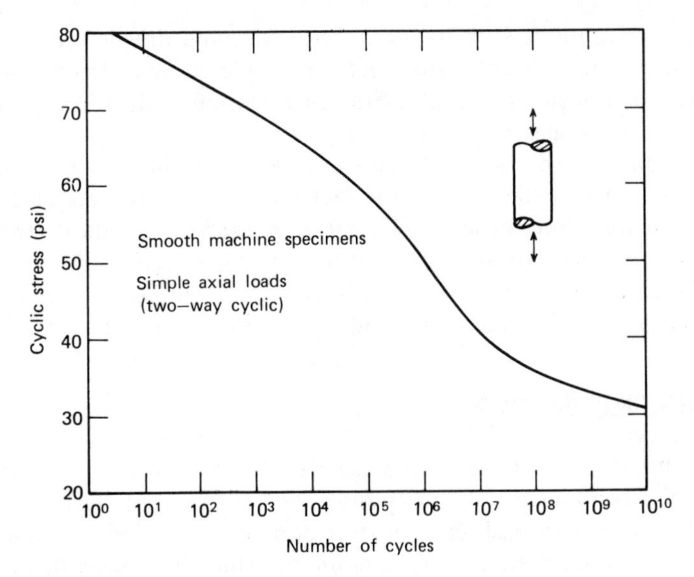

Figure 7.14 Fatigue behavior of aluminum alloy 7075, 755T6.

Throughout a normal flight a given component is subjected to a variety of cyclic stress levels depending on what the aircraft is doing at the time. For example, cyclic torsional loads of the main rotor shaft are higher when hovering OGE or performing a maximum rate vertical climb than in 1 *G* level flight at 60 knots. By analyzing the total flight load spectra one can assess the *cumulative* fatigue damage. If, in the example of Figure 7.14, 100 cycles at 70,000 psi were accompanied by 10,000 cycles at 50,000 psi and 100,000 cycles at 40,000 psi, the total effect would be calculated as follows:

1. For each 70,000 psi there are 10^3 cycles available, only 100 of which were used, that is, because of this loading alone $(100/1000) \cdot 100 = 10\%$ of the fatigue life was used.
2. For each 50,000 psi we have $(10{,}000/1{,}000{,}000) \cdot 100 = 1\%$.
3. For each 40,000 psi we have $(100{,}000/10{,}000{,}000) \cdot 100 = 1\%$.

Thus a *total* of 12% of the fatigue life has been used in this combined cyclic loading spectrum.

In Figure 7.14 we see also how relatively small increases in cyclic stress level cause large reductions in fatigue life. For example, by doubling cyclic stress from 35,000 psi to 70,000 psi the number of cycles to failure has been reduced from 10^9 to 10^3—a factor of a million! The importance of avoiding stress concentrations such as nicks, scratches, and drastic cross-sectional area changes can be appreciated. In the example above an inadvertant dent causing the local stress to double can cause a fatigue failure in this area one million times sooner than expected.

The nature of the fatigue failure progression is such that the fracture surface appears brittle, despite the fact that the material may act ductile to static loads. Concentric circular "stop marks" often indicate the origin of failure (usually a stress concentration) and the direction of propagation. The "instantaneous" portion of the fracture face reflects the true nature of the material and the manner of loading. Figure 7.15 provides examples.

7.5 STRUCTURAL MATERIALS

A revolution is occurring in the science of new structural materials for helicopter use. Elastomers, composites, and hybrid materials are proving to be better in every respect (even cost in many cases) than the families of steel, magnesium, titanium, and aluminum, which have been the mainstay helicopter materials to date. Though it will be some time before such exotic materials completely replace conventional metals, the changeover is certain and inevitable.

What are the characteristics of a good structural material? Before choosing the material the designer must determine the exact purpose of the component, the expected static loads, the oscillatory loads, the frequency of dynamic loading, temperature environment, deflection constraints, corrosive environment, and similar factors. The material, as well as the shape and size of the part, depends on the component's intended use. The finished part must meet rigid requirements in all these categories and must do so under severe weight restrictions. Helicopter blades, for example, must sustain high static centrifugal loads and at the same time retain their aerodynamic shape. They must be sufficiently flexible in bending to provide desired flapping behavior, but sufficiently rigid in torsion to avoid flap-pitch coupling. The severe cyclic load environment requires exceptional fatigue resistance, and their exposure to the elements, including blowing sand and other material, calls for high corrosive resistance. Cost—raw materials cost, manufacturing cost, and cost of ownership (e.g., maintenance)—is always a final consideration.

Metals

Aluminum alloys are by far the most common metals found in helicopter structures. The two thousand series (e.g., 2024), containing copper as the

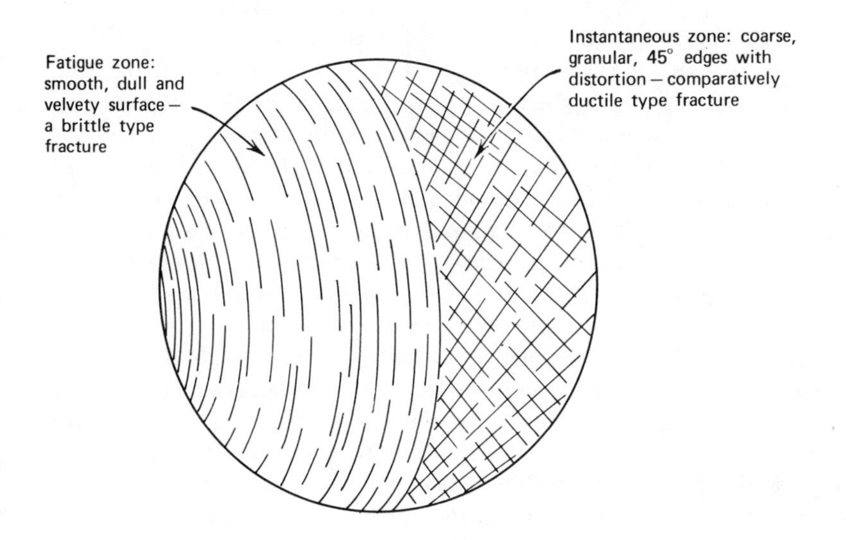

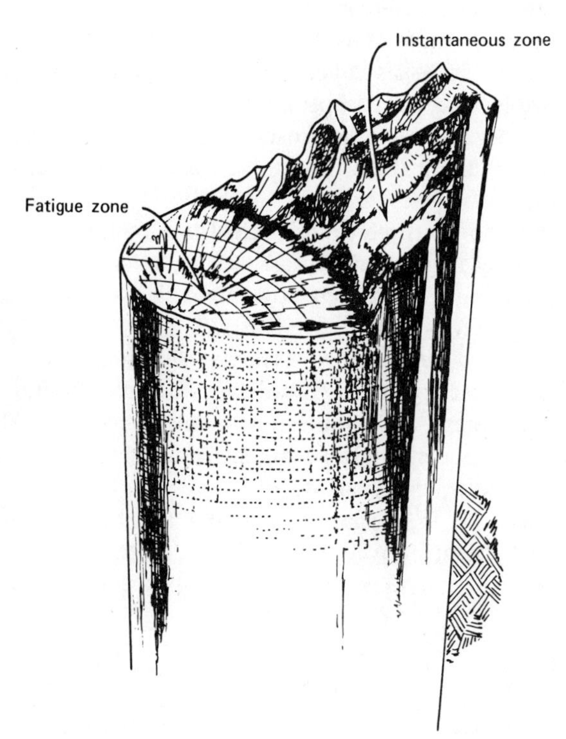

Figure 7.15 Technical fatigue fractures. (From reference 7.)

principal alloying ingredient, and the seven thousand series (e.g. 7075), containing zinc, enjoyed widespread application. Casting, extruding, rolling, bonding, and other manufacturing processes have been highly developed for aluminum alloys, and the confidence level is high. Base costs are very low (less than $1.00/lb), and, or course, the material combines high strength (about 75,000 psi ultimate tension for 7075-76) with low density (approximately $\frac{1}{10}$ lb/in.^{3}). Most aluminum alloys are not so resistant to corrosion as is pure aluminum (which, unfortunately, has low strength). But heat treatments and "alcladding" have resulted in the successful use of the high strength alloys in many corrosive environments.

Magnesium alloys enjoy the distinct advantage of low weight (about 63% that of aluminum per unit volume) and moderate strength (up to 50,000 psi ultimate tension) and have thus found application in some helicopter airframes. Their greatest disadvantage lies in their propensity to corrode because of their high standing in the galvanic series. Fatigue resistance in a corrosive environment has been a particular problem in some instances.

Steels, in many alloyed forms, have long been used where high strength and wear resistance are the dominant considerations. Many alloys, such as the martensitic stainless steels, have displayed excellent resistance to corrosion, heat, and wear, while offering exceptionally good strength (up to 300,000 psi) and stiffness. In many cases their exeptional strength is accompanied by high brittleness, making them unsuitable for many impact and dynamic loading environments. They are also the heaviest of all aircraft materials, having a density about three times that of aluminum.

Titanium has enjoyed increasing use in aircraft structures. Although it is about 62% denser than aluminum, its strength-to-weight ratio is up to 36% higher. Moreover, titanium alloys retain excellent strength, stiffness, and corrosion properties at elevated temperatures. Massive titanium rotor hub castings have been demonstrated on the Sikorsky S-61 and Lockheed AH-56A (Figure 7.16) helicopters, and titanium rotor blade spars are also operational. The superior fatigue strength-to-weight ratio of titanium has made it a candidate for rotating components.

Other metals have been tried in the laboratory, but few have reached regular inflight usage. Berryllium injoyed a brief flurry of attention, but, like most other metals, faded from view with the advent of composites.

Composites

Composites is the name given to a class of new materials that are manufactured by combining very fine threads of a base material in an epoxy plastic matrix. They are as strong and stiff as high strength steel, but about

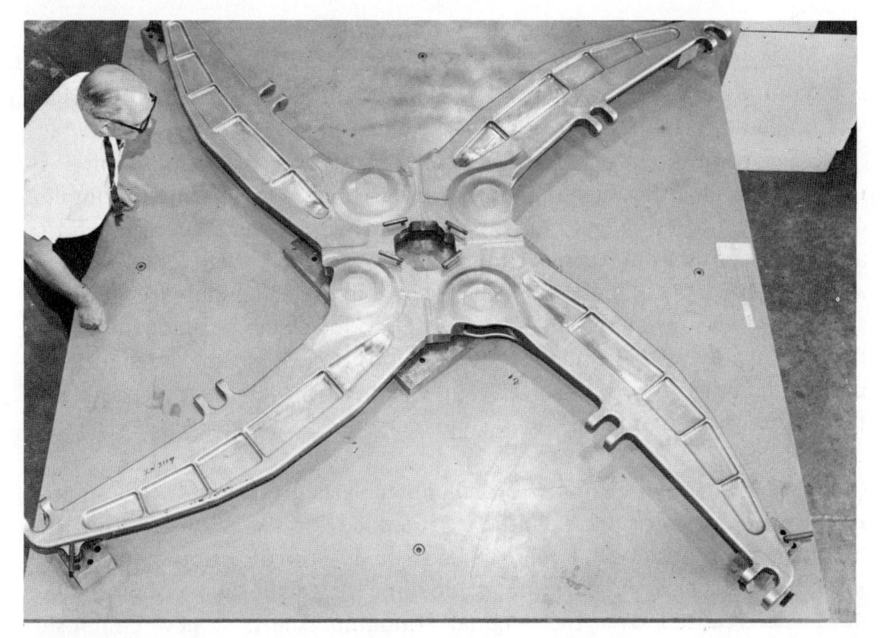

Figure 7.16 Titanium rotor hub casting for AH-56A helicopter.

75% lighter. They have demonstrated strengths three times that of aircraft aluminum, but are more than 25% lighter.

To illustrate, consider the most widely demonstrated of the composites, boron epoxy. Boron itself is a semimetallic element—the fifth element in the atomic table. In many of the most common forms of metals (e.g., when shaped by casting) boron is extremely brittle and unsuitable for helicopters. But just as glass is brittle in many forms but has high strength as filament or fiber, so boron filament has an extraordinarily high usable strength. And boron is very stiff—six times stiffer than glass. Boron filaments when mixed with an epoxy plastic exhibit the best qualities of both materials (aluminum and titanium matrices have also been used in place of epoxy).

The boron filament is made by drawing an extraordinarily fine wire of tungsten, heated to a bright red temperature, through a chamber into which boron trichloride and hydrogen gases have been pumped. In the vicinity of the hot tungsten wire, chemical reaction yields pure boron and hydrochloric acid. The particles of pure boron are deposited on the moving wire and the hydrochloric acid is removed from the chamber.

The final boron filament is 4/1000 in. in diameter—about as thin as a human hair. It is 95% pure boron and 5% wire core. To be used for building, these filaments must first be made into a composite in the form of a tape. About 212 filaments to the linear inch are coated with and embedded in epoxy on a glass-cloth backing to make a continuous tape in any desirable width. The tape is then rolled up for easy handling.

To form useful shapes from the composite tape, a basic "sculpture" is used as a mold, either of simple form for a flat panel or with many complex curves. Layer after layer of the tape is laid down on the form in much the same manner that any adhesive tape might be applied. Each layer is placed at a different angle (e.g., 0, 45 and 135°) to enable the laminate to withstand stress from various directions. Composite products may be made in varying numbers of layers, depending on the composition of weight, strength, and directional stress they must meet. When sufficient layers have been placed, the entire form is "cured" in an autoclave—essentially a large pressure cooker.

Figure 7.17 shows examples of helicopter parts fabricated from composites. In the tail rotor drive shaft case intended for the Sikorsky S-61, the filaments have been oriented at 45° to the axis—the direction of the maximum principal stress under torsional loading. A weight saving of more than 40% was realized over the original aluminum shaft. A new composite stringer was developed to increase the stiffness of the tail cone of the Sikorsky CH-54 Skycrane to solve a vibration problem. The new structure weighed 30 lb, compared to the 130 lb of aluminum previously used.

The most promising new use of composite materials in helicopters is for rotor blades. Not only are there substantial performance improvements offered by lower weight and dynamic tuning allowed by tailoring the properties of the material, but the nature of the composite fabrication process allows aerodynamic shapes that are difficult if not impossible to produce with present metal fabrication.

In one application, the use of boron epoxy for the spar allowed substantial improvements in the system, including a 40% weight saving in the spar, a 75% reduction in tip deflection, and reduced stresses. Improved stability, reduced control loads, longer life, and less maintenance resulted.

Corrosion is practically nonexistent in composites exposed to normal environments.

Vast improvements in fatigue behavior and damage tolerance can also be achieved, as evidenced in Figure 7.18. In this test the steady loads imposed were approximately the same, but the oscillatory amplitude on the composite blade was made four times that of the aluminum blade. Even so, no failure had occurred in the composite blade after half a million cycles, and the crack was still growing stably and was 20 in. long when the test was terminated.

Elastomers

Elastomeric bearings and dampers have enjoyed widespread acceptance in helicopter application since the late sixties. Bearings made from elastomers are used in main and tail rotors in both the flapping and feathering axes. Compared to conventional bearings they have fewer parts, have relaxed tolerances, require far less maintenance (they need no lubricants), can be tuned to control oscillatory blade loads, and are not singificantly more expensive. Elastomeric dampers have similar virtues, operate well between −65° and 200°F, and have exhibited service lives of more than 2000 flight hours. Adverse environmental effects such as weathering, oil, sand, and dust are virtually nonexistent.

Instead of the ordered and rigid crystalline arrangement of atoms and molecules in metals, elastomer atoms are arranged in a chainlike, structured configuration of great length and are in constant thermally induced motion, resulting in a tangled mass of kinked, twisted, and intertwined elements somewhat akin to a tangled mass of kite string.

Statistically, there is one most probable distance between any two atoms along a chain. When an applied force changes this distance, the thermal movement of the system automatically sets up a force to bring this distance back to its most probable location. This is the action that explains the elastic recovery of elastomer; "billions" of molecules unite in the act to make a relatively small piece of elastomer "snap back."

Within the elastic solid the tangled chains are relatively free to move with reference to one another except when, upon being vulcanized, they are "hooked" together at chemically reactive sites along the chain by cross-links. It is such cross bridging that brings about the structural integrity necessary for a piece of elastomer to perform its function.

Whether deformation is in shear, compression, tension, or torsion in an elastomeric product, the elastomer molecule does not really know the difference except in the degree of strain involved. Elastomer in this context has sometimes been called a "lubricant" or a "grease" with togetherness. Elastomeric dampers employ a viscoelastic polymer that is vulcanized and bonded to metallic members. Deformation of the viscocelastic material produces a total resisting force consisting of a damping and a spring component operating 90° out of phase because of the hystenesis inherent in the polymer. In other words, a piece of such material exhibits both stiffness and damping all in one. Moreover, the amounts of each can be controlled by design. The most important assets of elastomeric dampers are improved reliability and elimination of the costly maintenance usually associated with conventional energy dissipative devices such as friction or viscous dampers.

Figure 7.19 illustrates several applications of elastomeric bearings and dampers to helicopters.

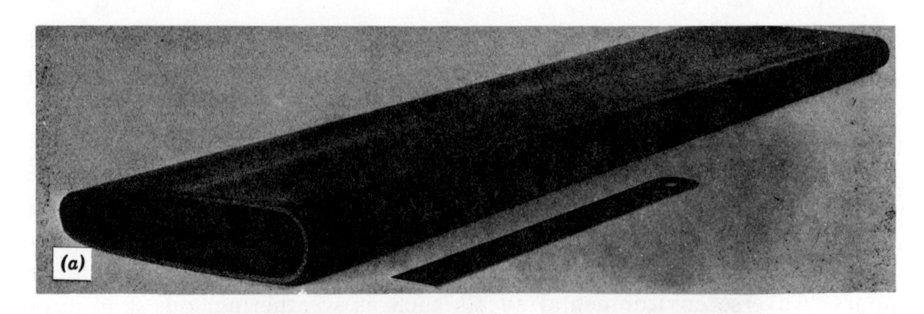

Figure 7.17 Composite helicopter components. (Courtesty Lockheed Aircraft Company.)

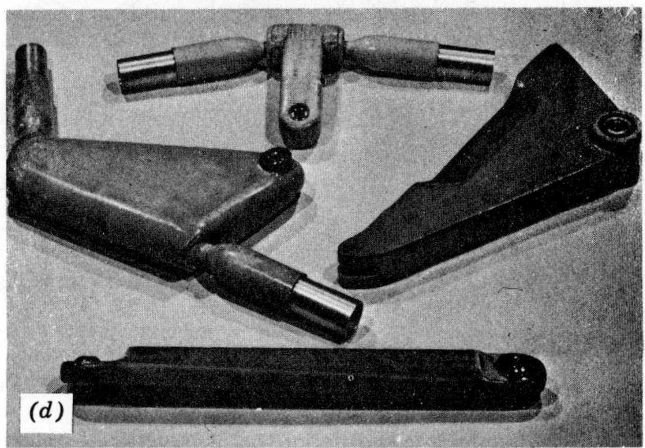

Figure 7.17 (*Continued*)

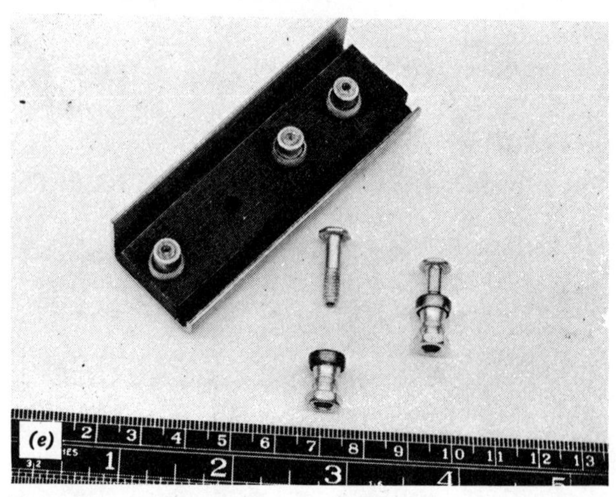

Figure 7.17 (*Continued*)

7.6 CRASHWORTHINESS

The potential for survival of the occupants of a helicopter involved in a crash depends on the following considerations:

1. Crashworthiness of aircraft structure—the ability of the aircraft structure to maintain living space.
2. Tie-down chain strength—the strength of the linkage preventing occupant, cargo, or equipment from becoming missiles during a crash.
3. Occupant acceleration environment—the intensity and duration of accelerations experienced by occupants (with tie-down assumed intact) during a crash.
4. Occupant environment hazards—barriers, projections, and loose equipment in the immediate vicinity of the occupant, which may cause contact injuries.
5. Postcrash hazard—the threat to occupant survival posed by such factors as fire, drowning, and exposure following the impact.

These five areas are usually lumped under the broader title of crashworthiness.

The structure's ability to maintain living space has been a severe problem in helicopters. Figure 7.20 illustrates typical failures of the structure in this

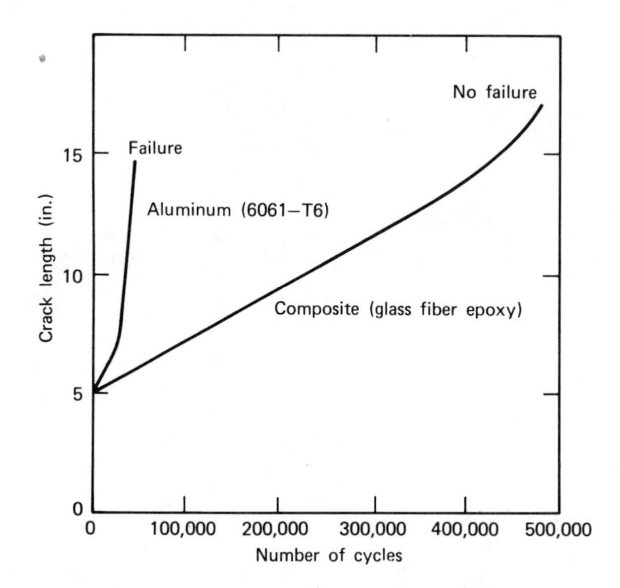

Figure 7.18 Fatigue of H-53 rotor blade sections. (From reference 30.)

respect. A study of 71 U.S. Army utility helicopter accidents revealed the following:

1. In 60% of the cases the aircraft either impacted directly on its side or rolled on its side at least once during the crash sequence.
2. The main rotor blade penetrated the cockpit sufficiently to cause crew injury in 13% of the cases.
3. The transmission or mast penetrated the troop space sufficiently to constitute a hazard to occupants 21% of the time.
4. In 16% of the crashes vertical decelerative forces were exerted on at least one occupant beyond human tolerance.
5. In 47% of the crashes one or more occupants received injuries or were trapped by inward movement of the fuselage shell or transmission.
6. In over one third of the cases at least one occupant was ejected from the helicopter during the crash sequence.

The 71 accidents—all of them army accidents occurring during a 15 month period, has the following common features: (1) same helicopter model, (2) at least one occupant survived, and (3) at least one occupant received a major injury.

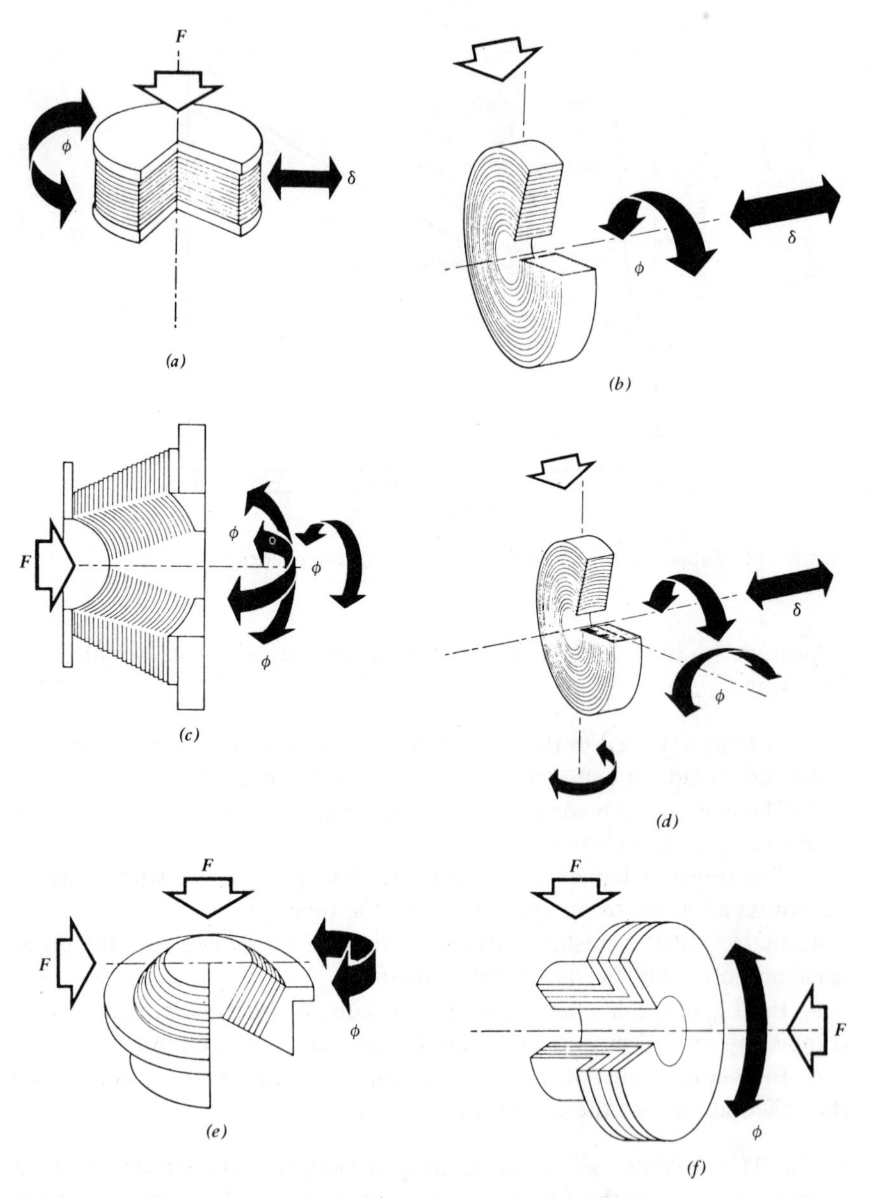

Figure 7.19 Elastomeric bearing configurations. (*a*) Typical axial bearing. (*b*) Typical radial bearing. (*c*) Spherical sandwich bearing. (*d*) Spherical tubular bearing. (*e*) Conical

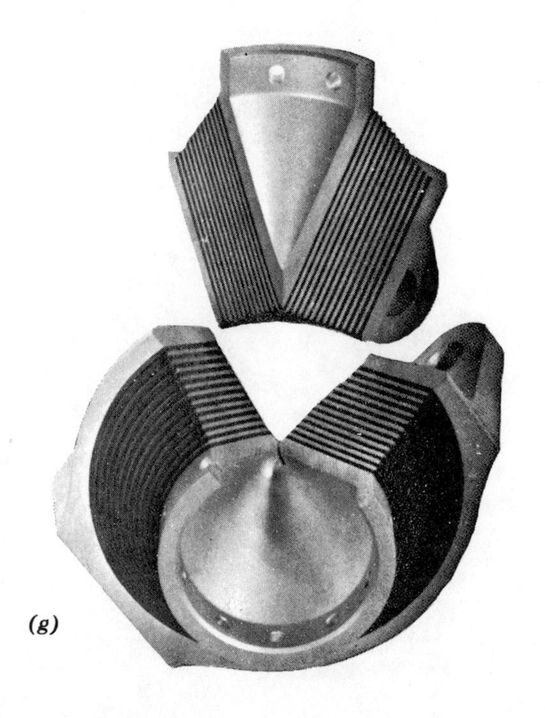

bearing. (*f*) Radial/axial bearing. (*g*) Bearing designed for AH-1 Cobra. (*h*) Closeup of elastomeric bearings installed in hub. (Courtesy Lord Manufacturing.)

Figure 7.20 Helicopter crash examples showing collapse of cockpit living space. (Courtesy U.S. Army.)

Load Limiting

The literature on crashworthy fuselage designs reveals that most of the work done has been experimental. Exceptions are the utilization of "load limiting" landing gears by several manufacturers. Bell Helicopter Company uses a tapered wall tube on their skid-type gear to good advantage. Hughes Aircraft used the plastic bending potential of their outrigger landing gears. Sikorsky incorporated crushable honeycomb into some of their landing gear struts to provide controlled deformation. The emergency sink

Figure 7.20 (*Continued*)

rates of all three manufacturers' products have been increased from 9 or 10 fps up to 15 fps.

"Load limiting" refers to restricting the load in a structure to a specific value by permitting controlled deformation to occur. Consider a vertical descent of a helicopter at 600 fpm (10 fps) (Figure 7.21).

The time history of landing gear deflection on touchdown may be very nonlinear from its initially undeflected state to its maximum deflection. Consequently the deceleration experienced by the fuselage floor may vary. For simplicity, assume that a constant deceleration has occurred over the short time it takes to completely arrest the vertical descent rate; that is,

$$V_0 = 10 \text{ fps}$$
$$V = 0$$
$$s = 1 \text{ ft}$$
$$V^2 - V_0^2 = 2as$$

Figure 7.20 (*Continued*)

where

$$a = \frac{V^2 - V_0^2}{2s} = \frac{-(10)^2}{2(1)} = -50 \text{ ft/sec}^2 = -1.55\ G$$

The minus sign refers to the deceleration process. If this deceleration were transferred directly to the pilot, he would perceive it as an incremental force in his positive G direction. Thus he would experience $1.0 + 1.55 = 2.55\ G$ positive during this time. The time period required for the deceleration is calculated from the constant acceleration formula previously derived:

$$V = V_0 + at$$

$$t = \frac{V - V_0}{a} = \frac{-10}{-50} = \tfrac{1}{5} \text{ sec}$$

The occupant's experience will in general differ from the prediction above for at least three reasons:

1. The load/deflection relationship of the gear structure may not be linear because of geometry and/or the proportional limit strength of the material being exceeded.

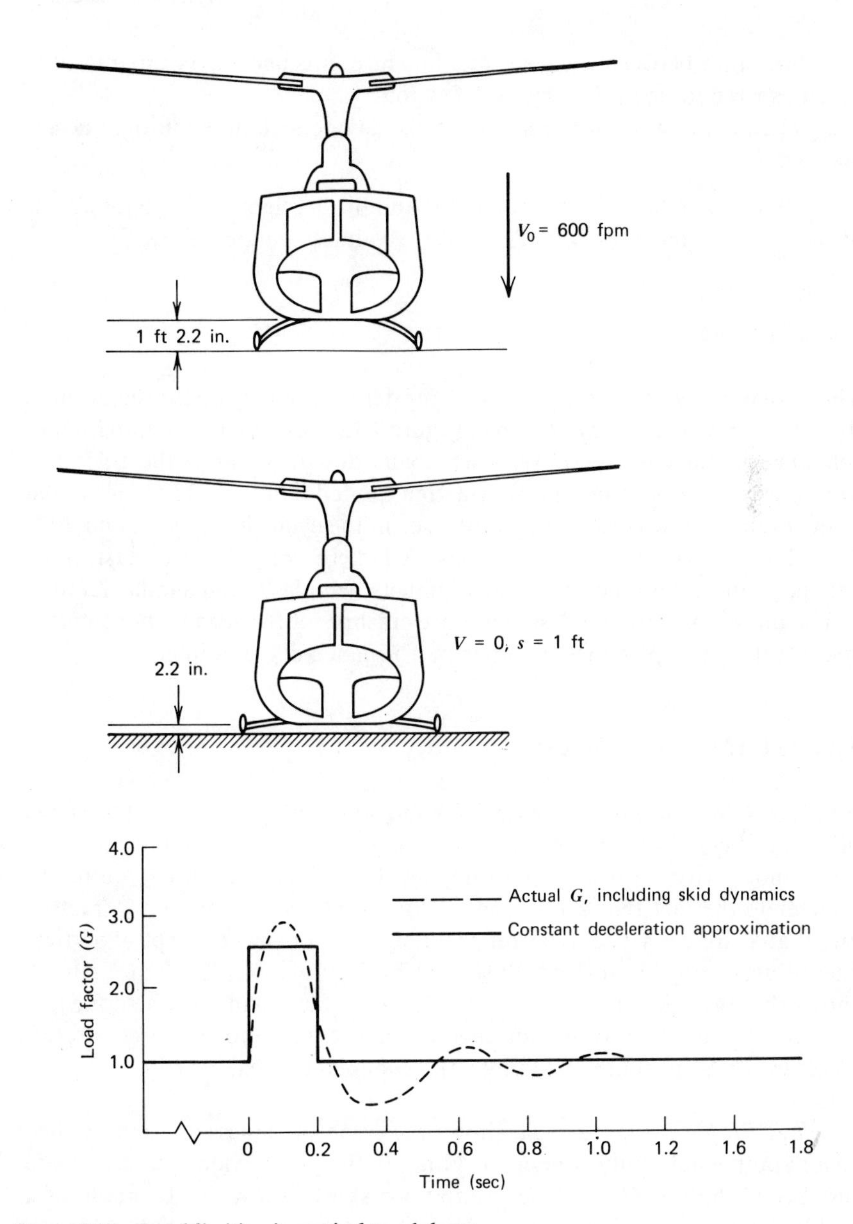

Figure 7.21 Load limiting in vertical touchdown.

2. Structure between the gear attachment points and the occupant's seat may absorb additional energy in deflection.

3. The "dynamics" of the gear system may contribute additional accelerations.

If the total maximum deflection is 1 ft and the deceleration is nonuniform, at times the momentary G will exceed the value calculated above.

Human Tolerance

The human body's ability to survive force depends in part on the magnitude, direction, and duration of the force. Figure 7.22 provides insight into human tolerance in the positive G sense (eyeballs down). Clearly, the tolerance decreases with increasing duration. Often quoted limits are 25 G for 0.1 sec in the eyeballs down case, 45 G for 0.1 sec in the eyeballs out case, and 20 G for 0.1 sec in sideward accelerations. All these are for a well-restrained occupant and do not consider hard impacts, whiplash, and similar factors.

The question is how to design a more crashproof fuselage without undue structural weight penalties or other performance degradations.

Airframe Crashworthiness Design

Fuselage Cross Section. Figure 7.23 illustrates in very simple terms the difference between a circular and a rectangular structure, the former being much more crush resistant on an impact. Little imagination is required to appreciate the fact that a box dropped on a corner will probably fracture and that a circular wooden barrel probably will not. The concept of vertical energy absorption is further illustrated in Figure 7.24. The figure simply shows that the inward crushing of the fuselage outer skin must be done in a controlled manner in order for the skin and frames not to force aircraft structure or large components into the occupiable area.

Fuselage Profile. Figure 7.25*a* shows the crashworthiness concept applied to a hypothetical utility helicopter. Note, in the profile view, the keel beam just below the floor level. The inside floor skin is shown to be made of a highly ductile material so that maximum resistance to penetration by rocks, tree stumps, landing gear, and other objects is afforded. The shallow, conventional high strength beams just below the floor could be used to provide a redundant load path for fuselage torsion, shear, and bending flight loads. This "subfloor" with the high strength sheet just below it could provide

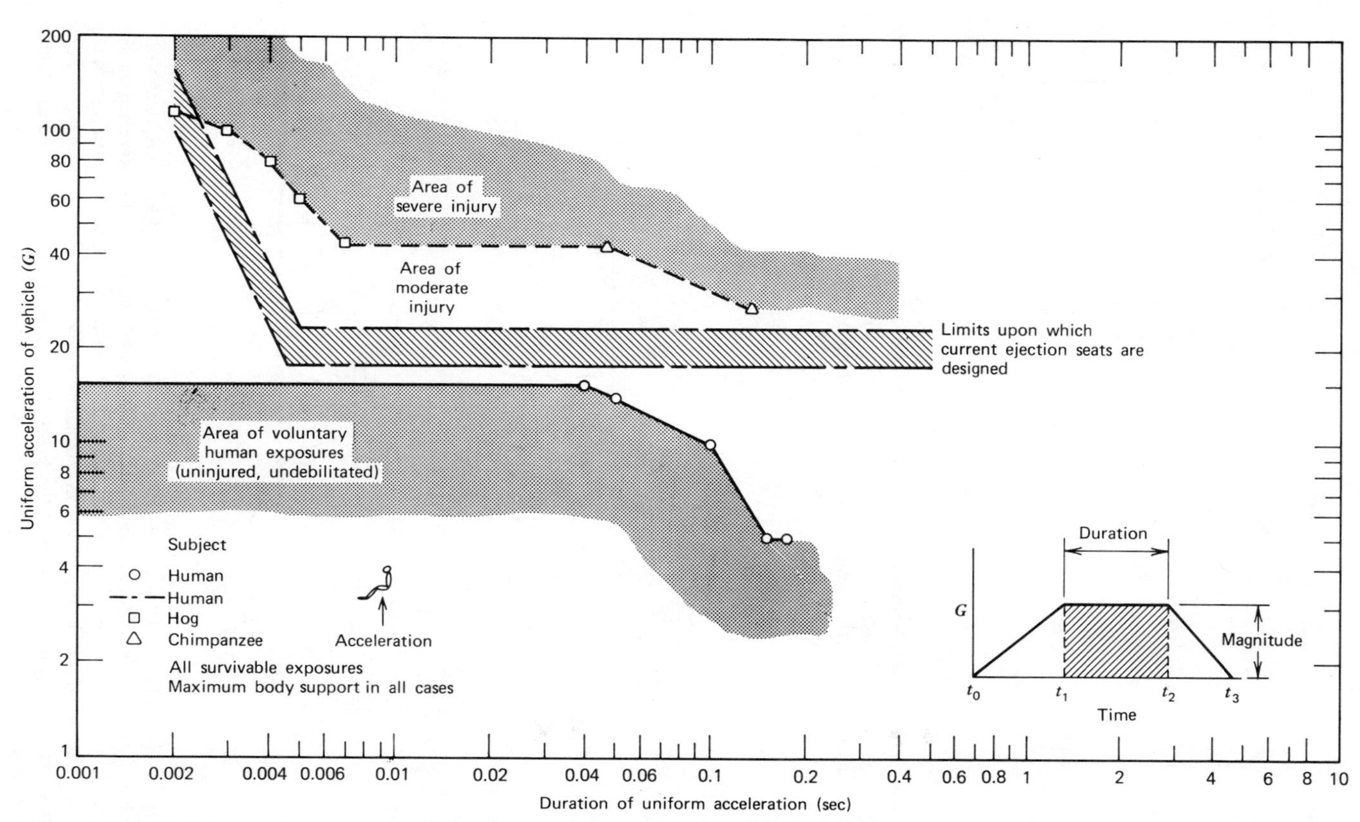

Figure 7.22 Duration and magnitude of headward acceleration endured by various subjects. (From reference 93.)

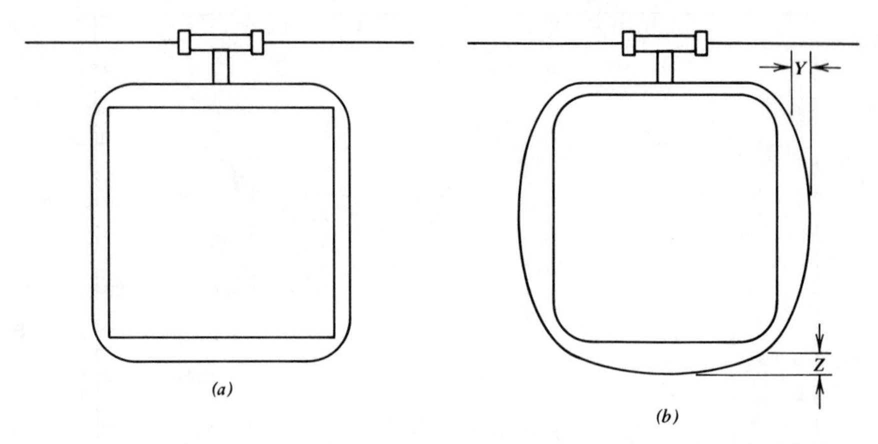

Figure 7.23 Desirable structural cross section to absorb maximum emergency sink rates. (*a*) Poor design. Rectangular cross section: (1) no crushable structure; (2) weak corners (square joint). (*b*) Better design. Circular cross section: (1) *Y* and *Z* crushable structure; (2) strong corners (round joints). (From reference 50.)

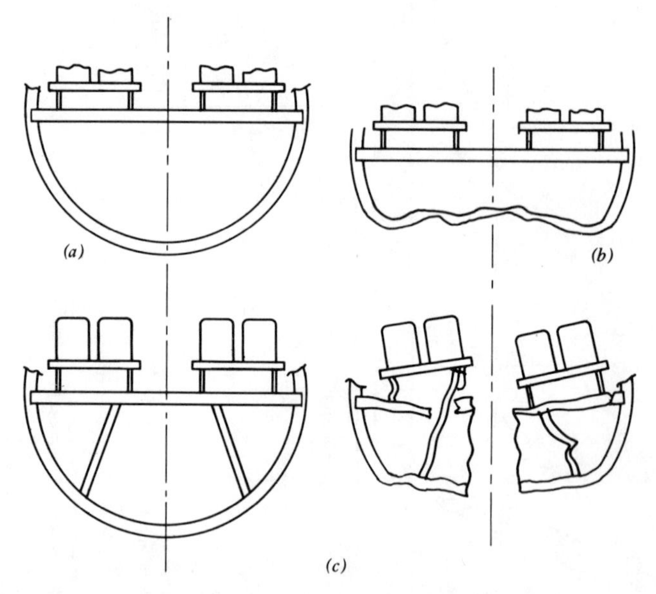

Figure 7.24 Effects of underfloor structure on survivability. (*a*) Floor beam supported at sidewall only. (*b*) Seat support unaffected by lower shell crushing. (*c*) Lower shell supported floor beam. As the lower shell is crushed or worn away, the underfloor support members may either protrude through the floor, damaging or destroying the seat or attachment, or they may fail locally. Either way the floor beam strength is radically reduced and will itself fail as seat loads are applied. (From reference 50.)

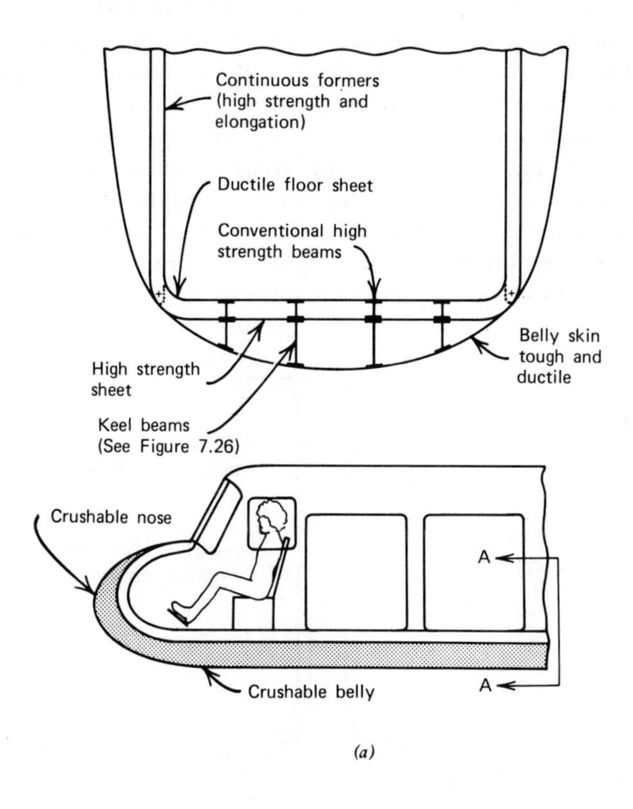

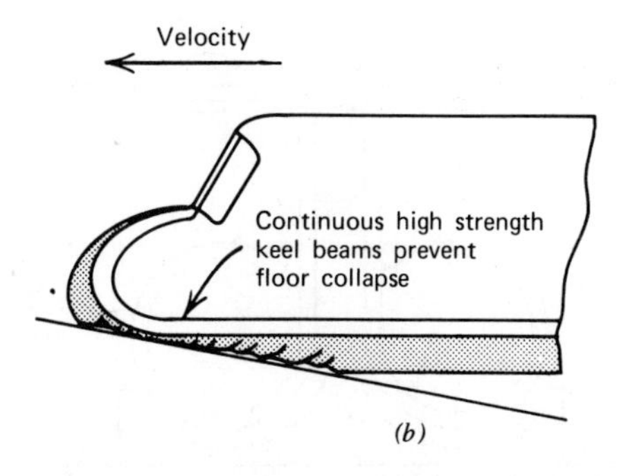

Figure 7.25 Structural design for crashworthiness. (*a*) Conceptual structural configurations to absorb maximum energy for sideward, longitudinal, and vertical impact forces. (*b*) Crushable belly deforms inward without "plowing" due to ductile outer skin. (From reference 50.)

space and protection for control cables, control rods, hydraulic lines, electrical lines, and similar items. The keel beam portion of the subfloor extends forward and upward in front of the crew member's feet to offer protection in the event of a nose-on crash or end-over crash.

The crushable belly is depicted to be made up of highly ductile outer skin, which would resist tears and would crush inward easily without tearing. This crushable belly skin could be supported by a variety of crushable materials. The concept shown in the top view of Figure 7.25*a* is simply one conventional idea that might be made to work. The concept of the crushable beams is shown in Figure 7.26.

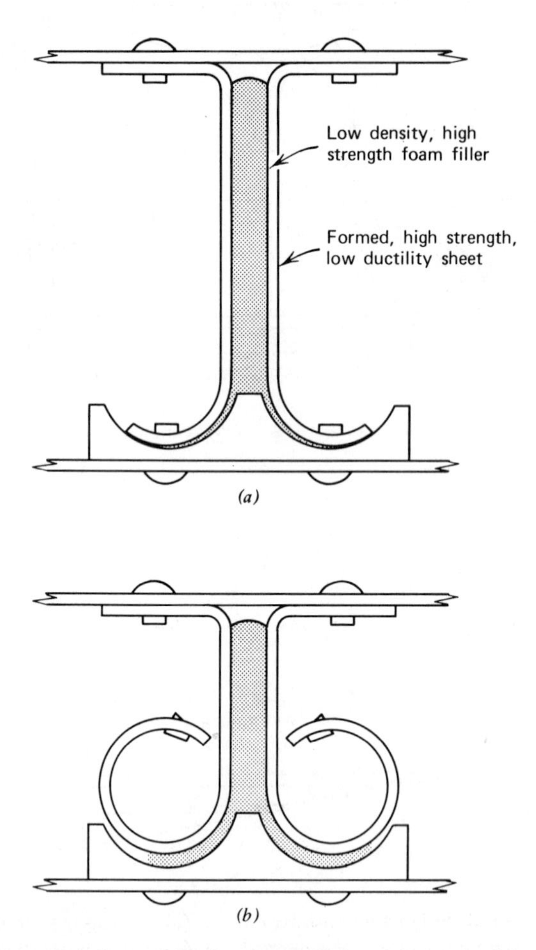

Figure 7.26 Cap and web combination beam design with potential energy absorbing capability. (*a*) Before impact. (*b*) After impact. (From reference 50.)

A profile view of the crushable belly concept is shown in Figure 7.25*b*. A moderate sink speed, combined with a slight nosedown attitude and some forward speed will result in inward deformation of belly structure. Control of this deformation is the design goal so that fractures, breaks, tears, and buckles cannot form an "earth scoop."

Another feature of the suggested utility helicopter fuselage shown in Figure 7.25*a* is the suggested low height door, which would be hinged at the floor level and would be provided with some type of stop similar to the "airstair" used on commercial airlines. These doors could be closed for all flight conditions, regardless of the shortness of the duration and thus provide protection against occupant ejection from the aircraft for any who may not use a restraint harness. The hinged doors would also (1) prevent, in their horizontal position, troops from inadvertently jumping between the fuselage and the skids in hovering-type troop discharges and (2) serve, in their closed position, as a structural member of the basic airframe and improve its integrity and continuity.

The overall optimum fuselage configuration to best absorb maximum energy is a sphere, followed by an ellipse. Both shapes would provide a large radius surface to resist inward curshing from any impact angle. The spherical or elliptical shape would also ensure minimum resistance on the part of the aircraft during end-over or lateral roll-over accidents. For very small aircraft (4 to 6 occupants), an elliptical shape could be used. In larger aircraft, a cylindrical shape must be used in order to reduce drag.

Tie-down of Heavy Components. The heavy masses of the helicopter such as transmissions, engines, and landing gear should be so located that they are unlikely to intrude into the occupiable area in severe crashes. The failure modes of the landing gear should be determined for all impact angles—from vertical to lateral configurations—to make certain that struts, cross tubes, or skids cannot penetrate the occupiable area. Engines should be tied down with enough strength to prevent their displacement into flammable fluids that may be spilled in a crash. On the basis of the navy's accident experience with 20 G strength transmissions and on the basis of measured loads in full scale tests, a tie-down strength of 20 G_z, 20 G_x, and 15 G_y appears to be needed.

Recommended Terrain Impact Conditions. This is a difficult topic because of the many different impact attitudes and terrain conditions. Some tentative impact conditions were agreed upon by a crashworthiness panel at the Second Department of Defense/Rand Symposium on "Increased Survivability of Aircraft" at Santa Monica, California, in February 1970. Some of the proposed conditions are presented here for consideration.

MINIMUM HELICOPTER DESIGN CRASH CONDITIONS

1. All occupants should survive without injury in a fuselage impact along the Z axis of 40 fps.*
2. All occupants should survive with minimum injury in a fuselage impact along the diagonal axis (45° from Y and Z axis) of 35 fps.*
3. All occupants should survive with minimum injury in a fuselage impact along the Y axis at 32 fps.*
4. The cockpit occupants (crew) should be able to survive without injury in an impact into a rigid wall at 20 fps.
5. All fuselage occupants seated aft of the cockpit should survive without injury in a longitudinal impact into a rigid wall at a velocity of 40 fps.
6. All occupants should survive without major injuries in an impact with sod-type terrain up to an impact angle of 5° and up to a velocity of 100 fps. This is a "roll-over" condition about any aircraft axis, sometimes caused by "running" landings after tail rotor failure
7. Landing Gear Design Criteria: (*a*) Limit sink speed*—8 fps minimum, flat impact. (*b*) Emergency sink speed*—18 fps minimum, flat impact. (Fuselage belly contact is acceptable.)

These conditions should be considered as minimum impact conditions for small 2500–3000-lb G.W. helicopters. Larger helicopters could sustain higher survivable impact speeds, but further analysis and/or experience is necessary before attempting to set definite limits.

Postcrash Fire

Accident records indicate that the greatest number of fatalities occur in accidents involving postcrash fire. Reference 8 and others indicate that the problem of survival in fire accidents is most critical in rotary wing aircraft. It is apparent from crash fire studies that once ignition has occurred in the presence of significant quantities of uncontained fuel, the chances of survival are greatly reduced, even where fire fighting equipment is immediately available.

Fires occur only when three basic elements are present: a fuel, an oxidizer, and an ignition source. Control of any one of these three elements will prevent a fire. Since it is hardly feasible to control the supply of oxygen immediately surrounding the aircraft, control is best exercised over the other two elements.

The ideal fuel system is one that completely contains its flammable fluids both during and after the accident. To accomplish this, all components of the system must resist rupture regardless of the degree of failure of the

* Rigid surface impact applies.

surrounding structure. Success of the system depends on proper design technique and selection of materials for fuel tanks and fittings, flammable fluid lines, fuel transfer system components, and vent systems. As a result of sad experience rapid advances in these areas have been recently demonstrated. Crashworthy fuel systems, retrofitted to existing helicopters have dramatically reduced injury and death due to postcrash fire. The U.S. Army has reduced postcrash fires from 1 in 11 crashes to 1 in 50 by converting to such a system. Moreover, more stringent detailed crashworthiness specifications are now being incorporated into procurement documents, which ensure a greater level of safety for minimum weight/performance penalties.

PROBLEMS

7.1 A helicopter hovering 15 ft above the ground suddenly experiences a complete power loss and falls vertically to the ground. Examination of the damage to the skids and fuselage indicates that a maximum compression of 2 ft has occurred. Determine: (*a*) the maximum rate of descent possible at the moment of impact and (*b*) the average deceleration experienced during impact.

7.2 A certain structural member of a helicopter has a cylindrical shape with a diameter of $\frac{1}{2}$ in. It is subjected to the following cyclic tension loads during 1 hr of flight: 1000 cycles at 10,000 lb, 5000 cycles at 8000 lb, 100,000 cycles at 6000 lb. What is this member's fatigue life (hr) if it has the fatigue characteristics of Figure 7.14?

Figure 7.27 Courtesy U.S. Navy.

ANSWERS TO PROBLEMS

1.1 (*a*) 8946 lb; (*b*) 18.16°.
1.2 (*a*) 268.3 knots; (*b*) 2572 lb.
1.3 2573 lb.

2.1 (*a*) 1696 psf; (*b*) 0.001868 slugs/ft^3; (*c*) 90.2 knots; (*d*) 3.13°.
2.2 (*a*) 2165 psf; (*b*) 48.94 psf; (*c*) 2153 psf.
2.3 (*a*) 88.8 knots; (*b*) 4.4°; (*c*) 1250 lb.
2.4 300 HP.

3.1 (*a*) 760 fps; (*b*) $M = 0.68$; (*c*) $M = 0.70$.
3.2 (*a*) 0.133; (*b*) 8.84 psf; (*c*) 79.5 fps.
3.3 $P_{pr} = 2336$ HP; $P_i = 5562$ HP; $M = 0.69$.

4.1 (*a*) 909 fps; (*b*) $M = 0.84$; (*c*) $M = 0.55$; (*d*) 0.21.
4.2 8.77°.
4.3 (*a*) 305 HP; (*b*) 264 HP; (*c*) 413 HP.
4.4 (*a*) 35 knots, 110 knots; (*b*) 68 knots.
4.5 1593 HP in hover, 926 HP at 100 knots.
4.6 (*a*) 719 ft; (*b*) 12.1°/sec; (*c*) 1.41; (*d*) 1100 HP.
4.7 (*a*) 2237 fpm; (*b*) 8.88 ft/sec^2.
4.8 (*a*) 0.773; (*b*) 0.802, (*c*) 0.783.

6.1 (*a*) 1979 ft; (*b*) 15,480 ft; (*c*) 19,059 ft; (*d*) 16,946 ft.

6.2 15°.

6.3 (*a*) 8.6 knots; (*b*) 23.5 knots; (*c*) 71.4 knots; (*d*) 18.2°.

6.4 2.71°.

6.5 1.11 *G*.

6.6 (*a*) 53 KIAS; (*b*) 1250 fpm; (*c*) 14 min; (*d*) 1000 fpm; (*e*) 360 fpm; (*f*) 8.4°.

7.1 (*a*) 1865 fpm; (*b*) 241.5 ft/sec^2.

7.2 164 hr.

BIBLIOGRAPHY

BOOKS

1. Anonymous, *Instrument Flying for Helicopter Aircraft*, U.S.A.F. Manual 51-13, Department of the Air Force, April 1967.
2. Anonymous, *The Jet Engine*, 3rd ed., Rolls-Royce Ltd., England, 1969.
3. Etkin, B., *Dynamics of Atmospheric Flight*, Wiley, New York, 1971.
4. Gessow, A. and G. Myers, *Aerodynamics of the Helicopter*, Macmillan, New York, 1952.
5. Green, D. L., *Helicopter Stability and Control*, Navy Test Pilot School Flight Test Manual #101, June 1968.
6. Hurt, H. H., *Aerodynamics for Naval Aviators*, Navair 00-80T-80, revised January 1965.
7. Hurt, H. H., *Fundamentals of Helicopter Structures*, University of Southern California, 1967.
8. Karman, Theodore von, *Aerodynamics*, McGraw-Hill, New York, 1963.
9. Liptrot, R. N. and J. D. Woods, *Rotorcraft*, Butterworths, London, 1955.
10. Nikolsky, A. A., *Helicopter Analysis*, Wiley, New York, 1951.
11. Payne, P. R., *Helicopter Dynamics and Aerodynamics*, Macmillan, New York, 1959.
12. Perkins, C. D. and Robert Hage, *Airplane Performance Stability and Control*, Wiley, New York, 1957.
13. Richards, R. B., *Principles of Helicopter Performance*, Naval Test Pilot School Textbook USNTPS-T-No. 1, March 1968.
14. Roland, H. E. and J. F. Detwiler, *Fundamentals of Fixed and Rotary Wing Aerodynamics*, University of Southern California, November 1967.
15. Seckel, E., *Stability and Control of Airplanes and Helicopters*, Academic Press, New York, 1964.
16. Shapiro, Jacob, *The Helicopter*, Macmillan, New York, 1957.
17. Shapiro, Jacob, *Principles of Helicopter Engineering*, McGraw-Hill, New York, 1955.
18. Young, Raymond A., *Helicopter Engineering*, Ronald Press, New York, 1949.

REPORTS, PAPERS, ARTICLES, AND OTHER SOURCES

19. Abzug, J. J., *Dynamics and Control of Helicopters with Two-Cable Sling Loads*, AIAA 2nd Aircraft Design and Operations Meeting, Paper No. 70-929, Los Angeles, Calif., July 1970.
20. Air Force Flight Dynamics Laboratory, *Proceedings of the V/STOL Technology and Planning Conference*, Las Vegas, 22–25 September, 1969.
21. Amer, K. B. and A. Gessow, *Charts for Estimating Tail-Rotor Contribution to Helicopter Directional Stability and Control in Low-Speed Flight*, NACA Report TR1216, 1955.
22. Anonymous, *Heavy Helicopter Tests Loop, Roll:* (CH-53A), Aviation Week and Space Technology, November 18, 1968.
23. Anonymous, Military Specification MIL-H-8501A, *Helicopter Flying and Ground Handling Qualities; General Requirements for*, September 1961 with Amendment April 1962.
24. Anonymous, *NACA Conference on Helicopters*, A Compilation of the Papers Presented, Langley Aeronautical Laboratory, May 1954.
25. Anonymous, *Special Study of Autorotational Procedures*, U.S. Army Aviation Test Activity, February 1968.
26. Asseo, S. J. and R. F. Whitbeck, "Control Requirements for Sling-Load Stabilization in Heavy Lift Helicopters," *Journal of the American Helicopter Society*, Vol. 18, No. 3, July 1973.
27. Bailey, F. J., *Simplified Theoretical Method of Determining the Characteristics of a Lifting Rotor in Forward Flight*, NACA Report 716, 1941.
28. Balke, R. W., *Development of the Kinematic Focal Insulation System for Helicopter Rotors*, 38th Shock and Vibration Symposium, St. Louis, May 1968.
29. Bartlett, F. D. et al., *Application of Antiresonance Theory to Helicopters*, American Helicopter Society 29th National Forum, May 1973.
30. Bettino, J. et al., *Development of the CH-53D High Performance Titanium Main Rotor Blade*, American Helicopter Society 29th Annual Forum, Paper No. 783, May 1973.
31. Blake, B. B. et al., *Flight Simulation of the CH-46 Helicopter*, American Helicopter Society 25th Annual Symposium, Paper No. 361, May 1969.
32. Brata, N. et al., *Tail Rotor Design, Park I—Aerodynamics*, and R. W. Balke, et. al., *Tail Rotor Design, Park II—Structural Dynamics*, American Helicopter Society 25th Annual Forum, May 1969.
33. Buss, M. W., *Sudden Engine Failure Problems of High-Performance Attack Helicopters*, Society of Experimental Test Pilots, 15th Annual Report, September 1971.
34. Carta, F. O. and R. G. Carlson, *Determination of Airfoil and Rotor Blade Dynamic Stall Response*, American Helicopter Society 28th Annual Forum, Paper No. 613, May 1972.
35. Cooper, G. E. and R. P. Harper, Jr., *The Use of Pilot Rating in the Evaluation of Aircraft Handling Qualities*, NASA TN D-5153, April 1969.
36. Crimi, Peter, *Theoretical Prediction of the Flow in the Wake of a Helicopter Rotor*, CAL No. B-1994-S-1, Cornell Aeronautical Laboratory, September 1965.
37. Curtiss, H. C. and E. Seckez, *Helicopter Rotor Forces and Moments*, Princeton University Aeronautical Engineering Report 659, 1963.

38. Dukes, T. A., *Elements of Hovering and Near-Hover Operations With Sling Load*, RDTR ECOM-02412-12, U.S. Army Electronics Command, Fort Monmouth, N. J., September 1972.

39. Dukes, T. A., "Maneuvering Heavy Sling Loads Near Hover, Part I, Damping the Pendulous Motion," *Journal of the American Helicopter Society*, Vol. 18, No. 2, April 1973; "Part 2, Some Elementary Maneuvers," *ibid.*, Vol. 18, No. 3, July 1973.

40. Dumond, R. C. and D. R. Simon, *Flight Investigation of Design Features of the S-67 Winged Helicopter*, American Helicopter Society 28th Annual Forum, May 1972.

41. Dutton, W. J., *Development of H-53 Elastomeric Rotor Head*, American Helicopter Society 29th Annual Forum, Paper No. 713, May 1973.

42. Empey, R. W. and R. A. Ormiston, *Tail Rotor Thrust on a 5.5 ft Helicopter Model in Ground Effect*, American Helicopter Society 30th Annual Forum, Paper No. 802, May 1974.

43. Fitch, J. B. and J. J. Shapley, *Investigation of Engine Rigging, Airspeed and Rotor RPM Effects on Steady State Autorotational Performance*, U.S. Army Aviation Systems Test Activity Report, December 1970.

44. Flannelly, W. G., *The Dynamic Anti-Resonant Vibration Isolator*, American Helicopter Society, 22nd National Forum, May 1966.

45. Gatlin, C. I. et al., *Analysis of Helicopter Structural Crashworthiness*, USAAVLABS Tech. Report 70-71A, January 1971.

46. Gessow, A., *Equations and Procedures for Numerically Calculating the Aerodynamic Characteristics of Lifting Rotors*, NACA TN3747, 1956.

47. Graham, G. L., *Combat Operational Flight Profiles on the UH-1C, AH-1G, and UH-1H Helicopters*, American Helicopter Society 26th Annual Forum, Paper No. 455, June 1974.

48. Green, D. L., *A Review of MIL-F-83300 for Helicopter Applications*, American Helicopter Society, 28th Annual Forum, May 1972.

49. Griffith II, W. E. and L. K. Brewer, *Helicopter Icing Handling Qualities*, American Helicopter Society 30th Annual Forum, Paper No. 844, May 1974.

50. Haley, J. L., *Helicopter Structural Design for Impact Survival*, Symposium on Environmental Effects of VTOL Design, University of Texas, November 1970.

51. Hanley, W. J. and G. DeVore, *An Analysis of the Helicopter Height Velocity Diagram Including a Practical Method for Its Determination*, FAA Report No. NA-67-1, October 1967.

52. Ham, N. D. and M. I. Young, "Torsional Oscillation of Helicopter Blades Due to Stall," *Journal of Aircraft*, June 1966.

53. Harned, Malcolm, *Development of the OH-6A for Maximum Performance and Efficiency*, American Helicopter Society, 20th Annual Forum, May 1964.

54. Harris, F. D. and R. R. Pruyn, "Blade Stall-Half Fact, Half Fiction," *Journal American Helicopter Society*, Vol. B, No. 2, 1968.

55. Hirsh, N. B. and H. W. Ferris, *Design Requirements for a Quiet Helicopter*, American Helicopter Society 28th Annual Forum, Paper No. 604, May 1972.

56. Hutto, A. J., *Qualitative Report on Flight Test of a Two-Point External Load Suspension System*, American Helicopter Society 28th Annual Forum, Paper No. 473, June 1970.

57. Johnston, J. A., *A New Approach to Helicopter H-V Testing with Preliminary Results from the OH-58 Kiowa and AH-1G Huey Cobra Helicopters*, 14th Annual Report, Society of Experimental Test Pilots, September 1970.

58. Jones, J. P., "The Helicopter Rotor," *The Aeronautical Journal of the Royal Aeronautical Society*, Vol. 74, No. 719, November 1970.

59. Kesling, P. H. and J. Schmidt, *Hingeless Circulation Control Rotor Blade Design*, American Helicopter Society 30th Annual Forum, Paper No. 813, May 1974.

60. Kidd, D. L. et al., *Recent Advances in Helicopter Vibration Control*, American Helicopter Society 26th National Forum, June 1970.

61. Laing, E. J., *Army Vibration Survey Methods and Results*, American Helicopter Society 29th Annual Forum, Paper No. 763, May 1973.

62. Landgrebe, A. J.,*The Wake Geometry of a Hovering Helicopter Rotor and Its Influence on Rotor Performance*, American Helicopter Society 28th Annual Forum, Paper No. 620, May 1972.

63. Lewis II, R. B., "Army Helicopter Performance Trends," *Journal of the American Helicopter Society*, Vol. 17, No. 2, April 1972.

64. Lewis II, R. B., *Determining Helicopter Instrument Flight Capability*, Proceedings of the 4th National Symposium of the Society of Flight Test Engineers, August 1973.

65. Lewis II, R. B. et al., *Engineering Flight Test, AH-1G Helicopter (Huey Cobra), Maneuvering Limitations*, Final Report, USAASTA, Project No. 69-11, March 1971.

66. Lewis II, R. B., *Huey Cobra Maneuvering Investigations*, American Helicopter Society, 26th National Forum, Paper No. 472, June 1970.

67. Liff, B. and R. Bossler, Jr., *The Starting of Turbine Engines in Helicopters*, American Helicopter Society 28th Annual Forum, Paper No. 662, May 1972.

68. Liu, D. T., *In-Flight Stabilization of Externally Slung Loads*—Phase I Summary Report, Contract No. DAAJ02-6-0067, Navigation Department, Electronics, Division, Northrop Corporation, 1973.

69. Livingston, C. L. and M. R. Murphy, *Flying Qualities Considerations in the Design and Development of the Huey Cobra*, American Helicopter Society 24th Annual Forum, Paper No. 217, May 1968.

70. Martin, J. M. et al., *A Detailed Experimental Analysis of Dynamic Stall on an Unsteady Two-Dimensional Airfoil*, American Helicopter Society 29th National Forum, Paper No. 702, May 1973.

71. McCroskey, W. J., *Recent Developments in Rotor Blade Stall*, AGARD Fluid Dynamics Panel, Aerodynamics of Rotary Wings, September 1972.

72. McCutcheon, R. et al., *S-67 Flight Test Program*, American Helicopter Society 28th National Forum, Paper No. 653, May 1972.

73. Melton, J. R., *Results of the Flight Test Investigation of the Reduced G Maneuver in the AH-1G Helicopter*, Bell Helicopter Company Report No. 209-099-309, Cctober 1969.

74. Mil, M. L. et al., *Helicopters—Calculation and Design, Vol. 1 Aerodynamics*, NASA Technical Translation TT F-494, September 1967.

75. Miller, R. H., *Rotor Blade Harmonic Air Loading*, Presented at the IAS 30th Annual Meeting, New York, January 1962.

76. Montgomery, John R., *Sikorsky Helicopter Flight Theory for Pilots and Mechanics*, Sikorsky Aircraft, 1964.

77. Mouille, R., *The World Speed Records of the SA. 341 Gazelle*, American Helicopter Society 28th Annual Forum, Paper No. 651, May 1972.

78. Odneal, W. L., *Effect of Nap-of-the-Earth Requirements on Aircrew Performance During Night Attack Helicopter Operations*, American Helicopter Society 30th Annual Forum, Paper No. 863, May 1974.

79. Paul, W. F., *The Main Rotor Bifilar Pendulum Vibration Absorber*, Vertiflite, Vol. 16, No. 2, February 1970.

80. Pegg, R. J., *An Investigation of the Helicopter Height-Velocity Diagram Showing Effects of Density Altitude and Gross Weight*, NASA TN D-4536, May 1968.

81. Putman, W. F. and J. J. Traybar, *An Experimental Investigation of Compound Helicopter Aerodynamics in Level and Descending Forward Flight and in Ground Proximity*, USAAMRDL Technical Report 71-19, July 1971.

82. Saunders, G. H., *Development of a Flying Qualities Specification for Military V/STOL Aircraft*, American Helicopter Society 25th Annual Forum, May 1969.

83. Saunders, G. H., *Requirements for Simulation of Helicopter Autorotations*, University of Southern California ISSM Working Paper, March 1972.

84. Saunders, G. H., *Stability Derivatives and Other Data Required for Simulation of the Bell UH-1C Helicopter*, Flight Systems Inc., Report 211-70-1, February 1970.

85. Saunders, G. H. et al., *V/STOL Flying Qualities Criteria Development*, Vol. 1, *A Proposed V/STOL Flying Qualities Specification*, Vol. 2, *Background Information and User's Guide*, Cornell Aeronautical Laboratory, October 1968.

86. Scarpati, T. et al., *The Heavy Lift Helicopter Rotor Blade*, American Helicopter Society 29th National Forum, Paper No. 710, May 1973.

87. Schane, W. P., *Effects of Downwash Upon Man*, U.S. Army Aeromedical Research Unit Report 68-3, November 1967.

88. Schmidt, W. E., *Design, Testing and Performance of Elastomeric Bearings*, American Helicopter Society 30th Annual Forum, Paper No. 883, May 1974.

89. Shipman, D. P. et al., *Fuselage Nodalization*, American Helicopter Society 28th National Forum, No. 611, May 1972.

90. Sinacori, J. B., *Application of the Northrop Rotational Simulator to Helicopters and V/STOL Aircraft*, USAAVLABS Technical Report 70-26, May 1970.

91. Spezia, E., *Fire in U.S. Army Helicopter Accidents*, Report HF 67-1, USABAAR, Ft. Rucker, Ala., January 1967.

92. Tangler, J. L. et al., *An Experimental Investigation of Vortex Stability, Tip Shapes, Compressibility, and Noise for Hovering Model Rotors*, Bell Helicopter Report 299-099-641, also NASA CR-2305, September 1973.

93. Turnbow, et al., *Crash Survival Design Guide*, U.S. Army Aviation Material Laboratories, Technical Report 70-22, August 1969.

94. Wallerstein, L. Jr., *A New Approach to Vibration Isolation for Low Frequency Sources*, ASME Design Engineering Conference and Show, April 1968.

95. Welge, R. T., *Application of Boron/Epoxy to the CH-54B Skycrane*, American Helicopter Society, 28th Annual Forum, May 1972.

96. Wells, C. D. and T. L. Wood, "Maneuverability-Theory and Application," *Journal of the American Helicopter Society*, Vol. 18, No. 1, January 1973.

97. Winn, A. L. and R. B. Lewis II, *Pilot Workload During Instrument Flight*, American Helicopter Society 30th Annual Forum, Paper No. 820, May 1974.

98. Wittlin, G., *A Consistent Crashworthiness Design Criteria Approach for Rotary Wing Aircraft*, American Helicopter Society 29th Annual Forum, Paper No. 781, May 1973.
99. Wolkovitch, J. et al., *Lateral Control of Hovering Vehicles With and Without Sling Loads*, TR 145-1, Systems Technology Inc., Hawthorne, Calif., May 1966.
100. Wolkovitch, J. and J. A. Hoffman, *Stability and Control of Helicopters in Steep Approaches*, USAAVLABS Technical Report 70-74A, 1971.
101. Wolkovitch, J. and R. P. Walton, *VTOL and Helicopter Approximate Transfer Functions and Closed-Loop Handling Qualities*, Systems Technology, Inc., Report 128-1, September 1963.
102. Zinberg, H., *An Advanced Composite Tail Boom for the AH-1G Helicopter*, American Helicopter Society 29th Annual Forum, Paper No. 785, May 1973.

SYMBOLS AND UNITS

a	Acceleration	ft/sec^2
a	Speed of sound	ft/sec (fps)
A	Disc area	ft^2
AR	Aspect ratio	—
b	Span	ft
c	Chord	ft
C_F	Force coefficient	—
C_D	Drag coefficient	—
C_L	Lift coefficient	—
d	Distance	ft
D	Drag	lb
DA	Density altitude	ft
DL	Disc loading	lb/ft^2 (psf)
e	Strain	—
e	Span efficiency factor	—
f	Equivalent flat plate area	ft^2
f	Stress	lb/in.^{2} (psi)
g	Gravitational acceleration (32.2)	ft/sec^2
G	Acceleration $= a/g$	—
h	Altitude	ft
HP	Horsepower	550 ft-lb/sec
I	Moment of inertia	slug-ft^2

KE	Kinetic energy	ft-lb
l	Length	ft
L	Lift	lb
m	Mass	slug
M	Moment	ft-lb
M	Figure of merit	—
p	Pressure	lb/ft^2 (psf)
P	Power	ft-lb/sec
PE	Potential energy	ft/lb
q	Dynamic pressure	lb/ft^2 (psf)
Q	Mass flow rate	slug/sec
R	Radius	ft
R_T	Radius of turn	ft
ROT	Rate of turn	deg/sec
s	Distance	ft
s	Solidity ratio	—
S	Blade area	ft^2
t	Time	sec
T	Torque	ft-lb
u, U, V	Velocity	ft/sec (fps)
W	Weight	lb

GREEK LETTERS

α	Angle of attack	deg
β	Angle of sideslip	deg
γ, Γ	Flight path angle	deg
δ	Pressure ratio	—
Δ	Change in a quantity	—
η	Propulsive efficiency	—
θ	Pitch angle	deg
Θ	Temperature ratio	—
Λ	Glidepath angle	deg
μ	Coefficient of friction	—
ρ	Density	$slug/ft^3$
σ	Density ratio	—
Σ	Summation	—
ϕ	Bank angle	deg
ψ	Heading angle	deg
ω	Rotation rate	rad/sec

APPENDIX: PERFORMANCE CHARTS

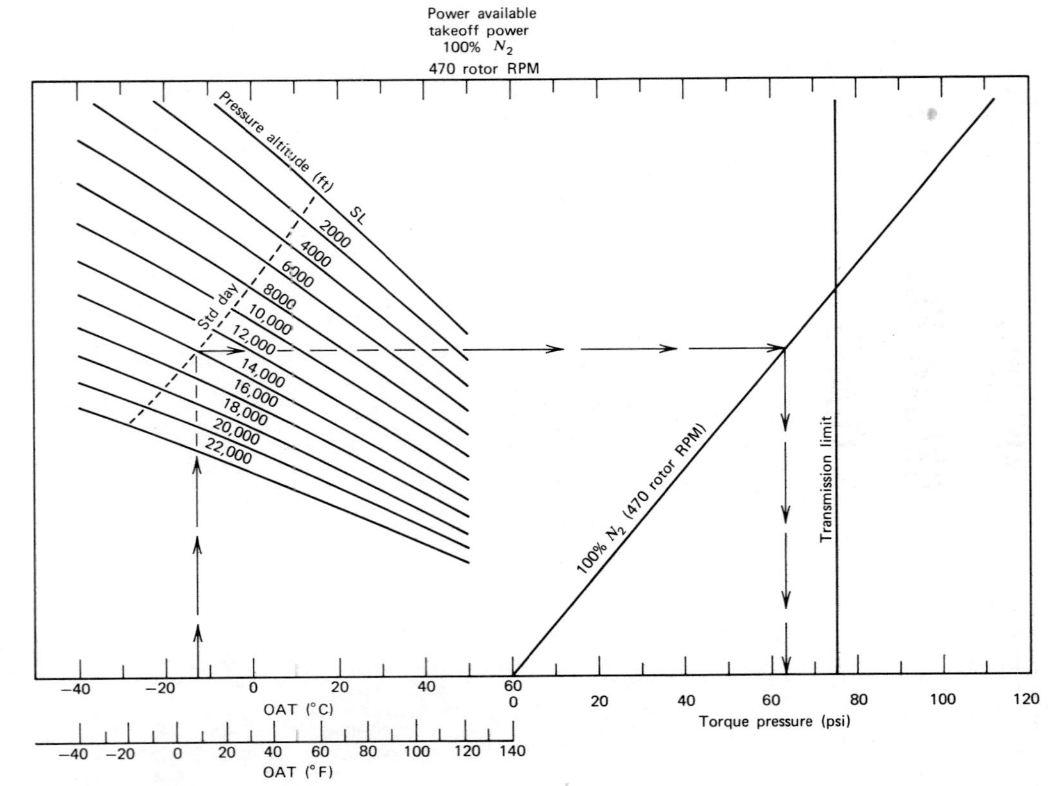

Figure A.1 Power available, takeoff.

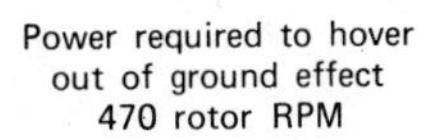

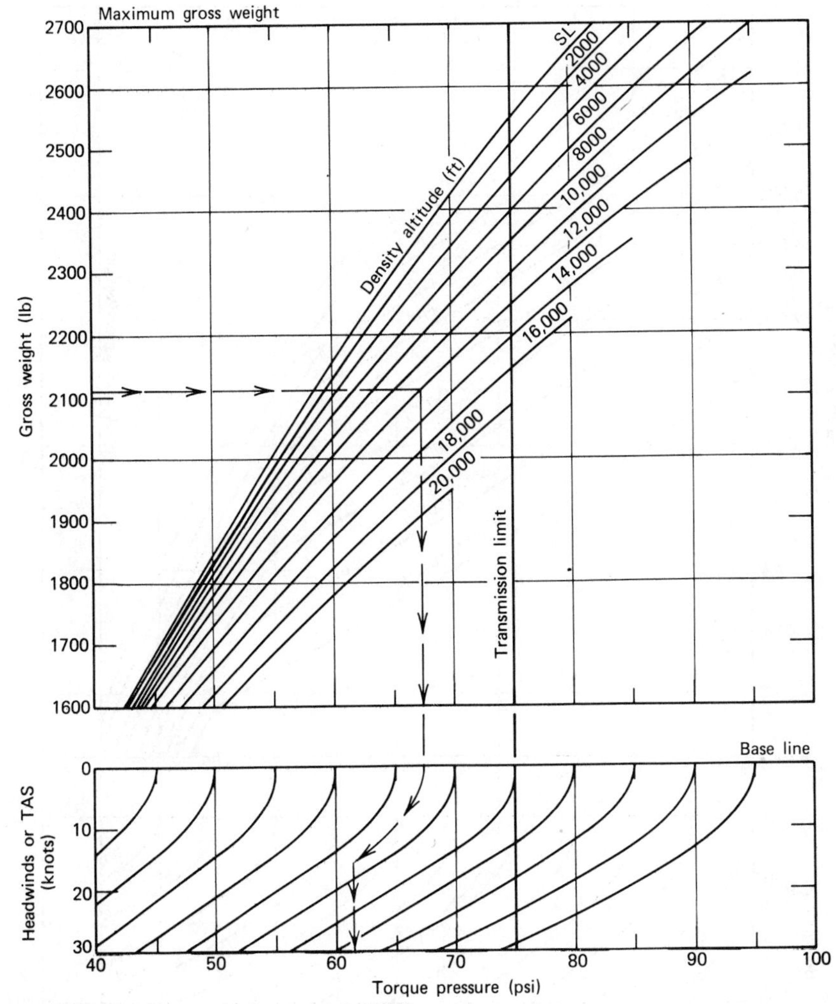

Figure A.2 Power required to hover, OGE.

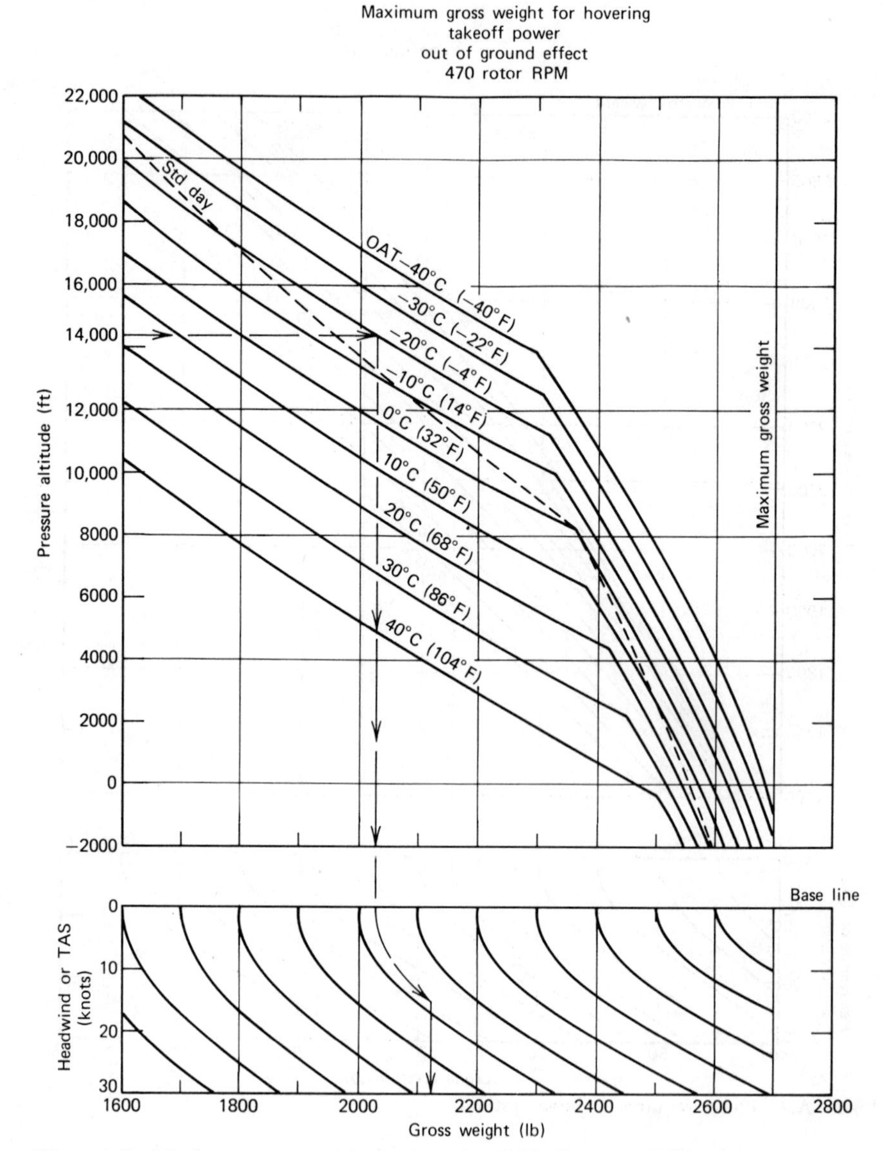

Figure A.3 Maximum gross weight for hovering, takeoff power, OGE.

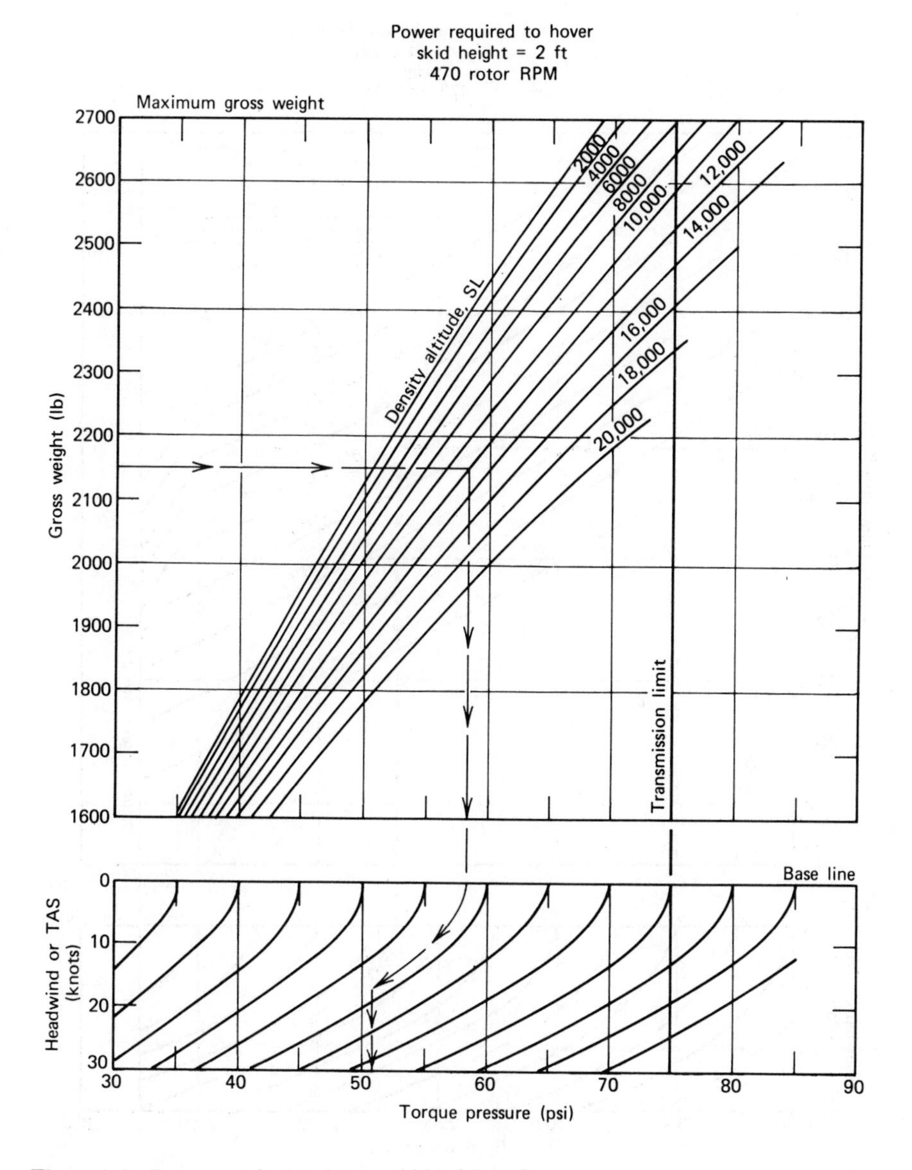

Figure A.4 Power required to hover, skid height 2 ft.

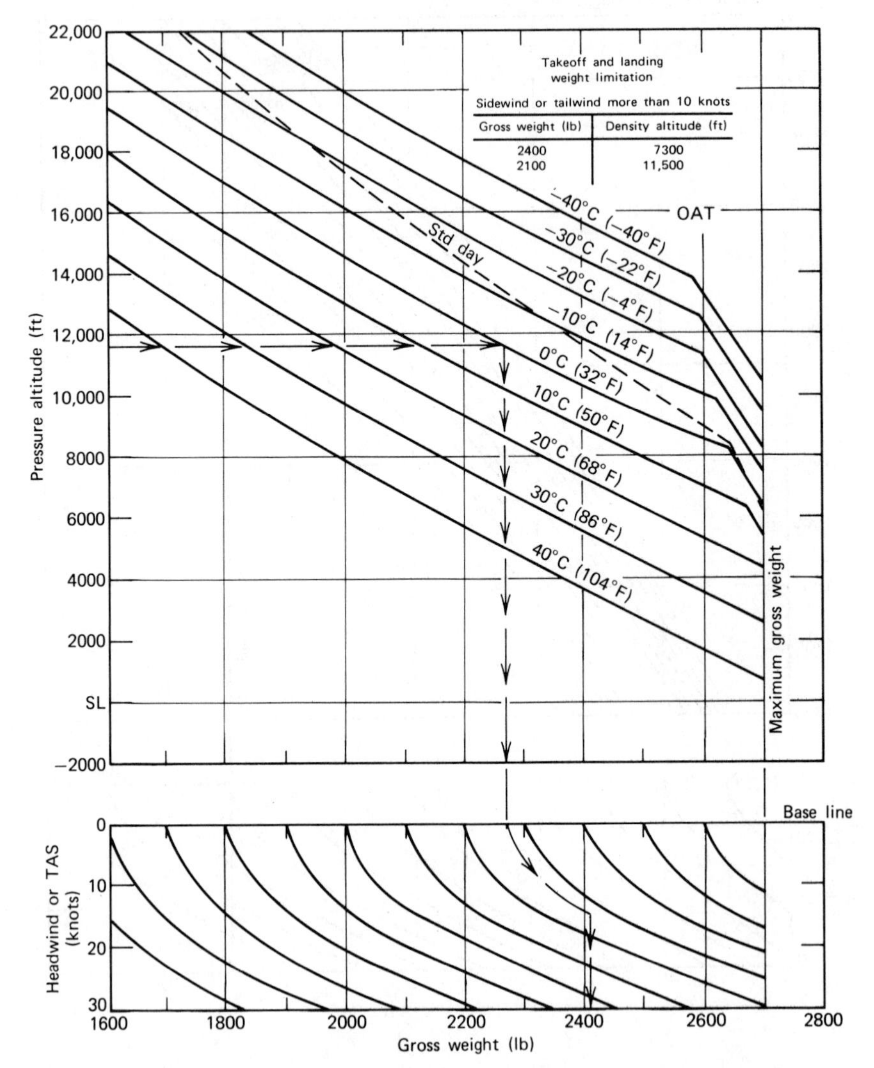

Figure A.5 Maximum gross weight for hovering, takeoff power, skid height 2 ft.

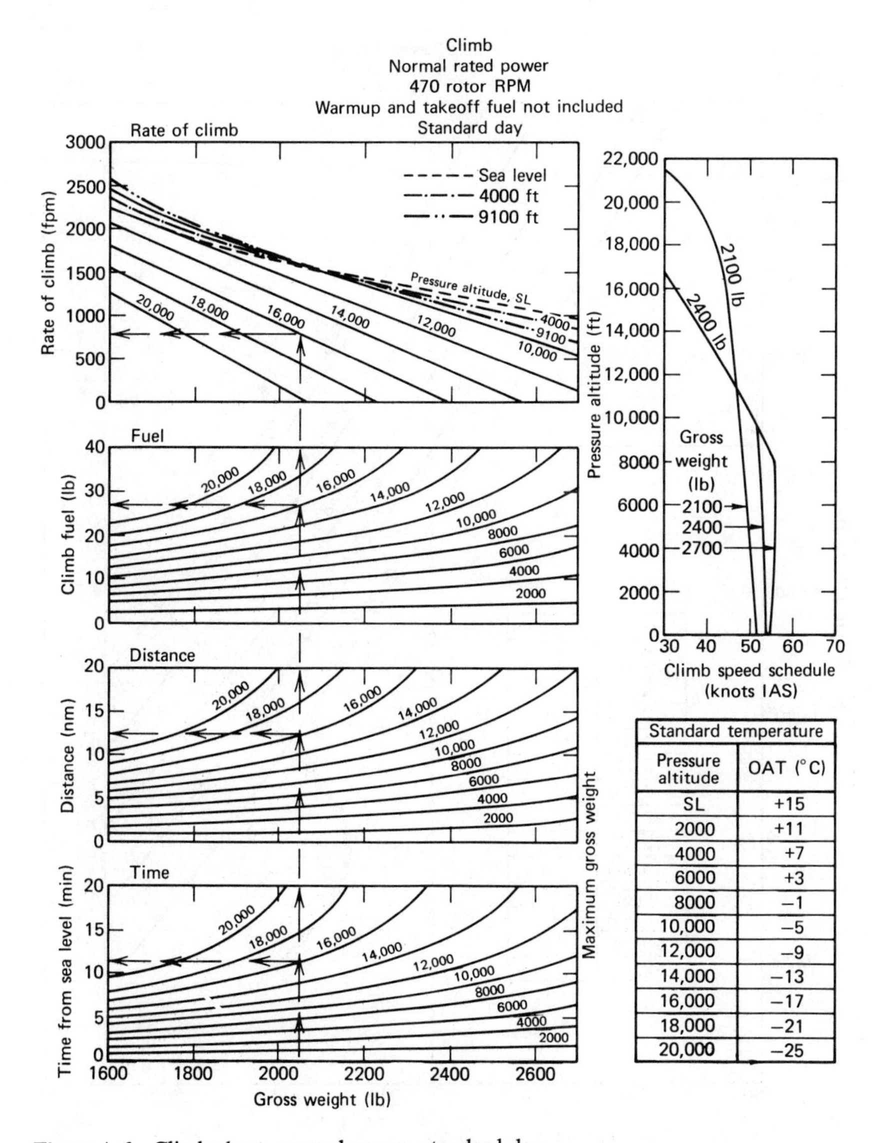

Standard temperature	
Pressure altitude	OAT (°C)
SL	+15
2000	+11
4000	+7
6000	+3
8000	−1
10,000	−5
12,000	−9
14,000	−13
16,000	−17
18,000	−21
20,000	−25

Figure A.6 Climb chart, normal power, standard day.

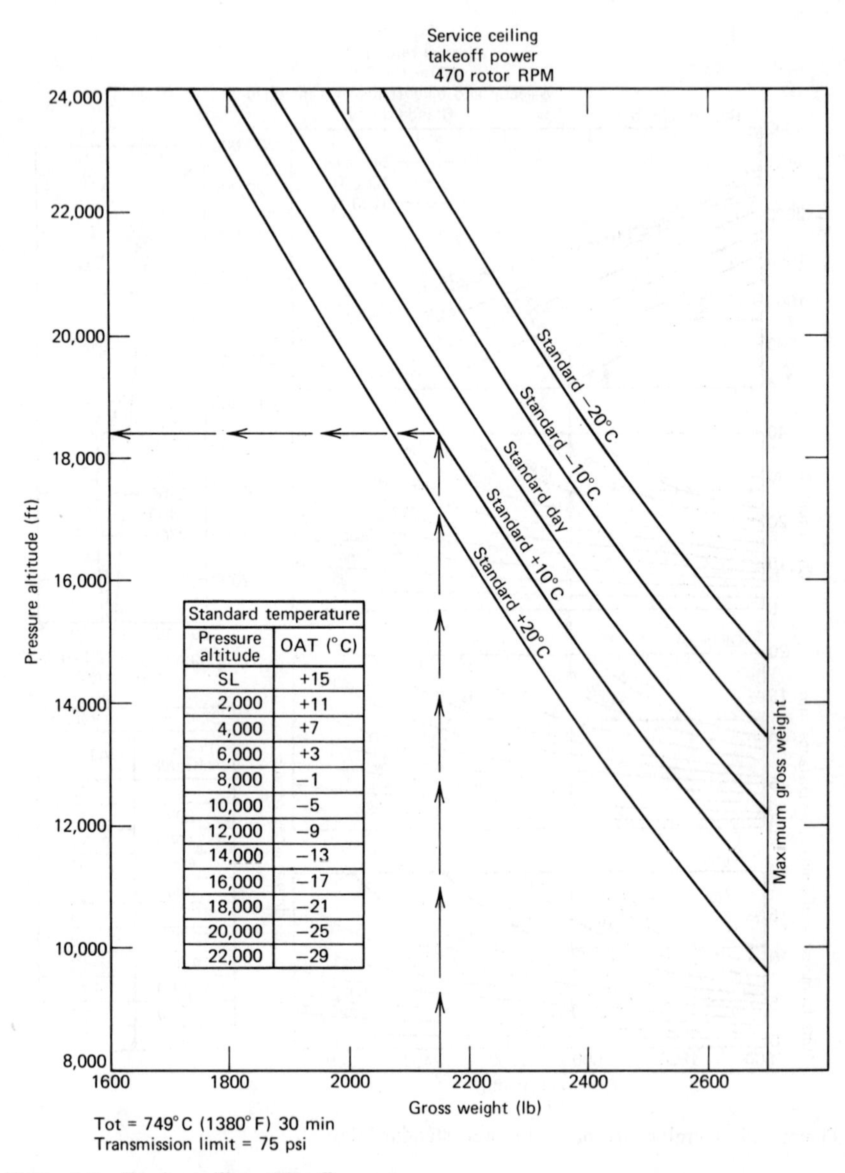

Standard temperature	
Pressure altitude	OAT (°C)
SL	+15
2,000	+11
4,000	+7
6,000	+3
8,000	−1
10,000	−5
12,000	−9
14,000	−13
16,000	−17
18,000	−21
20,000	−25
22,000	−29

Figure A.7 Service ceiling, takeoff power.

INDEX